Æ. *Occidentalis.*

CAMBRIDGE OBSERVED

Cambridge her ancient number wrote,
And what could Cambridge do but quote
THOMAS CHATTERTON

Portrait of John Nicholson, known as 'Maps' *by P. Reinagle*

CAMBRIDGE OBSERVED

AN ANTHOLOGY

——— ❋ ———

Charles Moseley and Clive Wilmer

COLT BOOKS
Cambridge

Colt Books Ltd
9 Clarendon Road
Cambridge CB2 2BH
tel: 01223 357047   fax: 01223 365866

First published by Colt Books in 1998

ISBN 0 905899 81 4

British Library Cataloguing-in-Publication Data
A catalogue record for this book is available from the British Library

Designed by Clare Byatt

Typeset by Ronset, Blackburn
Printed in Great Britain by Biddles Ltd, Guildford and King's Lynn

CONTENTS

———— ✸ ————

CONTENTS

ILLUSTRATIONS

———— ✹ ————

West view of the Gate of Cambridge Castle
by John Sell Cotman

PROSPECT

———— ✸ ————

Do not go to Cambridge, Sir, there are Alehouses, in which you will be drunk. There are Tennis-courts, and Bowling Greens that will heat you to an excess, and then you will drink cold small Beer and die. There is a River too, in which you will be drowned; and you will study yourself into a consumption, or break your Brain.

> ANON., *Animadversions on Two Late Books*, 1673

On the other hand...

Cambridge, wet, cold, abstract, formal as it is, is an excellent place to write, read and work.

> SYLVIA PLATH (writing to her mother, 1956)
> *Letters Home*, 1975

This town evokes, and always has evoked, the strongest of reactions – to its people, to its landscape, to what it stands for. If Rupert Brooke, in one of the best known poems romanticising Cambridgeshire, could joke that

> Cambridge people rarely smile,
> Being urban, squat, and packed with guile

(with more of the same sort about the people from the outlying villages), he was less damning (and less witty) than Byron, who remarked that

into Cambridgeshire the Emperor Probus transported a considerable number of Vandals ... There is no reason to doubt the truth of this assertion; the breed is still in high perfection.

Yet, over the last hundred years it is not difficult to find book after book celebrating, almost cloyingly, the delights of Cambridge – its serenity, its eccentricity, its pastoral setting, its architectural grandeur – all true enough, though the shine has been tarnished in patches.

Cambridge today is changing, far faster than ever before in its long history. The electrification of its railway and its lower house-prices allow a

1

substantial number of people to use the city as a base for commuting to London. It is a happy hunting-ground, with the enormous number of foreign visitors, for the Language Schools – only some three or four in 1960 and now as common as blackberries. Drive in from the Midlands and you pass land where, a generation ago, corn and sugar beet plotted and pieced the land of various farms owned by the University and Colleges. Now their crop is business, higher and higher tech: Cambridge has become the United Kingdom's Silicon Valley. Only a few years ago, in what was still an East Anglian provincial market town, life went on with only a grudging thought of the University that has made it famous, and dour unconcern greeted the achievements of a Newton, or a Russell, or a Crick. It is also a place where for centuries young men, and, later, young women, from all over the British Isles, spent, or mis-spent, crucial years of their lives before going away to make a noise, or not, in the big world. Some called it their alma mater, *their 'dear mother', and left money to beautify its colleges and to maintain the life of scholarship. Because of their benefactions, among other things, Cambridge has become, with Oxford, Stratford and London, one of the four places in England most visited by travellers from abroad. The visitors come alone, they come in fleets of buses that stand throbbing by the Silver Street bridge; they disembark with cameras poised, ready to frame their vision, so that they can know what they have seen. Yet Cambridge was already a tourist site when Elizabeth I came here and was entertained in the new chapel of King's College. Some of the visitors come, as a few always have done, as students and teachers.*

These days, the appeal of Cambridge is felt all over the world, though Americans, for some reason, often seem more deeply affected than most. Henry James was one of the first to write about his response. An oddly downbeat comparison to Oxford introduces a lovingly detailed description:

If Oxford were not the finest thing in England the case would be clearer for Cambridge. It was clear enough there, for that matter, to my imagination, for thirty-six hours. To the barbaric mind, ambitious of culture, Oxford is the usual image of the happy reconciliation between research and acceptance. It typifies to an American the union of science and sense – of aspiration and ease. A German university gives a greater impression of science and an English country house or an Italian villa a greater impression of idle enjoyment; but in these cases, on one side, knowledge is too rugged, and on the other satisfaction is too trivial. Oxford lends

2

sweetness to labour and dignity to leisure. When I say Oxford I mean Cambridge, for a stray savage is not the least obliged to know the difference, and it suddenly strikes me as being both very pedantic and very good-natured in him to pretend to know it. What institution is more majestic than Trinity College? what can effect more a stray savage than the hospitality of such an institution? The first quadrangle is of immense extent, and the buildings that surround it, with their long, rich fronts of time-deepened gray, are the stateliest in the world. In the centre of the court are two or three acres of close-shaven lawn, in the midst of which rises a splendid Gothic fountain, where the serving-men fill up their buckets. There are towers and battlements and statues, and besides these things there are cloisters and garden and bridges. There are charming rooms in a kind of stately gate-tower, and the rooms, occupying the thickness of the building, have windows looking out on one side over the magnificent quadrangle, with half a mile or so of decorated architecture, and on the other into deep-bosomed trees. And in the rooms is the best company conceivable – distinguished men who are remarkably good fellows. I spent a beautiful Sunday morning walking about Cambridge, with one of these gentlemen, and attempting, as the French say, to *débrouiller* its charms. These are a very complicated affair, and I do not pretend, in memory, to keep the Colleges apart. There are, however, half a dozen points that make ineffaceable pictures. Six or eight of the Colleges stand in a row, turning their backs to the river; and hereupon ensues the loveliest confusion of Gothic windows and ancient trees, of grassy banks and mossy balustrades, of sun-chequered avenues and groves, of lawns and gardens and terraces, of single-arched bridges spanning the little stream, which is small and shallow, and looks as if it had been 'turned on' for ornamental purposes. The scantily-flowing Cam appears to exist simply as an occasion for these enchanting little bridges – the beautiful covered gallery of John's or the slightly-collapsing arch of Clare. In the way of College-courts and quiet scholastic porticoes, of gray-walled gardens and ivied nooks of study, in all the pictorial accidents of a great English University, Cambridge is delightfully and inexhaustibly rich. I looked at these one by one and said to myself always that the last was the best. If I were called upon, however, to mention the prettiest corner of the world, I should draw out a thoughtful sigh and point the way to the garden of Trinity Hall. My companion, who was very competent to judge (but who spoke indeed with the partiality of a son of the house), declared, as he ushered me into it, that it was, to his mind, the most beautiful *small* garden in Europe. I freely accepted, and I promptly repeat, an affirmation so magnanimously conditioned. The little garden at Trinity Hall is narrow and crooked; it leans upon the river, from which a low parapet, all muffled in ivy, divides it; it has an ancient wall adorned with a thousand matted creepers on one side, and on the other a group of extraordinary horse-chestnuts. The trees are of prodigious size; they occupy half the garden, and are remarkable for the fact that their giant limbs strike down into the earth, take root again and emulate, as they rise, the majesty of the parent stem. The manner in which this magnificent group of horse-chestnuts sprawls about over the grass, out into the middle of the lawn, is one of the most heart-shaking features of the garden of Trinity Hall.

HENRY JAMES, *Portraits of Places,* 1883

D. H. Lawrence disagreed. He wrote to Bertrand Russell on 19 March, 1915:

Dear Russell: it is true Cambridge made me very black and down. I cannot bear its smell of rottenness, marsh-stagnancy. I get a melancholic malaria.

D. H. LAWRENCE, *Letters,* 1932

The guide books bought by tourists and visitors offer ambiguous advice and back-handed praise. Herr Baedeker, for instance, in 1887:

Oxford is on the whole more attractive than Cambridge to the ordinary visitor; and the traveller is therefore recommended to visit Cambridge first, or to omit it altogether if he cannot visit both.

Baedeker's Guide to Great Britain, 1887

Earlier, in a letter of 6 July, 1855, William Morris had written:

As to Cambridge, it is rather a hole of a place, and cannot compare for a moment with Oxford; it is such a very different kind of place, too, that one feels inclined to laugh, at least I do, when I think of it.

WILLIAM MORRIS

4

But Morris was an Oxonian. Other Oxonians have echoed him (they would, wouldn't they?), though not unanimously. None other than the renowned Master of Balliol, in a letter to Alfred Marshall of 5 January 1886, wrote:

At Oxford, you know, we follow the Cambridge lead, sometimes with uncertain steps.

BENJAMIN JOWETT

The rivalry between the two Universities is ancient. Of the sixteenth-century martyrs, Latimer and Ridley, Macaulay remarked:

Cambridge had the honour of educating those celebrated Protestant Bishops whom Oxford had the honour of burning.

THOMAS BABINGTON MACAULAY, *Essay on Bacon*, 1837

When George II gave the Royal Library to Cambridge University in the 1740s, the Oxford Professor of Poetry, Joseph Trapp, turned a neat little verse:

> The King observing with judicious eyes
> The state of both his universities,
> To Oxford sent a troop of horse, and why?
> That learned body wanted loyalty;
> To Cambridge books, as very well discerning,
> That loyal body wanted learning.

An unkind disposition might try to make much of the fact that Cambridge only replied in 1770; but in fact William Browne, Fellow of Peterhouse (according to Mrs Thrale, Dr Johnson's friend and confidante) made his reply extempore *in response to Johnson's triumphant quotation of Trapp:*

> The King to Oxford sent a troop of horse,
> For Tories own no argument but force;
> With equal skill to Cambridge books he sent,
> For Whigs admit no force but argument.

SIR WILLIAM BROWNE, 1692-1774

There have been many attempts, serious and not, to define the different tempers of the universities. While Oxford, to some, suggests lost causes and royalism, the historical disciplines, and a certain regret about the Reformation, Cambridge has long been linked with Puritanism, liberalism, the sciences and an intellectual toughness impatient with too many good manners.

But this is to anticipate: much in this vein will come later in this book. Nowadays, we arrive in Cambridge quickly, by the impersonality of road or rail, and forget how only a few generations ago it would have been impossible, in a slower progress to the city, to ignore the hinterland that made the town grow on the banks of its river in the first place. The panoramic view that opens up as you surmount the last of the high land before the level vastness of the Fens is still much as when Daniel Defoe saw it about 1720:

I first had a view of Cambridge from Gogmagog Hills. As we descended westward we saw the Fen country on our right, almost all covered with water like a sea, the Michaelmas rains having been very great that year. They had sent down great floods of water from the upland counties, and those fens being, as may be very properly said, the sink of no less than thirteen counties; that is to say, that all the water, or most part of the water of thirteen counties falls into them, they are often thus overflowed. The rivers which thus empty themselves into these fens, and which thus carry off the water, are the Cam or Grant, the Great Ouse and Little Ouse, and the river which runs from Bury to Milden-Hall. In a word, all the water of the middle part of England which does not run into the Thames or the Trent, comes down into these fens ...

As these fens appear covered with water, so I observed too, that they generally at this latter part of the year appear also covered with fogs, so that when the Downs and higher grounds of the adjacent country were gilded by the beams of the sun, the Isle of Ely looked as if wrapped up in blankets, and nothing to be seen, but now and then, the lanthorn or cupola of Ely Minster.

One could hardly see this from the hills and not pity the many thousands of families that were bound to or confined in those fogs, and had no other breath to draw than what must be mixed with those vapours, and that steam which so universally overspread the country.

DANIEL DEFOE, *Tour through the Whole Island of Great Britain*, 1724-27

Cambridge is an in-between place: not quite of the high land, not quite of the Fens, a border town between Mercia and East Anglia: small surprise that a bridge is in its name and on its coat of arms. It links the disparate and does so intellectually, too: a bridge from youth to maturity, subject to subject, idea to idea. Approaching it from any direction underlines this frontier status.

The Arms of the City of Cambridge, originally granted to the Borough
by the Clarenceux King of Arms in 1575

Defoe came from the South East, along, more or less, the line of the old Roman Road from Colchester that still makes the spine of the city – Hills Road, Regent Street, St Andrews Street, Sidney Street, Bridge Street, Huntingdon Road. In 1867, Charles Kingsley – naturalist, novelist, clergyman, Professor of Modern History – evoked the approach from the north in an eloquent lecture to a Mechanics' Institute in Cambridge. He remembers what the landscape had been only a short while previously, before the wholesale draining of the Fens had its effect. He had

7

*witnessed the destruction of a great natural phenomenon, which had turned
'a waste and howling wilderness' (the Great Fen was such in his boyhood),
into a Garden of the Lord, where*

> All the land in flowery squares
> Beneath a broad and equal-blowing wind
> Smells of the coming summer

And he comments:

And yet the fancy may linger without blame, over the shining
meres, the golden reedbeds, the countless water-fowl, the strange
and gaudy insects, the wild nature, the mystery, the majesty – for
mystery and majesty there were – which haunted the deep fens for
many a hundred years. Little thinks the Scotsman, whirled down
by the Great Northern Railway from Peterborough to
Huntingdon, what a grand place, even twenty years ago, was that
Holme and Whittlesea, which is now but a black unsightly
steaming flat, from which the meres and reed-beds of the old
world are gone, while the corn and roots of the new world have
not as yet taken their place.

But grand enough it was, that black ugly place, when backed by
Caistor Hanglands and Holme Wood and the patches of the
primeval forest; while dark-green alders, and pale-green reeds,
stretched for miles round the broad lagoon, where the coot
clanked, and the bittern boomed, and the sedge-bird, not content
with its own sweet song, mocked the notes of all the birds around;
while high overhead hung, motionless, hawk beyond hawk,
buzzard beyond buzzard, kite beyond kite, as far as eye could see.
Far off, upon the silver mere, would rise a puff of smoke from a
punt, invisible from its flatness and white paint. Then down the
wind came the boom of the great stanchion-gun; and after that
sound, another sound, louder as it neared; a cry as of all the bells
of Cambridge and all the hounds of Cottesmore; and overhead
rushed and whirled the skein of terrified wildfowl, screaming,
piping, clacking, croaking – filling the air with the hoarse rattle of
their wings, while clear above all sounded the wild whistle of the
curlew and the trumpet note of the great wild swan.

They are all gone now. No longer do the ruffs trample the sedge into a hard floor in their fighting-rings, while the sober reeves stand round, admiring the tournament of their lovers, gay with ruffs and tippets, no two of them alike. Gone are ruffs and reeves, spoonbills, bitterns, avosets; the very snipe, one hears, disdains to breed. Gone, too, not only from Whittlesea, but from the whole world, is that most exquisite of butterflies – *Lycaena dispar* – the great copper; and many a curious insect more. Ah, well, at least we shall have wheat and mutton instead, and no more typhus and ague; and, it is to be hoped, no more brandy-drinking and opium-eating; and children will live and not die. For it was a hard place to live in, the old Fen; a place wherein one heard of 'unexampled instances of longevity,' for the same reason that one hears of them in savage tribes – that few lived to old age at all, save those iron constitutions which nothing could break down.

CHARLES KINGSLEY, *Prose Idylls*, 1874

'Any fool can appreciate a hill', as the old Fen saying has it. Those great skies and level plains many found the fabric of memory, though, when land-scape began to be seen in terms of the picturesque, it was difficult to say precisely what was picturesque about Cambridgeshire. Wordsworth writes memorably about the University but has little to say about the landscape. William Gilpin, an influential theorist of 'the picturesque' was not impressed with Cambridge, either approaching, or in it, or when leaving by the Ely road:

The country beyond Audley-end grows chalky, bare, exposed, ridgy and unpleasant; and, after we leave Chesterford, it becomes flat also. The distances, such as they are (nowhere furnished with variety of Objects, nor ever remote) are term-inated with one even line of horizon: and the foregrounds are spungy Swamps, producing only rushes, the natural appendages of a fenny country. Gog-magog hills, which we leave on the right, so little deserve the name of *hills*, that we should not have observed them, unless they had been pointed out to us.

Cambridge makes no appearance at a distance. King's-college chappel is the only object, which presents itself with any dignity, as we approach.

At the end of Queen's walk, Clare-hall makes a good *perspective*. When you see it *in front*, as you do from Clare-hall-piece, it loses half its grandeur. In full view, you are sure you see the whole: whereas a perspective view leaves the imagination room to extend the idea ...

The senate-house is a heavy building; and the gallery makes it heavier ...

The public-library, however richly stored with books, is not any object to be shewn. Nor are the public-schools any ornament to the university ...

His comments on some of the colleges were not much kinder and, as he left, his spirits sank further at the prospect of the road to Ely:

From Cambridge the road to Ely led us immediately among fens. Trees, groves, extensive distances, and all the variety of land-scape, are now totally gone. All is blank. The eye meets nothing but dreary causeways ... Stretches of flat, swampy ground; and long ditches running in Strait lines; and intersected, at right angles, in various parts, by other ditches, make the whole of the scenery on each side. In the room of such beautiful objects as often adorn landscape, the only ornaments of this dreary Surface are windmills.

WILLIAM GILPIN, *Observations on several parts of the Counties of Cambridge, Norfolk, Suffolk and Essex. Also on several parts of North Wales; relative chiefly to picturesque beauty. In two tours, 1809*

❋

Defoe saw the town from somewhere near Wandlebury Ring, on the Gog Magog Hills with a prosaic eye. One curious fantasy about those hills is in Michael Drayton's PolyOlbion, Or, a Chorographical Description of Tracts, Riuers, Mountaines, Forests and other parts of this renowned Isle of Great Britaine, *where we find the love song of Gogmagog and Granta. The pastoral eclogue was never before like this! (Alas, Drayton's Owls and Urchins are not Senior Members and Undergraduates, as one wildly, momentarily, hoped, but simply the hedgehogs and owls of the Gogs.)*

... these ancient Dykes neglected in their ground,   [The great Cambridge-
Through the sad aged earth, sent out a hollow sound,   shire ditches, Fleam,
Brent and Devil's, here
To gratulate her speech; when as we met againe,   strangely loquacious]
With one whose constant heart, with cruell love was slaine:
Old Gogmagog, a Hill of long and great renowne,
Which neere to Cambridge set, o'rlookes that learned Towne.
Of Balshams pleasant hilles, that by the name was knowne,
But with the monstrous times, he rude and barbarous growne,
A Gyant was become; for man hee cared not,
And so the fearefull name of Gogmagog had got:
Who long had borne good will to most delicious Grant: [Granta]
But doubting lest some god his greatnesse might supplant.
For as that daintie Flood by Cambridge keepes her course,
He found the Muses left their old Beotian source,
Resorting to her banks, and every little space,
He saw bright Phoebes gaze upon her Christall face,
And through th'exhaled Fogs, with anger looked red,
To leave his loved Nymph, when he went down to bed.
Wherefore this Hill with love, being fouly overgone:
And one day as he found the lovely Nymph alone,
Thus wooes her; Sweeting mine, if thou mine owne wilt be,
C'have many a pretty gaud, I keepe in store for thee.   [I have]
A nest of broadfac'd Owles, and goodly Urchins too;
Nay Nymph take heed of me, when I begin to wooe:
And better yet then this, a Bulchin twa yeares old,   [bullcalf]
A curld-pate Calfe it is, and oft could have beene sold:
And yet beside all this, c'have goodly Beare-whelps twa,
Ful daintie for my Joy, when shee's dispos'd to play,
And twentie Sowes of Mead, to make our wedding Ring;
Bezides, at Sturbridge Fayre, chill buy thee many a thing: [I shall]
Chill zmouch thee every morne, before the Sunne can rise,   [kiss]
And looke my manly face, in thy sweet glaring eyes.

Thus said, he smug'd his Beard, and stroked up his hayre,   [smoothed]
As one that for her love he thought had offered fayre:
Which to the Muses, Grant did presently report,
Wherewith they many a yeare shall make them wondrous sport ...

Later in the poem, the river Granta 'entertains the Muses' with her own song – every other feature in the landscape has already sung – and concludes:

O noble Cambridge then, my most beloved Towne,
In glory flourish still, to heighten thy renowne:
In womans perfect shape, still be thy Embleme right,
Whose one hand holds a Cup, the other beares a Light ...
MICHAEL DRAYTON, PolyOlbion, 1613

Just such a conceit is expressed in the device of the University, used some-times still as a colophon in books from the University Press.

Coming into Cambridge along the London road, you pass through Trumpington, where Chaucer set The Reeve's Tale. *A pamphlet of 1700 describes a hilarious journey to Cambridge from London:*

... nothing remarkable till we came within four Mile of Cambridge, at which distance the top of Kings Colledge Chappel was discernable, appearing in a Figure resembling a Cradle, and by Travellers is so call'd; which happen'd to draw into my Noddle, the following scrap of Poetry.

> *Old Cambridge brings forth Men of learning and parts,*
> *   Dame Natures dark Laws to unriddle;*
> *Since she's the Midwife of Science and Arts,*
> *   'Tis fit she be known by a Cradle.*

When from thence we had travel'd about three Mile further, we came to a small Village call'd Trumpington, a mile on this side Cambridge. This Town is not a little famous for the great Conveniences it affords the young scholars of the University, for here the Fresh Men first learn to be good Companions, and afterwards, when in Orders, practise to be good Preachers; for here they commonly Drink their first merry cup with their Friends after their initiation, and generally deliver their first Sermon when qualified by the Bishop for the Ministerial Function; as we pass'd thro' Trumpington, where the Scholars at their leisure hours, are some or other of 'em usually refreshing themselves, we saw several Black Gowns pop in and out of the little Country-hovels, like so many Black Rabbits in a Warren, bolting out of their Coney-Burroughs; I have some reason to be jealous, the Name of this Place was Originally given for no good, but rather from some wild Schollars, who being Libidinously given, had usual recourse thither, and kist the Wenches till they Farted again, from whence, as some Sages conjecture, in process of time, it gain'd the Name Trumping-Town.

> *Where Women, doubtless, are possest,*
> *Of Faculties discerning;*
> *Since they (kind Souls) so oft are Blest,*
> *With Men of Parts and Learning.*
>
> *One Pulpit's Common to the Gown,*
> *For Teachers to be seen in;*
> *But they have Numbers in the Town,*
> *Where Preachers oft have been in.*
>
> *All standing stifly to their Text,*
> *Till clear'd the Point most fairly;*
> *Whilst those they 'nstruct are never vext,*
> *But when they've done too Early.*

EDWARD (NED) WARD, 'A Step to Stur-Bitch Fair, with Remarks upon the University of Cambridge', *The London Spy*, 1700

Visitors to the town, if important enough, could expect a lengthy reminder of its civic pride and of its fanciful history:

Touchinge the antiquitie and denomination, historians testifie it was builded before Christs incarnation, with a castle, towers, and walls of defence, by Duke Cantaber, the sonne of the Kinge of Spayne, who was entertained in England by Kinge Gurguntius; and the Towne being situated and united with a bridge upon the River then called Canta, was denominated Cantabridge; and in tract of tyme the name of the River being altered to Granta, the Towne likewise to Grantabridge; and after it was called Cam, and the Towne Cambridge, which yet remaineth and consisteth of fourteen parishes. This river is current throughe the hearte of the Shire, with navigation to the sea, and is the life of trafficke to this Towne and countie; and no bridge is over the same but at Cambridge, and it is maintayned by fowerscore hides of land lye-ing *sparsim* [scattered] in this Shire, which are holden of your Majestie by pontage, appropriate to this bridge only ...

The Muses did branch from Athens to Cambridge, and were lovinglie lodged in the houses of Citizens untill Ostles and Halls were erected for them without endowments, and nowe the materials of the castle, towers, and walls are converted into Colleges, beautifieing this famous universitie. It hath bin trulie saide *Quid Musis cum Marte?* ['What have the Muses to do with Mars?'] but never saide *Quid Musis cum Mercatore?* ['What have the Muses to do with the Merchant?'] It hath bin saide of the Abbies, *Religio peperit divitias, et filia devoravit matrem*, ['Religion brought forth wealth, and the daughter devoured the mother'] which we hope shall never be truly applyed to the University and this Towne.

FRANCIS BRACKYN, Recorder of Cambridge (from a speech delivered to James I), March 7, 1614/5

Where did this fanciful history start? John Lydgate (?1370-1449), monk of Bury St Edmunds, poetic heir of Chaucer, and on his day capable of a certain long-paced, slow-chap't power, wrote a poem on the origins of the town and university. It was doubtless intended to enhance Cambridge's reputation: it hardly flatters his. But a stanza or two is worth quoting, if only for the fantastic account of Cambridge's origins:

Like as I finde – reporte I can none other –
This Canteber tyme of his lyvynge

To Pertholyne he was germayne brother,
    Duke in tho dayes, in Ireland a great kynge,
    Chieffe & principall cause of that buildyng;
The wall about & towers as they stoode
Was sett & builte upon a large floode,

Named Cantebro, a large brode ryver,
    And after Cante called Cantebro.
This famous citie, this write the cronicler,
    Was called Cambridge; rehersing eke also
    In that booke theis authors bothe twoe.
Towching the date, as I reheartse can,
Fro thilke tyme that the world began

Fower thowsand complete, by accomptes clere,
    And three hundreth by computacion,
Ioyned therto eight & fortie yeare,
    When Cantebro gave the foundacion
    Of thys cytie & this famous towne,
And of this noble universitie,
Sett on this ryver which is called Cante…

JOHN LYDGATE

Cantaber also, says Lydgate, brought 'folke experte in philosophie', *such as Anaximander and Anaxagoras, from Athens to start the University. Julius Caesar took Cambridge men back to Rome. And, says Lydgate,* 'all clarks seyne the same, / Of heresie Cambridge bare never blame': *perhaps an important detail, considering the increasingly intolerant atmosphere of his time.*

    Did Lydgate start the myth of Cantaber? Whether he did nor not, it certainly ran and ran, just as did the myth of King Alfred founding the university of Oxford. Such foundation myths, after all, could be and were appealed to in legal wrangles over authority, property, precedence and so on: they were invented because they legitimated, authorised a status quo.

According to many guidebooks, the advantages of Cambridge's situation were patent:

The Air of Cambridge is very healthful, and the Town plentifully supplied with excellent Water, not only from the River and Aqueduct [Hobson's Conduit] already mentioned, but from the numerous Springs on every Side of it; some of them medicinal. Nor is it better supplied with Water, than it is with other Necessaries of Life. The purest Wine they receive by the Way of Lynn: Flesh, Fish, Wild-Fowl, Poultry, Butter, Cheese, and all Manner of Provisions, from the adjacent Country: Firing is cheap; Coals from Seven-pence to Nine-pence a Bushel; Turf, or rather Peat, four Shillings a Thousand; Sedge, with which the Bakers heat their Ovens, four Shillings per hundred Sheaves: These, together with Osiers, Reeds, and Rushes used in several Trades, are daily imported by the River Grant. Great Quantities of Oil, made of Flax-Seed, Cole-Seed, Hemp and other Seeds, ground or pressed by the numerous Mills in the Isle of Ely, are brought up this River also; and the Cakes, after the Oil is pressed out, afford the Farmer an excellent Manure to improve his Grounds. By the River also they receive 1500 or 2000 Firkins of Butter every Week, from Norfolk and the Isle of Ely, which is sent by Waggons to London: Besides which, great Quantities are made in the neighbouring Villages, for the useof the University and Town, and brought fresh to Market every Day, except Monday. Every Pound of this Butter is rolled and drawn out to a Yard in Length, about the Bigness of a Walking-Cane; which is mentioned as peculiar to this Place. The Fields near Cambridge furnish the Town with the best Saffron in Europe, which sells usually from 20 to 30 Shillings a Pound.

Cantabrigia Depicta, 1763

It is of course still a place of market. Cattle are still sold, on the outskirts now, and since a collection of clothes stores routed the full range of serious, practical shops from the centre of the town, the historic Market Hill – yes, one can feel it as a hill under the wheels of a bicycle – once more provides on its stalls an essential service of fresh food and vegetables, books, fish, meat, cooked food and so on. Every so often 'they' try to tidy it away ...

THE MARKET-PLACE AT MIDNIGHT

No moon,
but lamp light.

The fountain dead,
planks fallen.

Row upon row, still,
of stalls:
crude boards roped across
trestles, and slack canvas.
CLIVE WILMER, 1968 (in *Selected Poems*, 1995)

The town in December, in that lull at the end of the afternoon when the market stalls are closing, and torn paper and discarded fruit litter the gutters, still has its enormous, seductive charm, a place my heart delights in. But – perversely? – I miss the hissing Tilley lanterns that used to light the market stalls in late afternoons, as November hardened into December. I miss their pulsing light on the face of Mr Human, greengrocer, as he used to blow on his hands in his brown fingerless gloves, stamping his feet in the cold, calling out the virtues of the sprouts I knew he had bought cheap at the produce auction at the old Cattle Market by the railway. Long gone. As I come out of the light and the warmth and the smell – leather, paper, ink, mould – of David's Bookshop in the dusk, I hear King's bell ringing for Evensong, the ancient sounds echoing in the steelwork of the new Arts Theatre. As I pass St Edward's, a sudden glimpse through the open door of a small orchestra and the sound of an impassioned, fast, rendering of Mozart 35: steal closer, and look in: every face is rapt, and the young shoulders of the conductor are putting everything they have got into the sound. Those young folk think their audience is only themselves. And two ladies pass by, talking of Michelangelo.

In A. E. Clothier's window, I notice that the turn-ups my youth despised are coming back into fashion: I suppose I shall wear my trousers rolled, once more. Such fashions return, like the flowered waistcoat and stiff collar sported by some young fogeys, an allusion to a set of attitudes rather than their natural expression. And as I turn, the light of the window catches two world-famous faces as they come round the corner. They pass, deep in conversation. I catch, 'And seventhly ...'

CHARLES MOSELEY, 1997

Until well into the twentieth century, the countryside pressed in – a long tongue of green and trees still does reach from the heart of the city out along the river towards Grantchester, and from Jesus Green towards Ely. The old names remain: Laundress Green, Sheep's Green, Coe Fen, Paradise, Grantchester Meadows. Towards the end of the eighteenth century, Henry Gunning (1768–1854), for many years one of the two Esquire Bedells – roughly, marshals – of the University, had, like many of his contemporaries and successors, a passion for the relatively new sport of 'shooting flying'. His Reminiscences *give a glimpse of a just recognisable Cambridge.*

The great source of idleness, which consumed more time than all my other employments put together, was my passion for shooting, for which diversion Cambridge afforded the most extraordinary facilities. In going over the land now occupied by Downing-Terrace, you generally got five or six shots at snipes. Crossing the Leys, you entered on Coe-Fen; this abounded with snipes. Walking through the osier-bed on the Trumpington side of the brook, you frequently met with a partridge, and now and then a pheasant. From thence to the lower end of Pemberton's garden was one continued marsh, which afforded plenty of snipes, and in the month of March a hare or two. If you chose to keep on by the side of the river, you came to Harston-Ham well known to sportsmen; and at no great distance from this you arrived at Foulmire Mere, which produced a great variety of wildfowl ...

HENRY GUNNING, *Reminiscences of the University, Town and County of Cambridge*, 1854

There are still kingfishers along the little brook (Vicar's Brook) – and in the Botanical Gardens.

Gunning's shooting trip entailed what many would now call a prodigious walk. Many dons, living a sedentary life of scholarship, felt the need for exercise, and long walks, and later long bicycle rides, were common. A. C. Benson, Eton Master, Fellow, President and then Master of Magdalene, describes in his diary his response to the Cambridgeshire countryside to which his exercise took him:

Magdalene, May 5 [1905] – I dabbled about with letters all morning. ... Then I got a bike out. I had slept indifferently and was a little heavy. But the day was simply enchanting – a cool north wind, the air exquisitely clean and clear.

. . . There is a wold, perhaps sixty feet high, above Swaffham; and Swaffham is just on the edge of the huge fen that stretches to Ely and Soham, and of which one bit, Wicken, is still (undrained) fen. Well, by the mill up there the view was gigantic and glorious: the long, pure lines of fen and dykes from verge to verge: and on the edge was Ely, in a dim, blue majesty, the sun shining on the leads as [Edward] FitzGerald saw it from Newmarket heath sixty years ago !

The Diary of Arthur C. Benson

The structure of the University year means that the town has always had a floating population: as indeed now, except that while only a couple of decades ago August was quiet and peaceful, now it is the busiest and noisiest time of year with the tourists and the summer schools. Thomas Gray liked the town in the Long Vacation.

August 12, 1760: Cambridge is a delight of a place, now there is nobody in it. I do believe you would like it, if you knew what it was without inhabitants. It is they, I assure you, that get it an ill name and spoil all.

The Letters of Thomas Gray

'Nobody in it'? Not even the townsfolk?

Similarly, the quiet impressed an anonymous writer just before Gray. (Dockrill was Master of Robin's, one of the fashionable coffee-houses.)

> No Barbers trim are now! no more with Wig
> Well-powder'd, white or brown, of Don more grave,

Or Scholar blythe meet Emblems, haste those Sires
Of News, and sprucest God-fathers of Dress!
No more the jolly Jips, with Heart a Foe
To Thought or Sorrow, carol out their Songs,
Loud-ecchoing thro'the Mirth-devoted Court,
As to the Butteries, with their Paper Friend
Jocund they jog along, and o'er their Ale
Measure their Masters Merits by their Gifts !
To Penury, alas, and pinching Want
Condemn'd, the long Vacation loud they curse,
And pray with me, October's Bell to hear,
To Sophs more dread than Curfeu! so thro' Life
The Weal of one still proves another's Woe.

Vain is it, once the Coffee-House supplied
Reviving Coffee, or Heart-chearing Tea,
And with them Pamphlets in long happy Roll,
Food for the hungry Mind ! How dreary all
As ent'ring there, I pace along the Room !
The languid *Dockrill* drops his wonted Smiles,
Pale *Dockerilla* on her Elbow leans,
And views the long, long Order, shining trim,
(Ah that they shine!) of Coffee-Pots forlorn !
While each with me in deep Complaining joins,
And ruminates full sad on happier Days.

A Day in Vacation at College, 1751

A similar moment of vacation quiet is caught – tongue in cheek – in the Tennysonian manner, by S. C. Roberts, Syndic of the University Press and Master of Pembroke. Trams from the railway station went to the Senate House, whence a hansom cab could be hired to take one on to the final destination. Jehu, for generations that knew the history of the kings of Israel, was a byword for a reckless driver.

… They came unto a town
Where it seemed always Thursday afternoon.
Adown the street the languid tram did glide,
Swaying like one that hath an empty life,
And at the college gate the porter lone

Would idly gaze, as downward in the court
Slow-dropping leaves on primmest lawn did fall.
While others through the corridors did bear
The furniture of yester-term afar,
In Autumn stillness stood the royal fane –
Four silent pinnacles, and silent, too,
The organ thunder. By the Senate House
The fareless Jehus sleep – no more to roam.

S. C. ROBERTS, *Granta (May Week Number)*, 1912

If, to the folk from the Fens, Cambridge was the main market, a place for exchange of news, goods, clothes, even work, to new undergraduates it was a place where arrival itself was almost a rite of passage.

They waited for the other tram by the Roman Catholic Church, whose florid bulk was already receding into twilight. It is the first big building that the incoming visitor sees. 'Oh, here come the colleges!' cries the Protestant parent, and then learns that it was built by a Papist who made a fortune out of movable eyes for dolls. 'Built out of dolls' eyes to contain idols' – that, at all events, is the legend and the joke. It watches over the apostate city, taller by many a yard than anything within, and asserting, however wildly, that here is eternity, stability, and bubbles unbreakable upon a windless sea.

A costly hymn tune announced five o'clock, and in the distance the more lovable note of St. Mary's could be heard, speaking from the heart of the town. Then the tram arrived – the slow stuffy tram that plies every twenty minutes between the unknown and the market-place – and took them past the desecrated grounds of Downing, past Addenbrooke's Hospital, girt like any Venetian palace with a mantling canal, past the Fitzwilliam, towering upon immense substructions like any Roman temple, right up to the gates of one's own college, which looked like nothing else in the world.

E. M. FORSTER, *The Longest Journey*, 1907

Map of Cambridgeshire with street plan of Cambridge by John Speed,
1610

A LITTLE CITY ON
A RIVER

———— ❀ ————

The shape of the town shows, if you know where to look, the marks of its long history – like lines upon a face that has seen many summers. William the Conqueror, getting to grips with his new kingdom, set Sheriff Picot to keep the little town by the bridge. Before that, the Danes made this a strong point in their East Anglian settlement; before them the monks of Ely, as the Venerable Bede describes in his Ecclesiastical History, *sailed along the river* 'to a little city left uninhabited ... which, in the tongue of the English, is called Granta caestir' *to find a marble coffin (doubtless a Roman sarcophagus) for the royal abbess, St Etheldreda. The Romans built the first bridge at the bottom of Castle Hill –* 'the most famous bridge in England: the one bridge that gives its name to a county', *as F. W. Maitland said (*Township and Borough, *1898).*

Quite possibly, more books have been written about Cambridge than any other town in the British Isles, except London and Oxford. It is remarkable how many antiquarians of the first ability have chosen to write about the town they made their home and workplace. One of the best is John Willis Clark, through whose prose one hears the tones of Victorian civic pride – and some reliable history.

If however we transport ourselves back to a remote period, some seven or eight centuries ago, we shall find a town of peculiar and considerable importance before the University had come into existence ... Ancient Cambridge was spread out along the right bank of the Cam from the Mills to the Great Bridge; and the busiest part of it lay between the street leading to those Mills and the river. Here were the numerous wharfs or hythes at which the merchandise brought in barges up the stream was landed, and the numerous lanes connecting the hythes with Milne Street or High Street. On the side remote from the river the extent of the town was defined by a ditch, called the King's Ditch, planned by King John and completed by King Henry the Third in 1267. The area included between these boundaries was in shape like the section

23

of a pear; and near the end where the stalk would grow was the Bridge leading to a steep road which climbed the Castle Hill. Whatever may be the date of that mound it seems certain that the castle at its foot was built on the site of a Roman settlement, as the antiquaries of the eighteenth century maintained; and that the Norman castle was never more than a third-class fortress which may have lent a certain dignity to the town but could not have afforded it any serious protection.

The river was originally called the Granta, or more familiarly, *le Ee* and *Le Ree*. The earliest form of the town's name was *Grantanbrycge* or *Grentebrige*, which in process of time became *Cantbrigge* and *Caumbrege*. Lastly, in the Sixteenth and Seventeenth centuries, when it became necessary to find a name for the river, the old name of the town having been forgotten, *Cam* was adopted from *Cam-bridge*, the shortened form of *Caumbridge*. Thus the river derived its name from the town, and not the town from the river, as was formerly supposed.

To the commercial interests of Cambridge [*as a market and as a port connecting with Lynn*] there was added, at an unknown period, and by an unknown agency, the corporation of teachers which we describe as the University. It must not, however, be supposed that someone said: 'Let us found a University at Cambridge.' No University, so far as we know, was ever founded anywhere. Such an institution started from very small beginnings, and 'broadened slowly down, from precedent to precedent,' till, in this case, it became one of those stately associations of learned men of which the two English examples are now the sole survivors. Nor, again, must it be supposed that the word *Universitas* or University meant in the Middle Ages what it means now. It meant simply 'the whole of' any persons to whom a document was addressed.

What, then, was the probable beginning in Cambridge of what we call the University? Some teacher on his travels – perhaps at the time of Stourbridge Fair – may have attracted an audience; his lectures may have been popular and he may have been asked to repeat them in the following year; the great monasteries of the Fenland, and the smaller houses of the same Orders in Cambridge, may have associated themselves with this educational movement; the required element of permanency may have thus been gained; and so, very gradually, the little body may have developed an organisation of the required type, with a Rector and a body of Masters; after which the distinction of being called a *Studium Generale* – the medieval equivalent for a modern University – would in a very short time be conferred upon the new body.

JOHN WILLIS CLARK, *A Concise Guide to the Town and University of Cambridge*, 1910

❊

Many wrote about the town a century ago as a place to which the discerning visitor would make his way. In the immensely popular Highways and Byways *series of guidebooks published by Macmillan, the Cambridge and Isle of Ely volume is one of the best: its author, the Rev. Edward Conybeare, Vicar of Barrington, wrote with a blend of imaginative history, anecdote and evident affection for the place:*

Should [the reader enter the town] from the railway station he will have to face a mile or so of 'long unlovely street' to begin with. For when railroads were first made – (the Great Eastern line from London to Cambridge being constructed in 1845) – they were regarded with extreme suspicion and dislike by the authorities of both Universities. The noise of the trains, it was declared, would be fatal to their studies; the facility of running up to London would hopelessly demoralise their undergraduates; bad characters from the metropolis would come down in shoals to prey upon them. Thus both Oxford and Cambridge strenuously opposed any near approach of this new-fangled abomination to their hallowed precincts. Oxford actually succeeded in keeping the main line of the Great Western as far off from it as Didcot, ten miles away, whence it did not penetrate to the city itself till a considerably later date, when prejudice[1] had been overcome by the patent advantages of the new locomotion, and a station hard by was welcomed. At Oxford, therefore, no such distance divides the

---

[1]According to Conybeare, the Vice-Chancellor of the time wrote to the Directors of the Company to say that the proposals were as 'distasteful to the University authorities as they must be offensive to Almighty God and all right-minded Christians'.

railway and the Colleges as at Cambridge, where from the first the station stood in its present place. This, at the date of its construction, was far beyond even the outermost buildings of the town, with which it is connected by the old Roman road, the main artery of Cambridge, running straight, as Roman roads do run, for miles on either side to the 'Great Bridge'. To antiquarians this road is known as the Via Devana, because its objective is supposed to have been the old Roman city of Deva (Chester); during its passage through Cambridge it has no fewer than seven official designations to the frequent discomfiture of strangers ...

The best approach to Cambridge is by the westward road of the four, which leads into the London Road (or Trumpington Road, as it is here called), that umbrageous avenue of leafage ... Keeping along this towards the town, we find ourselves confronted with one of the prettiest and most uncommon amongst the minor attractions of Cambridge, the runlets of clear water which sparkle along the side of either pavement.

REV. EDWARD CONYBEARE, *Highways and Byways in Cambridge and the Isle of Ely*, 1910

The runlets are part of Hobson's Conduit. For Hobson, himself, see page 200.

A less deferential eye – that of Ned Ward – saw things rather differently:

The next place we arriv'd at, was our Journeys-end, Cambridge ... After the Coach had set me down and I had taken a fair Leave of my Fellow-Travellers, I walk'd about to take a more compleat survey both of the Town and University. The Buildings in many parts of the Town were so little and so low, that they look'd more like Hutts for Pigmies, than Houses for Men; and their very Shop-keepers seem'd to me to be so well-siz'd to their Habitations, that they appear'd like so many Monkeys in their Diminutive Shops mimicking the Trade of London. Amongst the rest of the Pomps and Vanities of this Wicked Corporation, there is one very famous Inn, distinguished by the sign of the Devils Lap-dog in Petty-Cury; here I went to refresh myself with a Glass or two of Canary; where I found an Old grizly Curmudgion, Corniferously Wedded to a Plump, Young, Brisk, Black, Beautiful, good Landlady, who I afterwards heard had so great a kindness for the University, that she had rather see two or three Gown-men come into her House, than a Cuckoldy Crew of Aldermen in all their Pontificalibusses; and indeed I had reason to believe there was no love lost, for the Scholars crept in as fast and as slily, for either a Kiss, a kind Look, or a Cup of Comfort, as Hogs into an Orchard after a High-wind, or Flys into a Pig-sauce, for the sake of the Sugar; I lik'd my pretty Hostess so wonderfully well, and was so greatly Delighted with the pleasant Conversation I met with in the House, that I determin'd with myself to make this my place of residence during my continuance in the Town, so bespeaking a Bed, I afterwards took a Walk in order to view the University, of which I shall proceed to give you a sober and Concise Description.

The Colledges stand without side the Town, which in plain Terms is a Corporation of Ignorance, hem'd round with Arts and Sciences, a Nest of Fools, that dwell on the Superfluities of the Learned, an ingrateful Soil where the Seeds of Generosity are daily scatter'd, but produce nothing in return but the Wicked Weeds of Unthankfulness and Ingratitude …

EDWARD (NED) WARD, 'A Step to Stur-Bitch Fair, with Remarks upon the University of Cambridge', *The London Spy*, 1700

William Soone had been Regius Professor of Civil Law between 1561 and 1563. His career was varied: he had also been professor of law at Louvain, but got involved in cartography, and assisted Abraham Ortelius on the Theatrum Orbis Terrarum *of 1570. Then he published maps on his own account, and made a version of Richard Lyne's map of Cambridge drawn for John Caius'* History of the University *(1574), publishing it in Braun and Hogenberg's* Civitates Orbis Terrarum *– ('The Cities of the World'). That such a work could be published indicates the growing interest in topography, and in the human geography of cities. In early 1575, Soone wrote a description of the University in a letter to George Bruin.*

The common dress of all is a sacred cap; (I call it sacred, because worn by priests); a gown reaching down to their heels, of the same form as that of priests. None of them live out of the colleges in the townsmen's houses; they are perpetually quarrelling and fighting with them; and this is more remarkable in the mock fights which they practise in the streets in summer with shields and clubs. They go out in the night to shew their valour, armed with monstrous great clubs furnished with a cross piece of iron to keep off the blows, and frequently beat the watch. When they walk the streets they take the wall, not only of the inhabitants, but even of strangers, unless persons of rank ... In standing for degrees, the North country and South country men have warm contests with one another; as at Oxford the Welsh and English, whom the former call Saxons. In the months of January, February, and March, to beguile the long evenings, they amuse themselves with exhibiting public plays, which they perform with so much elegance, such graceful action, and such command of voice, countenance, and gesture, that if Plautus, Terence, or Seneca, were to come to life again, they would admire their own pieces, and be better pleased with them than when they were performed before the people of Rome; and Euripides, Sophocles, and Aristophanes, would be disgusted at the performance of their own citizens.

The officers of the University which are perpetual, are, the Chancellor, who is now William Cecil, Lord Burghley, Principal Secretary of State; High-Steward, Robert Earl of Leicester; Syndic, a person well versed in the common law, Gilbert Gerard Attorney General; the Chancellor's Commissary, John Ithell, LL D. These offices are held only by persons of the highest rank, who by their influence can protect the rights of the University. The annual officers are, the Vice-chancellor, to whom all matters are referred; the Proctors, who moderate in the schools, take care of the watch, and of the meat, to see that it is wholesome; the Taxors, who take care of the corn; the Scrutators, who collect the votes in the senate-house; the Professors, who give lectures extraordinary, in Divinity, Civil Law, Physic, Hebrew, and Greek, and have each a salary of £40 per annum. The Apparitors, commonly called Bedels, have all titles, except one, who is the Vice-chancellor's Marshal. When the different ranks are assembled in the senate House, which is done by the Marshal going round to all the colleges and halls, and standing in the court with his gilded staff in one hand and his hat in the other, and with a loud voice proclaiming the day and hour of the congregation, you would think the wisest and gravest senators of some great republic were met together. To conclude, the way of life in these colleges is the most pleasant and liberal: and if I might have my choice, and my principles would permit, I should prefer it to a kingdom.

WILLIAM SOONE

Soone refers to Town/Gown scraps. Their origin is apparently ancient.

It must be admitted with regret that from the first appearance of a corporation of scholars in this place there dates also a long series of bitter feuds with the Town; the Scholars claiming for themselves complete immunity from authority and taxation, and, further, insisting upon their rights to carry the war into the camp of the common enemy, by testing their weights and measures, by prescribing what amusements should be allowed and what forbidden, and by trying to enforce morality by action in the court of the Vice-Chancellor ...

JOHN WILLIS CLARK
A Concise Guide to the Town and University of Cambridge, 1910

Such scraps still went on in the 1960s, when Bonfire Night was a time for more or less acknowledged, and not always bad-tempered, mayhem; the tradition is venerable. Long before Bonfire Night was invented, the townsfolk in the 1380s burnt down Corpus Christi, the College one of the town guilds had founded. Roger Ascham wrote on 17 September 1547 to Sir William Paget to complain of how the 'gentleness of the peaceful university' needed defence against the behaviour of the townsfolk in the time, just past, of the annual Stourbridge Fair. He complains that the proctors, patrolling as was their duty, had apprehended some 'nefarious persons' 'committing evils too great to be mentioned', and on seeking the key to the jail or Tollbooth (on the site of the present Guildhall) from the Mayor, were insultingly refused by him. Then they took their prisoners to the castle, where they imprisoned the miscreants – only to find them promptly set free by the Mayor's son. Calculated insult to the privileges and duties of the University, of course; so taken indeed, probably so intended.

Defoe, too, notices the tensions between the Town and the University resulting from their distinct jurisdictions:

I come now to the town, and university of Cambridge; I say the town and university, for though they are blended together in the situation, and the colleges, halls, and houses for literature are promiscuously scattered up and down among the other parts, and some even among the meanest of the other buildings; as Magdalen College over the bridge, is in particular; yet they are all incorporated together, by the name of the university, and are governed apart, and distinct from the town, which they are so intermixed with. The town is governed by a mayor, and aldermen. The university by a chancellor, and vice-chancellor, &c. Though their dwellings are mixed, and seem a little confused, their authority is not so; in some cases the vice-chancellor may concern himself in the town, as in searching houses for the scholars at improper hours, removing scandalous women, and the like. But as the colleges are many, and the gentlemen entertained in them are a very great number, the trade of the town very much depends upon them, and the tradesmen may just be said to get their bread by the colleges; and this is the surest hold the university may be said to have of the townsmen and by which they secure the dependence of the town upon them, and consequently their submission.

Thus I say, interest gives them authority; and there are abundance of reasons why the town should not disoblige the university, as there are some also on the other hand, why the University should not differ to any extremity with the town; nor, such is their prudence, do they let any disputes between them run up to any extremities, if they can avoid it. As for society; to any man who is a lover of learning, or of learned men, here is the most agreeable under heaven, nor is there of want of mirth and good company of other kinds. But 'tis to the honour of the university to say, that the governors so well understand their office, and the governed their duty, that here is very little encouragement given to those seminaries of crime the assemblies, which are so much boasted of in other places. Again, as dancing, gaming, intriguing, are the three principal articles which recommend those assemblies; and that generally the time for carrying on affairs of this kind, is the night, and sometimes all night; a time as unseasonable as scandalous; add to this, that the orders of the university admit no such excesses: I therefore say, as this is the case, 'tis to the honour of the whole body of the university, that no encouragement is given to them here.

DANIEL DEFOE, *Tour through the Whole Island of Great Britain*, 1724-27

❄

A proclamation, from about 1630, by the Town authorities reminds us that problems of riotous youth, streetlighting, water-supply and pollution are not new. They were certainly acute in a very crowded little town, still largely within the tiny compass of its ancient walls:

... divers disordered people ... not regarding the good of this Universitie, and Town of Cambridge, do suffer their chanels, streets, and lanes, to lie unpaved, ungravelled, and uncleansed; and do lay their muck, mire, dung, dust and other filth, in the open streets ... to the great annoyance, as well of the Students in the Colledges, as the Inhabitants of this Town.

There were other nuisances: dung heaps against the walls of houses and colleges, the streets running with the blood of beasts slaughtered by the butchers more or less where they pleased, 'guts, filth, entralls, and bloud of all their beasts', *not being dumped* 'unto the usuall common place, called the Pudding-pits, and the valley beyond the Castle-hills ... hog or hogs, pig or pigs' *being kept in the close-packed houses. The new conduit of fresh water (Hobson's Conduit) was clearly being misused for washing, and was also being polluted, for the edict forbids any washing of clothes or dyeing, except in the river itself. The streets were noisome with dead dogs, kitchen waste, and other rubbish; and a town where it was necessary to forbid people to* 'hang or lay any fish, skins, bedding, apparell, haires, or such other like things upon the walls of any Church, or Church-yard, payls, rayls of any bridge, or shambles, upon the like pain of vi shillings viii pence for every offence' *would have been colourful, to say the least. The well-remembered smell of fish in the 1960s by where old Falcon Yard used to join Petty Cury, where MacFisheries' shop spread its wares, is a faint echo of the malodorous town. But there were positive things: the proclamation also makes provision for streetlighting.*

That every Inhabitant in this Town do every fourth night hang out candle and lanthorn before his doore, from five of the clock in the evening untill the bell hath done ringing eight: and for the more convenient ordering hereof, we will that they take due course with their next neighbours, that by turns every night every fourth house have a candle light the said houres, untill fourteen days after Candlemas next …

❉

The Victorian installation of a sewerage system must surely have improved matters more than the Rev. Professor W. W. Skeat, one of Chaucer's and Langland's most distinguished editors, allows. Perhaps the fun in this extract is the tissue of quotations from Chaucer's Franklin's Tale:

THE DRAINS

This subtil clerk swich routhe had of this man,
That night and day he spedde him that he can,
To wayte a tyme of his conclusioun,
This is to say, to make illusioun.
By swich an apparence or jogelrye –
I n'can no termes of astrologye –
That he and every wight shold wene and seye,
Of Cauntebrigge the smelles were aweye,
Or elles they were sunken under grounde.
So thurgh his magik, for a wyke or tweye,
It seemed that the smelles were aweye.
Aurelius, which that yet despaired is,
Wher he shal han his hope or fare amis,
Awaiteth night and day on this miracle,
And when he knew that ther was noon obstacle,
That voided were thise smelles everichon,
Down to his maistres feet he fil anon,
And seyde, I woful wrecche Aurelius,
Thanke you, lord, that ben propitious,
That me han holpen fro my cares colde.

W. W. SKEAT, 1898

As it happens, 'they' are still digging up the streets to build a sewer, regardless of expense.

❉

Before the sewers, everything, in the end, drained into the river. For, as well as remaining a commercial waterway through the Backs until the late nineteenth century, it was still a major drain for the town's refuse and sewage, fed by the King's Ditch (which still, running under Pembroke and Downing Streets, debouches into the Mill Pool through a discreet pipe). There is a story that Queen Victoria, in Trinity on one of her visits, asked the Master on crossing the bridge what those pieces of paper were in the water. With great presence of mind he replied, 'Those, Ma'am, are notices prohibiting bathing'. But by the end of that century the drains celebrated by Professor Skeat had begun to make the river take on its present aspect as an amenity, a place of pleasure and social display. Even before then, the Backs appealed to the taste for the picturesque – landscape valued because it reminded of, could be seen in the static terms of, a painting. And so now: for many visitors do not see Cambridge when they are here; they see it in the photos into which they have dismembered it.

These grounds, then, as they are now disposed, consist of several walks with plantations of majestic elms, except one of a grand row of chestnuts, and two or three of limes. The walks are in general strait, and Cam moves near them; not crowned about here with much of his sedge, nor yet with cheerful underwood, but with slow, sullen course. Milton, therefore, was always for abusing him, whether writing in Latin or English. The narrow bed of the river does not admit of large magnificent bridges, but one by the late Mr. Essex, an ingenious architect, formerly of this town, is of great elegance, and universally admired ...

But, still our walks have their peculiar beauties adapted to the place, and the walk planted with limes from Clare Hall forms a vista, lengthened, and of admirable effect. You might say, perhaps, that Oxford has not anything of the kind equal to this: the eye is also carried across the river through a fine vista, formed by rows of lime and elm, as you come from Trinity library, terminating in Coton Church; the view of Clare Hall piece, as seen from King's College or Clare Hall, with the adjoining objects, forms a most pleasing landscape as seen over the Cam, and opening through a plantation of venerable elms to the adjacent fields. Any eye that can perceive rural beauty may dwell on these pictures with delight ...

GEORGE DYER, *History of the University and Colleges of*
Cambridge, 1814

❁

Charles Kingsley's hero, Alton Locke,

... wandered up and down, feeding my greedy eyes, till I found myself again upon the bridge where I had stood that morning, gazing with admiration and astonishment at a scene which I have often expected to see painted or described, and which, nevertheless, in spite of its unique magnificence, seems strangely overlooked by those who cater for the public taste, with pen and pencil. The vista of bridges, one after another spanning the stream; the long line of great monastic palaces, all unlike, and yet all in harmony, sloping down to the streams with their trim lawns and ivied walls, their towers and buttresses; and opposite them, the range of rich gardens and noble timber trees, dimly seen through which, at the end of the gorgeous river avenue, towered the lofty buildings of St. John's. The whole scene, under the glow of a rich May afternoon, seemed to me a fragment out of *The Arabian Nights* or Spenser's *Fairy Queen*. I leaned upon the parapet, and gazed, and gazed, so absorbed in wonder and enjoyment, that I was quite unconscious, for some time, that Lord Lynedale was standing by my side, engaged in the same employment.

CHARLES KINGSLEY, Alton Locke, 1850

It is difficult to work out where Kingsley envisaged his character as standing for him to achieve this view.

Just upstream of the town, along the Grantchester path, lie Grantchester Meadows, in early summer full of meadowsweet and buttercups. One American student here saw more in it than most:

WATERCOLOUR OF GRANTCHESTER MEADOWS

There, spring lambs jam the sheepfold. In air
Stilled, silvered as water in a glass
Nothing is big or far.
The small shrew chitters from its wilderness
Of grassheads and is heard.
Each thumb-size bird
Flits nimble-winged in thickets, and of good colour.

34

Cloudrack and owl-hollowed willows slanting over
The bland Granta double their white and green
World under the sheer water
And ride that flux at anchor, upside down.
The punter sinks his pole.
In Byron's pool
Cat-tails part where the tame cygnets steer.

It is a country on a nursery plate.
Spotted cows revolve their jaws and crop
Red clover or gnaw beetroot
Bellied on a nimbus of sun-glazed buttercup.
Hedging meadows of benign
Arcadian green
The blood-berried hawthorn hides its spines with white.

Droll, vegetarian, the water rat
Saws down a reed and swims from his limber grove,
While the students stroll or sit,
Hands laced, in a moony indolence of love –
Black-gowned, but unaware
How in such mild air
The owl shall stoop from his turret, the rat cry out.

SYLVIA PLATH, *The Colossus*, 1960

Messing about on the river is something almost every undergraduate did (does) and it is very much part of the 'Cambridge Experience' for visitors. Not so very long ago, when taking a punt along the Backs, there was a certain formality: smart clothes – blazer and flannels for the men, perhaps – certainly no radio, and decorous behaviour. To punt with elegance and courtesy was expected of all. A far cry from the Bedlam of a summer day now, when it is impossible to work in riverside rooms because of the shouting and screaming.

At the end of the last century, the favoured craft had been a Canadian canoe, and Scudamore's boatyard still has one or two for hire. They are not the easiest of craft to master, but are certainly easier than the punt. After the canoe as a craft had become unfashionable and the common drudge of the Fenman had become the elegant plaything of the leisured, its great advantage was revealed: in it one could be accompanied, preferably by a lady.

With a twinge of shameless pleasure I remember the dreamy flow of punts and canoes on the Cam, the Hawaiian whine of gramophones slowly passing through sunshine and shade and a girl's hand gently twirling this way and that the handle of her peacock-bright parasol as she reclined on the cushions of the punt which I dreamily navigated. The pink-coned chestnuts were in full fan; they made overlapping masses along the banks, they crowded the sky out of the river, and their special pattern of flowers and leaves produced a kind of *en escalier* effect, the angular figuration of some splendid green and old-rose tapestry. The air was as warm as in the Crimea, with the same sweet, fluffy smell of a certain flowering bush that I never could quite identify (I later caught whiffs of it in the gardens in the southern States). The three arches of an Italianate bridge, spanning the narrow stream, combined to form, with the help of their almost perfect, almost unrippled replicas in the water, three lovely ovals. In its turn, the water cast a patch of lacy light on the stone of the intrados under which one's gliding craft passed. Now and then, shed by a blossoming tree, a petal would come down, down, down, and with the odd feeling of seeing something neither worshipper nor casual spectator ought to see, one would manage to glimpse its reflection which swiftly, more swiftly than the petal fell – rose to meet it; and, for the fraction of a second, one feared that the trick would not work, that the blessed oil would not catch fire, that the reflection might miss and the petal float away alone, but every time the delicate union did take place, with the magic precision of a poet's word meeting halfway his, or a reader's, recollection.

VLADIMIR NABOKOV, *Speak, Memory: A Memoir*, 1951

A more recent phenomenon is the Chauffeur Punt, which does a very good trade indeed. And the river is still a good place for people-watching:

Now that undergraduates have to work so hard the most common sighting on the Cam is the Tourist Punt. These novices seem oblivious to the fact that punting is the Fens' revenge on tourists. Every summer they throw themselves at Scudamore's boat yard, waving money. And every summer a good percentage end up in the Cam waving their arms and, later, wringing out drenched Benetton sweaters. Poor technique and a deceptive current can usually be blamed, or perhaps one glass too many at the Baron of Beef beforehand ...

QUENTIN LETTS, in *CAM* (Cambridge Alumni Magazine), Easter Term 1993

❀

Not only the Lower River through the Backs is punting territory. The Upper River, to Grantchester, offers as much or more delight. Gwen Raverat recalls incidents from her childhood spent in the house that is now Darwin College:

... some things were very queer. For instance, there were the river picnics. All summer, Sheep's Green and Coe Fen were pink with boys, as naked as God made them; for bathing drawers did not exist then; or, at least, not on Sheep's Green. You could see the pinkness, dancing about, quite plain, from the end of our Big Island. Now to go up the River, the goal of all the best picnics, the boats had to go right by the bathing places, which lay on both sides of the narrow stream. These dangerous straits were taken in silence, and at full speed. The Gentlemen were set to the oars – in this context one obviously thinks of them as Gentlemen – and each Lady unfurled a parasol, and, like an ostrich, buried her head in it, and gazed earnestly into its silky depths, until the crisis was past, and the river was decent again.

Sometimes we children were sent off to fetch a compass round about the danger zone, and to be picked up by the boats further on; but sometimes we went in the boats with the grown-ups. And then I – but not Charles, which was so unfair – was given a parasol, and told to put it up, and not to look 'because it was horrid'. I obediently put up the parasol and carefully arranged it between myself and the ladies, so that I could see comfortably, without hurting their feelings. For I thought the bathing place one of the most beautiful sights in the world: the thin naked boys dancing about in the sunlight on the bright green grass; the splashing, sparkling river; the reckless high dives, when the slim bodies shot down through the air like angels coming down from heaven: it was splendid, glorious, noble; it wasn't horrid at all. It was the ladies who were horrid; but then, poor things, they always were even stupider than most other grown-ups.

I had not the faintest idea why they objected to passing the bathing sheds; though, with the fuss they made, it was really extraordinary that they never succeeded in putting ideas into my head. But they never did.

GWEN RAVERAT, *Period Piece*, 1953

Another view of bathers comes from A. C. Benson, in his diary:

Magdalene, July 8 [1911] – The heat insupportable … Biked alone round Horningsea: had some talk to my little gatekeeper at Clayhithe. Then along by the river; in this heat all decency goes to the winds – there were people bathing frankly all along – but it was very nice and summery, and gave a sense of holiday and golden age. What a pretty thing the human body is! I saw a fine radiant boy come out of the water, looking like a little god: in five minutes he was clothed and shouting, a horrible cad! Then I wrote an article on Oratory. It has been a happy day. In the evening sate out for an hour in the dusk, with Salter and Maitland. The electric works [*which used to be on Quayside*] throbbed, and a large orange moon went slowly down over the Pepys building. Vague scents wandered, obscure sounds thrilled in the twilight.

The Diary of Arthur C. Benson

Cambridge has a larger range of architectural style and manner in smaller compass than almost anywhere in England. Some buildings are of superlative quality – one thinks especially of King's Chapel or the Wren Library. Working in such a context must be daunting for any architect with an ounce of imagination – indeed, the silent audience of the past seems to bring out the worst as well as the best in new performers on this stage. Nikolaus Pevsner took on the joint task of adjudication and of educating new readers in the appreciation of buildings with some gusto.

One essential thing has to be borne in mind as of the highest importance for the future: the past at Cambridge has never been afraid of contrasts of style and scale. The chapel and Gibbs' building at King's remain as one of the classic instances in the architecture of all countries of the success which can crown fearless modernity, if handled sensitively ...

But as Pevsner observed, between the fifties and the seventies there was a dramatic change.

In the thirties and most of the fifties modern architecture was crisp, logical, of few words, and easy to convince anybody, one would have thought, yet the committees shied away from it. Now architecture tends to be overdramatic, aggressive, highly individual, and committees lap it up, even when carried to the excesses of the Faculty of History and the new Zoology and Mathematics Building on the site north of Downing Street.

The result of this dare-devil attitude of committees anyway is that Cambridge is now one of the happiest hunting-grounds in Britain for specimens of the architectural style and fashions of the 1960s, large and small, elephants and butterflies.

There are a few buildings of this century in Cambridge about which nobody can be without an opinion. Pevsner had many. Of Giles Gilbert Scott's University Library, (1931–4), he remarks:

An odd lack of decision goes through the whole design ... one is never sure whether the building was meant to be functional or for display; modern or traditional ... all the detailing is oddly small and busy.

He does not mention the similarity to Southwark Power Station, or that King George VI, visiting the town, is reputed to have congratulated the University on the acquisition of a 'power-house of learning'.

Of the Faculty of Arts on Sidgwick Avenue, within a stone's throw of

Basil Champneys' courteous homage to Norman Shaw's 'Queen Anne' style in the buildings of Newnham:

... picturesque layout is easier to manage than picturesque architecture, and picturesque architecture is what [Sir Hugh Casson and Neville Conder] have aimed at ... the visual effect is wilful or perhaps only playful, or one may be permitted to call it witty. That is what must have maddened the architect of the [adjacent] Faculty of History, who ... seems to be shouting rude words at the Arts Faculty. Don't think, he seems to imply, you can play at architecture ...

And of the History Faculty:

... visually, alas, part of the Faculty of Arts buildings. Perhaps if Sir Hugh Casson had not been so playful, James Stirling would not have been so rude. People in the last ten years have spoken about anti-art. Here – and only here at Cambridge – is anti-architecture. Here is an intelligent, resourceful architect making it his business to design a building which fulfils all the functional demands and yet is actively ugly – not ugly in the vociferous way of the brutalists, but ugly more basically by avoiding anything that might attract ... But never mind, it hits you, the architecture hits you, and that is what the facade – and the whole building – are meant to do.

On the other side of the building [*from the harsh red Accrington brick*] there is almost entirely glazing, and the glazing is of an industrial kind which is aesthetically as neutral as the glazing of a tomato-frame. The brick, where it appears, will never go mellow, let alone picturesque, and the glazing won't – so that is all right ...

To this criticism [*and there is more*] of James Stirling it must be added in fairness that *Cambridge New Architecture* asserts that 'Stirling has come as near as anyone to finding a physical expression of the "why" as well as the "how" of a modern university', and that consequently 'it has, internally at least, the inexplicable obviousness of a great work of architecture'. So that seems to be where the young stand.

NIKOLAUS PEVSNER, *The Buildings of England: Cambridgeshire*,
1954 and 1970

❂

Cambridge is not only Colleges and public buildings. Much is terraced streets, which, built for artisans of the last century, have become the 'des. res.' regions of the professionals and academics. When P. D. James described such a house in one of her novels, it was not yet owned by an editor of this anthology:

Norwich Street was a one-way thoroughfare and, initially, Cordelia approached it from the wrong direction. It took her some time to find her way back to Hills Road, past the Roman Catholic church and down the fourth turning to the right. The street was terraced with small brick houses, obviously early Victorian. Equally obviously, the road was on its way up. Most of the houses looked well cared for; the paint on the identical front doors was fresh and bright; lined curtains had replaced the draped lace at the single ground-floor windows and the bases of the walls were scarred where a damp course had been installed. Number fifty-seven had a black front door with the house number painted in white behind the glass panel above ... The front door was wide open. Cordelia pressed the bell and stepped tentatively into a narrow white hall. The exterior of the house was immediately familiar to her. From her sixth birthday she had lived for two years in just such a Victorian terraced cottage with Mrs. Gibson on the outskirts of Romford. She recognized the steep and narrow staircase immediately ahead, the door on the right leading to the front parlour, the second door set aslant which led to the back parlour and through it to the kitchen and yard. She knew that there would be cupboards and a curved alcove on each side of the fireplace; she knew where to find the door under the stairs ...

P. D. JAMES, *An Unsuitable Job for a Woman*, 1972

The 1960s and 1970s were a time of rapid change to the physical environment of the city. The pressure of new patterns of work, new patterns of shopping and provision of services, and of the motor car led to major re-development. But few cities, even in those barbarous decades, can have had quite so much of their ancient heart ripped out of them, to be replaced with the tawdry: Lion Yard and the new Petty Cury are already dated, and the City Fathers responsible immortalised their vandalism with their names grandiose and smug on a stumpy, ugly

pillar outside St Andrew's church. Further away, the Kite, that area of solid, sensible, well-mannered and unassuming Victorian housing between East Road and Maid's Causeway almost went the same way: much of it did.

ON THE DEMOLITION OF THE 'KITE' DISTRICT: CAMBRIDGE, 1980

On the smashed hearthstone or the fallen lintel
Carve words to witness:
> That men who called themselves
Conservatives, lying in their teeth, tore down
Good rooms, good walls of weathered brick, erasing
A wordless register of birth and death.

CLIVE WILMER, Devotions, 1982

A lost domain? That is what the sixteen year-old Frances Cornford seems to have captured in the following poem. She was Charles Darwin's grand-daughter and Gwen Raverat's sister.

AUTUMN MORNING AT CAMBRIDGE

I ran out in the morning, when the air was clean and new
And all the grass was glittering and grey with autumn dew,
I ran out to an apple-tree and pulled an apple down,
And all the bells were ringing in the old grey town.

Down in the town off the bridges and the grass,
They are sweeping up the leaves to let the people pass,
Sweeping up the old leaves, golden-reds and browns,
Whilst the men go to lecture with the wind in their gowns.

FRANCES CORNFORD, 1902

SOME CAMBRIDGE
VIEWS

———— ✱ ————

Visitors' impressions say quite as much about their expectations as they do about what they found and saw. Even as early as the sixteenth century, there is a sense of Oxford and Cambridge being places worthy of note and of possible moral profit to the curious traveller; indeed, it was in the last years of Elizabeth I that cultured men and women, not scholars or students, begin to visit the sights: the colleges and their libraries. The collegiate system, which had parallels in some of the mediaeval universities of Europe, was already intriguing visitors from abroad.

✱

Stephen Jorevin de Rocheford is given the Cambridge Tour:

I was introduced to the Principal of this college [St. John's], who had resided a long time in Italy, and spoke Italian well. He would not quit me till I had seen all the colleges, and every thing worth notice in the town. During the five days I remained at Cambridge, he conducted me over his college, and made me observe curiously the library, and the garden, which extends along the bank of the great canal of the river, where there is a long walk of several rows of trees. King's college, and that of the university, called Clerhal [Clare] are also remarkable, particularly the church of the former, which is the handsomest in the town. Its outside is ornamented with many little miniatures, and pyramids, which make it appear as if crowned with flowers. The windows seem to be of chrystal, of every colour, representing the history of the Old Testament; and under them, in bas-relief, are the blasons of the greatest lords of the country, which serve round about that fine church like tapestry. Its lobby or interval between the nave and choir, is in the fashion of a lattice, covered with leafwork, accompanied by all sorts of fruit and birds, represented according to nature, and so well, that the Principal, who had, as well as I, made the voyage of

43

Italy, obliged me to acknowledge that nothing more beautiful, or of better workmanship, was to be seen there. The whole of divine service is sung there every day to music. I think I there counted more than fifty musicians, as many clerks, and the like number of ministers. We ascended to the top of the church, which has a platform surrounded with balustrades, with four small turrets at the four corners, which gives much grace to this great edifice. The fourth college to be noted is Christ Church [*sic*], situated almost at one end of the town. Its fountain istolerably handsome. What are the most wonderful to see in Cambridge are the many fountains, although the town is situated on a low spot; and that there are so many people, and so many rich shopkeepers, that the scholars are scarcely perceived in the town, although they are in great numbers. Besides the two great streets, there is the large market-place, where a market is held several days in the week: it has a fountain in the middle, and round about it some good public houses, in one of which was my inn, where I treated the before-mentioned head of the college with some good French wine.

The Travels of Monsieur Jorevin de Rocheford, 1672

The French composer Saint-Saëns writes impressionistically of the Cambridge he visited to receive an honorary degree:

Writers more skilful than I have described the English Universities for the benefit of Continental readers. I am therefore free to write simply of the pleasure which I derived from my visit to the charming city of Cambridge. It is a nest of pointed arches rising out of foliage: strikingly original, with all its 'colleges', sprawling Gothic or Renaissance buildings, some ancient, some modern in the same style, with immense courts, magnificent lawns, and immemorial trees. They often adjoin one another, and, communicating thus, form complexes of monumental buildings and wide spaces, in which newcomers can easily lose themselves. Each college has splendid grounds, where the students take their leisure, not to speak of the river … where the famous oarsmen train. This open-air life, in which physical exercise plays a major part, is very different from that of our French students, and the pleasant shades of Oxford and Cambridge have nothing in common with the Latin Quarter ... Unfortunately, this form of education is expensive and therefore not available to everyone. Each college has a chapel – so they call it, though anywhere else it would pass for a cathedral – and there every day the students attend service and sing clothed in surplices. Not the least curious aspect of these Universities is their religious character – French students would find it difficult to take. But the English religion is not very burdensome. The services are very short and consist mainly of good music very well sung, for the English tend to make admirable choristers.

CAMILLE SAINT-SAËNS, *Portraits et Souvenirs*, 1900

Soon after de Rocheford, Celia Fiennes and John Evelyn visited. Celia Fiennes saw the town first, like Defoe, from the Gog Magog hills:

You have a great prospect of the whole Country and of Cambridge which is 3 mile off; the town which lyes in a bottom and marshy ground all about it several miles which is garnish'd with willows; the Buildings are old and indifferent the Streets mostly narrow except near the Market place which is pretty spacious, there stands the University Church.

Trinity Colledg is the finest yet not so large as Christchurch College in Oxford; in the first Court there is a very fine fountaine in the middle of the Quadrangle with a carved top and Dyals round; there are large Cloysters [in] the Second and the Library [*Wren's, then brand new*] runns all the rang of building at the end and stands on 3 rows of stone pillars; it opens into the Gardens and Walk with 3 large Gates or doores of iron carv'd very fine with flowers and leaves; the river runs at the back side of most of the Colleges; they have fine stone bridges over it and gates that lead to fine walks, the rivers name is Cam; the Library farre exceeds that of Oxford, the Staires are wanscoated and very large and easye ascent all of Cedar wood, the room spacious and lofty paved with black and white marble, the sides are wanscoated and decked with all curious books off Learning their Catalogue and their Benefactors; there is two large Globes at each end with telis-copes and microscopes and the finest Carving in wood in flowers birds leaves figures of all sorts as I ever saw; there is a large Balcony opens at the end that answers to the Staires.

A breathless lady, whose enjoyment survives her poverty of adjectives.

King's College Chapple is the finest building I have heard off, curious Carvings of Stone on the out side, 12 large windows and two at each end very large, all finely painted all over the history of the new testament; its a hundred and twenty steps to the roofe and supported by noe pillars all arch of stone, you walke on the arch or cradle as its term'd, there is 32 little windows cut in stone just as you ascend to the cradle or arch which runns on either side, and a pair of staires of 8 stepps to every three windows which lead up to the arch; thence you ascend the Leads over all which are fine secured by battlements round, there are 4 large Spires, at each corner one: on these Leads you may see a vast Country round, you see Ely-Minster and the towers; this is a noble building and stands on so advantagious a ground and so lofty built that its perspicious above the town; this is in lieu of the theatre at Oxford there being none here.

St Johns College Garden is very pleasant for the fine walks, both close shady walks and open rows of trees and quickeset hedges, there is a pretty bowling green with cut arbours in the hedges; Queens College is old but a stately and lofty building; Claire Hall [*Clare College*] is very little but most exactly neate; in all parts they have walks with rows of trees and bridges over the river and fine painted gates into the fields; Katherine Hall [*St Catharine's College*] is new built the Chapple was not quite finish'd, the apartments for the Fellows and Gentlemen Commoners are very fine, a large dineing-roome a good Chamber and good Studdy and this for £8 a year.

The Journeys of Celia Fiennes, 1697

More coolly and circumspectly, the diarist John Evelyn, one of the founding Fellows of the Royal Society:

This evening, to Cambridge; and went first to St. John's College, well built of brick, and library, which I think is the fairest of that University ... Trinity College is said by some to be the fairest quadrangle of any university in Europe, but in truth is far inferior to that of Christ Church, in Oxford; the hall is ample and of stone, the fountain in the quadrangle is graceful, the chapel and library fair ...

Thence to Caius, and afterwards to King's College, where I found the chapel altogether answered expectation, especially the roof all of stone, which for the flatness of its laying and carving may, I conceive, vie with any in Christendom. The contignation of the roof (which I went upon), weight, and artificial joining of the stones is admirable. The lights are also very fair. In one aisle lies the famous Dr Collins, so celebrated for his fluency in the Latin tongue. From this roof we could descry Ely, and the encampment of Sturbridge fair now beginning to set up their tents and booths; also Royston, Newmarket, &c., houses belonging to the King. The library is too narrow ...

Catherine-Hall, though a mean structure, is yet famous for the learned Bishop Andrews, once Master. Emmanuel College, that zealous house, where to the hall they have a parlour for the Fellows. The chapel is reformed, *ab origine*, built north and south, and meanly erected, as is the library ...

The Schools are very despicable, and Public Library but mean, though somewhat improved by the wainscoting and books lately added by the Bishop Bancroft's library and MSS. They showed us little of antiquity, only King James's Works, being his own gift, and kept very reverently.

The market-place is very ample, and remarkable for old Hobson the pleasant carrier's beneficence of a fountain. But the whole town is situate in a low dirty unpleasant place, the streets ill-paved, the air thick and infected by the fens, nor are its churches, (of which St. Mary's is the best) anything considerable in compare to Oxford.

JOHN EVELYN, *Diary*, 1654

So that's that.

❀

47

From Frankfurt came Zacharias Conrad von Uffenbach, book collector, scholar, antiquarian. He contemplated settling in England, but disliked the place, and Oxford and Cambridge in particular: so much so that he simply went home again. He visited in July and August 1710, when he was 38; his account gives an invaluable glimpse of the state of Cambridge, the College Libraries and their manuscripts at that time.

The town, which however, excepting the colleges, is no better than a village ... the state of the university ... is certainly very bad. ... Nor is the entertainment good; one must dine every day pretty nearly alike, as on mutton, etc.

We were amazed that no course of lectures at all are delivered, and only in winter three or four lectures are given by the professors to the bare walls, for no-one comes in.

Uffenbach on the different Colleges is worth balancing against the awe that very soon travellers would feel, or pretend to feel. He visited Trinity, and dined with its Master, Richard Bentley, arguably the greatest Classical scholar of his generation. He spoke, says Uffenbach, 'good and tolerably intelligible Latin'. Uffenbach was not impressed by Trinity:

The Hall: Very large, but ugly, smoky, and smelling so strongly of bread and meat that it would be impossible for me to eat a morsel in it. On both sides there are placed long narrow tables, and wooden benches ...The Library [*Wren's; begun 1675–6, completed 1684–5, at a cost of £12,213.16.1d*] ... a large building, exceedingly handsome, and set apart for the purpose. It is very light, long and well lighted, and also highly decorated. For not only is the floor inlaid with white and black marble, but all the cases are of oak ...

Or Magdalene:

After spending a couple of hours with Dr Bentley, we took leave, and went to see Magdalene College. It is one of the meanest here, of which king James used to say in jest, that he would go to stool there. It is a very old, and as I said, mean building; the library, which stands at the top under the roof, is also very small, and may perhaps consist of 600 volumes. All the books, with hardly one single exception, are entirely overgrown with mould.

Peterhouse depressed him:

In Peterhouse ... the library is in a poor room of moderate size. The MSS stand partly over the door and at the very top of the cases, and were so buried in dust that the librarian was forced to send for a towel, for me to wear as a pinafore, that I might not dirty myself too much. They were also in [much] disorder.

But he did like what was becoming a feature of Cambridge as of London life, the coffee house. There was one kept by a Greek:

In this coffee-house, particularly in the morning and after three o'clock in the afternoon, you meet the chief professors and doctors, who read the papers over a cup of coffee and a pipe of tobacco, and converse on all sorts of subjects; thus you can make their acquaintance. For here they are universally far more polite than scholars in London and elsewhere, and are also delighted to see strangers, fewer of whom come hither than to Oxford.

ZACHARIAS CONRAD VON UFFENBACH

Some found it was Cambridge society rather than its buildings that was interesting, even diverting. Charles Victor de Bonstetten, a Swiss visitor who became a friend of Thomas Gray, visited Cambridge in 1770. The man of fashion (which is what Bonstetten was) found Cambridge society tolerably amusing. He writes to his mother:

Cambridge, 6 February, 1770
So you want me, dear mother, to go to Paris. You imagine, doubtless, that I still know how to bow and to greet a pretty woman. One does not do anything like that in Cambridge. Face long and stiff, a gait deliberate and measured, bows with one's hat still on one's head – that is what is called decent behaviour in the homeland of Newton. Here people only meet each other formally, for in the morning you ask permission to see someone, and in the evening there are visits rather like ours between three and four. You will find three or four ladies sitting on chairs, and men in long black gowns taking up the sofas and armchairs. You enter,

removing your hat, and greet each person with 'Your servant, Sir', or 'Your servant, Madam'. To hold your hat under your arm, to have a smiling face, to give a lady a well-turned compliment, to cross your legs, to address courteous remarks to the men, to pick up a dropped handkerchief, to take a cup from a lady – in this place that would be the most ridiculous, the most unbecoming manners in the world; I several times nearly behaved like that, but I checked myself quickly, for fear I was taken for a well-schooled monkey. In France, and among us, silence in company is the most embarrassing thing in the world; sometimes I have seen it put the host and hostess in a cold sweat, and we are not embarrassed to break such a silence with a platitude, or by ...'Nice weather, is it not?' ... Only in England do people know how to be silent. I have seen about fifteen persons, men and women, sitting in a circle, not saying anything at all for a full quarter of an hour. There wasn't that feeling of embarrassment that there certainly would have been anywhere else in such a situation; nobody broke the silence simply for the sake of breaking it, but because they really had something to say. So, dear mother, you may believe these folk do have a different sort of mentality, a different taste, a different way of thinking and feeling ...

CHARLES VICTOR DE BONSTETTEN,
from The Letters of Thomas Gray

A very different, far less worldly visitor was George Fox, founder of the Quakers or Society of Friends, who came in 1694.

That Evening I passed to Cambridge: And when I came into the Town, the Scholars hearing of me, were up, and were exceeding Rude. I kept on my Horse's Back, and rid through them in the Lord's Power: but they Unhorst Amor Stoddart, before he could get to the Inn. When we were in the Inn, they were so rude there in the Courts, and in the Street, that the Miners, the Colliers and Carters could never be Ruder. The People of the House asked us, What we would have for Supper? as is the usual way of Innkeepers: 'Supper!' said I, 'were it not, that the Lord's Power is over them, these Rude Scholars look, as if they would pluck us in pieces, and make a Supper of us.' They knew, I was so against their Trade, the Trade of Preaching, which they were there as Apprentices to learn: that they raged as bad, as ever Diana's Craftsmen did against Paul. At this place John Crook met us. When it was within Night, the Mayor of the Town, being friendly, came and fetched me to his House: and as we walked through the Streets, there was a Bustle in the Town; but they did not know me, it being darkish. But they were in a Rage not only against me, but against the Mayor also; so that he was almost afraid to walk the Streets with me, for the Tumult. We sent for the Friendly People, and had a fine Meeting there in the Power of God, and I stay'd there all Night. Next Morning, having ordered our Horses to be ready by the sixth Hour, we passed peaceable out of Town; and the Destroyers were disappointed: for they thought, I would have stay'd longer in the Town, and intended to have done us Mischief; but our passing away early in the Morning, frustrated their Evil Purposes against us.

GEORGE FOX, *Journal*, 1694

❋

Many Colleges generate affection, in varying qualities and degrees, though few were as lucky as St John's in having a Wordsworth to recall his youthful years in its precincts. In fact, St John's was lucky even without Wordsworth, for one of the finest tributes to any institution had been paid to it earlier by Thomas Nashe. His preface to his friend the dramatist Robert Greene's 'Menaphon', in the middle of a general overview of the state of letters, scholarship, religion, the universities and the stage, includes this lovely tribute:

... yet was not Knowledge fullie confirmed in hir Monarchie amongst vs till that most famous and fortunate Nurse of all learning, Saint Iohns in Cambridge, that at that time was as an Vniuersitie within it selfe; shining so farre aboue all other Houses, Halls, and Hospitalls whatsoever, that no Colledge in the Towne, was able to compare with the tythe of her Students; hauing (as I haue hearde graue men of credite report) more candles light in it, euerie Winter Morning before fowre of the Clocke, than the fowre of clocke bell gaue stroakes; till Shee (I saie) as a pittying Mother, put too her helping hand and sent from her fruitefull wombe, sufficient Schollers, both to support her owne weale, as also to supplie all other inferiour foundations defects, and namelie that royall erection of Trinitie Colledge, which the Vniuersitie Orator, in an Epistle to the Duke of Somerset, aptlie tearmed *Colona diducta*, from the Suburbes of Saint Iohns. In which extra-ordinarie conception, *vno partu in rempublicam prodiere*, the Exchequer of eloquence Sir Ihon Cheeke, a man of men, super-naturally traded in al tongues, Sir Ihon Mason, Doctor Watson, Redman, Aschame, Grindall, Leuer, Pilkington: all which, haue either by their private readings, or publique workes, repurged the errors of Artes, expelde from their puritie, and set before our eyes, a more perfect Methode of Studie. But howe ill their preceptes haue prospered with our idle Age, that leaue the fountaines of sciences, to follow the riuers of Knowledge, their ouer-fraught Studies, with trifling Compendiaries maie testifie: for I knowe not howe it comes to passe, by the doating practise of our Diuinitie dunces, that striue to make their Pupills pulpet men, before they are reconciled to Priscian: but those yeares, which shoulde bee employed in Aristotle, are expired in Epitomes; and well too, they maye haue so much Catechisme vacation, to rake vp a little refuse Philosophie ...

THOMAS NASHE, 1589

❀

Mary Lamb could write at least as acutely as her more famous brother Charles, and with an equally sharp eye. She writes, on August 20, 1815, to Sarah Hutchinson:

In my life I never spent so many pleasant hours together as I did at Cambridge we were walking the whole time – out of one College into another. If you ask me which I like best I must make the children's traditionary unoffending reply to all curious enquirers – 'Both.' I liked them all best. The little gloomy ones, because they were little gloomy ones. I felt as if I could live and die in them and never wish to speak again. And the fine grand Trinity College, oh how fine it was! And King's College Chapel, what a place! I heard the Cathedral service there, and having been no great church goer of late years, *that* and the painted windows and the general effect of the whole thing affected me wonderfully.

MARY LAMB, 1815

Thomas Rowlandson (1757–1827) studied in London and Paris, and first exhibited at the Royal Academy at the age of eighteen. At twenty, he set up as a painter of portraits in London. Quite soon, however, he began to develop his talent for outrageous but very skilfully executed caricatures. He published much with Ackermann's monthly Poetical Magazine *and many of these illustrations were later collected into volume form as the* Tour of Dr Syntax *(1812) – an irreverent picture of town and country life. This work, and his comic engravings and watercolours, now secure his reputation. A master of elegant line and graceful composition as well as of, at times, ingenious pornography, he visited both Oxford and Cambridge and his view of the universities were characteristically both anarchic and closely observed. What, one wonders, was the future of this young student in the Public Library (the old University Library), who is far more interested in the elegant lady than he is in the weight of learning that threatens to crush his seniors.*

The Public Library, Cambridge

The Undergraduate Room

Bucks of the First Head

Smuggling In

Jemmy Gordon's Frolic

Emmanuel College Garden

Of buildings, it is King's Chapel, beyond question, that has generated the most writing from residents and from visitors. While most college chapels are small and intimate, this one has the dimensions and the grandeur of a cathedral, and it is so recognisable as 'Cambridge' that a travesty of its delicate outline adorns many an advertisement or logo for the town and for firms that trade within and from it. But such a treatment of the most adventurous of Perpendicular buildings was well in the future when Henry James saw it:

Of course the single object at Cambridge that makes the most abiding impression is the famous chapel of King's College – the most beautiful chapel in England. The effect it attempts to produce within is all in the sphere of the sublime. The attempt succeeds, and the success is attained by a design so light and elegant that at first it almost defeats itself. The sublime usually has more of a frown and straddle, and it is not until after you have looked about you for ten minutes that you perceive the chapel to be saved from being the prettiest church in England by the accident of its being one of the noblest. It is a cathedral without aisles or columns or transepts, but (as a compensation) with such a beautiful slimness of clustered tracery soaring along the walls and spreading, bending and commingling in the roof, that its simplicity seems only a richness the more. I stood there for a quarter of an hour on a Sunday morning; there was no service, but in the choir behind the great screen which divides the chapel in half the young choristers were rehearsing for the afternoon. The beautiful boy-voices rose together and touched the splendid vault; they hung there, expanding and resounding, and then, like a rocket that spends itself, they faded and melted toward the end of the building. It was positively a choir of angels.

HENRY JAMES, *Portraits of Places*, 1883

Some saw no such beauty: D. H. Lawrence remarked that the Chapel of King's reminded him of nothing so much as a sow on its back without its piglets. Coleridge, by contrast, sees transcendent beauty:

The principle of the Gothic architecture is infinity made imaginable. It is no doubt a sublimer effort of genius than the Greek style: but then it depends much more on execution for its effect. I was more than ever impressed with the marvellous sublimity and transcendant beauty of King's College Chapel: it is quite unparalleled.

SAMUEL TAYLOR COLERIDGE, *Table Talk: Conversations at Cambridge*, 29 June, 1833

For some, the Chapel illustrated the revenges of Time. George Santayana notes the irony: the Chapel, founded by the saintly but ineffectual Henry VI, was completed in the reign of that king, Henry VIII, who would preside over the destruction in England of the old religion that would have called Henry VI a saint:

Unhappy King, look not upon these towers,
    Remember not thine only work that grew.
The moving world that feeds thy gift devours,
    And the same hand that finished overthrew.
GEORGE SANTAYANA, *A Hermit of Carmel*, 1902

During the Second World War, many feared attacks on Cambridge's historic buildings, like the 'Baedeker raids' on places like Bath. The windows of King's were especially vulnerable. The historian John Saltmarsh, with his mutton-chop whiskers and field-worker's knapsack, was a classic Cambridge figure, a Fellow of King's and the world's greatest expert on the history of the Chapel:

Sir – Panel by panel the stained glass of King's College Chapel is daily borne away to a place of safety, where we trust it will survive the chances of war, to shine again in its former glory when peace is restored. The ancient problem inevitably recurs: by what happy chance has it survived so long? …

That each Fellow, when the Civil War broke out, made himself responsible for one window, took it down with his own hands and removed it by a secret passage to the College manor-house at Grantchester – this seems to be no more than a picturesque invention of the romantic nineteenth century. For one thing, we have before our eyes at this moment a tangible demonstration of the time, labour and skill required in removing the windows; I leave it to you, Sir, to judge whether the Fellows of King's were ever equal to such a task. The only tangible piece of evidence which lends verisimilitude to the tale is the secret passage. The Grantchester end of it is still there. From the cellars of the manor house it runs down into the bowels of the earth; but no one knows where it ends. A fiddler, they say, once tried to find out. Playing his fiddle as he went, he descended the passage; by the sound of his fiddle the people of Grantchester followed his progress further and further into the fields, till the notes grew fainter and fainter and died away; and the fiddler was never seen again. An old survey of Grantchester marks a field by the name of Fiddler's Close, not far from the Grantchester end of the present footpath to Cambridge. Perhaps the name records the spot where the fiddler was last heard on earth.

In deference to tradition, Canon Milner-White and I visited Grantchester Manor House, just before war broke out, to see whether the secret passage would lead us to a suitable hiding-place for the windows; but it did not. However, we were more fortunate than the fiddler; for we returned.

JOHN SALTMARSH, Letter to the *Cambridge Review*,
10 October, 1939

Josef Haydn, during his time in England, followed the tourist route. What one would give for his opinion on the music of King's rather than the stonework!

The King's Chapel is famous for the carved work of the roof, which is all of stone, but so delicate that nothing more beautiful could have been made of wood. It has endured already four hundred years [*actually about 250*], and everybody judges its age at about ten years, because of the firmness and peculiar whiteness of the stone.

JOSEF HAYDN, *Note Book,* August 1791

Maria Edgeworth, the novelist, visited on May 1, 1813, and wrote to her husband:

Now for the beauty of Cambridge – the beauty of beauties – King's College Chapel! on the first entrance I felt silenced by admiration. I never saw anything at once so beautiful and so sublime. The prints give a good idea of the beauty of the spandrilled ceiling, with its rich and light ornaments; but no engraved representation can give an idea of the effect of size, height and *continuity* of grandeur in the whole building. Besides, the idea of DURATION, the sublime idea of having lasted for ages, is more fully suggested by the sight of the real building than it can be by any representation or description: for which reason I only tell you the effect it had upon my mind.

The organ began to play an anthem of Handel's while we were in the chapel: I wished for you ... particularly at that moment! Your friend took us up the hundred stairs to the roof, where he was delighted with the sound of the organ and the chanting voices rising from the choir below. My father was absorbed in the mechanical wonders of the roof: that stone roof of which Sir Christopher Wren said, 'Show me how the first stone was laid, and I will show you how the second is laid.'

Mr Smedley exclaimed, 'Is not the sound of the organ fine?' To which my father, at cross purposes, answered, 'Yes, the iron was certainly added afterwards.'... At last, to Mr. Smedley's great joy, he got my father alive off this roof, and on his way to Downing, the new college of which Leslie Foster talked so much, and said was to be like the Parthenon. Shockingly windy walk: thought my brains would have been blown out. Passed Peterhouse, and saw the rooms in which Gray lived, and the irons of his fire-escape at the window ... I nearly disgraced myself, as the company were admiring the front of Emmanuel College, by looking at a tall man stooping to kiss a little child. Got at last ... within view of Downing College, and was sadly disappointed – It will never bear comparison with King's College Chapel.

MARIA EDGEWORTH, 1813

William Gilpin was less impressed:

King's college chappel gives us on the *outside*, a very beautiful form: *within*, tho it is an immense, and noble aisle, presenting the adjunct idea of lightness, and Solemnity; yet its disproportion disgusts. Such height, and such length, united by such straitened parallels, hurt the eye. You feel immured. Henry the Sixth, we are told, spent twelve hundred pounds in adorning the roof. It is a pity he had not spent it in widening the walks. We should then have had a better form, and should have been relieved from the tedious repetition of roses and portcullises; which are at best but heavy, and unpleasing ornaments.

WILLIAM GILPIN, *Observations on several parts of the Counties of Cambridge, Norfolk, Suffolk and Essex. Also on several parts of North Wales; relative chiefly to picturesque beauty. In two tours,* 1809

But the chapel is not simply a building. It is a place primarily for worship. Wordsworth wrote three of the Ecclesiastical Sonnets *on* King's. *Here is one that captures its sublimity:*

> Tax not the royal Saint with vain expense,
> With ill-matched aims the Architect who planned,
> Albeit labouring for a scanty band
> Of white robed Scholars only, this immense
> And glorious work of fine intelligence!
> Give all thou canst; high Heaven rejects the lore
> Of nicely-calculated less or more;
> So deemed the Man who fashioned for the sense
> These lofty pillars, spread that branching roof
> Self-poised, and scooped into ten thousand cells,
> Where light and shade repose, where music dwells
> Lingering – and wandering on as loth to die;
> Like thoughts whose very sweetness yieldeth proof
> That they were born for immortality.

WILLIAM WORDSWORTH, 1821

The Varsity Handbook (the students' guide) for 1959 warned against the emotional response to candlelit evensong in King's. Some needed no warning. One of the most delightful of Cambridge books is Period Piece *by Gwen Raverat, Charles Darwin's grand-daughter. She was sensibly acerbic about such sentiments as Wordsworth's:*

College chapels usually have the Litany instead of a sermon; this seemed to me the lowest layer of the dust-and-ashes of boredom and misery. I never listened to any part of the service except the Psalms; I liked them because I always liked poetry. For the same reason I did not like the hymns. I lived through the Litany by thinking what horrid words *Vouchsafe* and *Beseech* were, and wondering if they meant something frightfully improper; or by hoping that the pigeons would get inside the roof again.

For it was to King's College Chapel that we were usually taken; and that was another trouble: I couldn't bear the music there! I don't expect anyone to understand about this, but I simply hated the unfair, juicy way in which the organ notes oozed round inside the roof, and sapped your vitals, and made you want to cry about nothing at all. I liked my music dry, not wet, in those days, just as I still do. Dr. Mann was organist then, and I dare say that he was rather soulful; at any rate, I have never yet been able to dissociate music at King's Chapel from the kind of emotional appeal which I find most antipathetic of all.

GWEN RAVERAT, *Period Piece*, 1953

Virginia Woolf was notably less sensible – perhaps less observant too – about the chapel and its mysteries.

They say the sky is the same everywhere. Travellers, the shipwrecked, exiles, and the dying draw comfort from the thought, and no doubt if you are of a mystical tendency, consolation, and even explanation, shower down from the unbroken surface. But above Cambridge – anyhow above the roof of King's College Chapel – there is a difference. Out at sea a great city will cast brightness into the night. Is it fanciful to suppose the sky, washed into the crevices of King's College Chapel, lighter, thinner, more sparkling than the sky elsewhere ? Does Cambridge burn not only into the night, but into the day?

Look, as they pass into service, how airily the gowns blow out, as though nothing dense and corporeal were within. What sculptured faces, what certainty, authority controlled by piety, although great boots march under the gowns. In what orderly procession they advance. Thick wax candles stand upright; young men rise in white gowns; while the subservient eagle bears up for inspection the great white book. An inclined plane of light comes accurately through each window, purple and yellow even in its most diffused dust, while, where it breaks upon stone, that stone is softly chalked red, yellow, and purple. Neither snow nor greenery, winter nor summer, has power over the old stained glass. As the sides of a lantern protect the flame so that it burns steady even in the wildest night – burns steady and gravely illumines the tree-trunks – so inside the Chapel all was orderly. Gravely sounded the voices; wisely the organ replied, as if buttressing human faith with the assent of the elements. The white-robed figures crossed from side to side; now mounted steps, now descended, all very orderly.

VIRGINIA WOOLF, *Jacob's Room*, 1922

Actually it is Henry VI, the Founder, who stands over the lectern. Artistic licence or faulty memory has put a Johannine eagle in the precincts of King's.

King's Chapel at Evensong. The coloured windows faded gradually out: only a twilight blue was left beneath the roof: and that died too. Then, only the double rows of candle-flames gave light, pointing and floating above the immemorial shadows of the floor and the shadows of benches and the shadowed faces of old men and youths. Hushed prayer echoed; and the long rolling organ-waves rose and fell half-drowning the singing and setting it free again. All was muffled, flickering, submerged deep under cloudy water. Jennifer sat there motionless, wistful-eyed and unconscious, neither kneeling nor standing with others, but leaning rigidly back with eyes fixed and brilliant.

And afterwards came the emerging into a strange town swallowed up in mist. White surprising faces glimmered and vanished under the lamps. The buildings loomed formlessly in the dense sky, picked out by dimly-lit windows, and forlorn lanterns in the gateways. The life of Cambridge was thickly enshrouded; but under the folds you felt it stir more buoyantly than ever, with sudden laughter and talk dropping from the windows, weighing oddly in the air: as if the town were encouraging her children to sleep by drawing the curtain; while they, very lively at bedtime, went on playing behind it.

ROSAMOND LEHMANN, *Dusty Answer*, 1927

✺

Trinity has not only the finest of all courts, but also more Nobel Prizewinners than France. The two may go together. It has other virtues as well: it provides one of the finest climbing pitches in the town.

The flat land of the Fens provides no diversion for those given to various ways of disporting themselves on mountains. The fashion for rock-climbing grew greatly in the nineteenth century; Cambridge men began that long association, still maintained, with the Scottish and Welsh hills, the Lakes and the Alps. But Cambridge, too, had to be used. Quite soon, climbs of all levels of difficulty were developed over major Cambridge buildings. Handbooks were published, but, because of the illegality of the pastime, all these climbs had to be made in silence, at night.

A view seen by few visitors to Trinity:

... Crossing the corner on to the Hall by a convenient sloping parapet we get our first glimpse of the impressive summits of the Great Court range. The newcomer's attention will, however, be more probably drawn to the nearer heights of the Hall roof, which rises above him in somewhat threatening proximity. A step up on to the creaky wooden path that fringes it and all else is shut out by the impossible slopes of its smooth slates. Time and nerve sufficing an ascent may be attempted, and the slightly raised stone coping which edges either end of the slate-slopes gives the key. Holding its square edges with both hands and placing his feet on the narrow lead gutter, the climber pulls up hand over hand, the tension on the arms keeping the feet from slipping. The stone pilaster on the summit is generally embraced with panting satisfaction, as the height makes the strain upon the muscles considerable. A few moments can well be spared to the view, and few could be insensible to its charms. The distant towers of the Great, New and Cloister Courts looming against the dark sky, lit by the flickering lamps far below; the gradations of light and shadow, marked by an occasional moving black speck seemingly in another world; the sheer wall descending into darkness at his side, above which he has been half-suspended on his long ascent; the almost invisible barrier that the battlements from which he started seem to make to his terminating in the Cloisters if his arm slips, all contribute to make this deservedly esteemed the finest view point in the College Alps.

The Roof-Climber's Guide to Trinity, 1899

Buildings of one purpose can, clearly, be adapted to another, and not only by man. For beneath the path of these intrepid climbers, a considerable community of sparrows once roosted in the Hall; as is recounted by Vincent Bourne, (1695–1747), master at Westminster School, writer of Latin verse. This poem was translated by his pupil, William Cowper:

> None ever shared the social feast,
> Or as an inmate or a guest,
> Beneath the celebrated dome
> Where once Sir Isaac had his home,
> Who saw not (and with some delight
> Perhaps he view'd the novel sight)
> How numerous, at the tables there,
> The sparrows beg their daily fare.
> For there, in every nook and cell
> Where such a family may dwell,
> Sure as the vernal season comes
> Their nest they weave in hope of crumbs,
> Which kindly given may serve with food
> Convenient their unfeather'd brood;
> And oft as with its summons clear
> The warning bell salutes their ear,
> Sagacious listeners to the sound,
> They flock from all the fields around,
> To reach the hospitable hall,
> None more attentive to the call.

Arrived, the pensionary band,
Hopping and chirping, close at hand,
Solicit what they soon receive,
The sprinkled, plenteous donative.
Thus is a multitude, though large,
Supported at a trivial charge;
A single doit would overpay
The expenditure of every day,
And who can grudge so small a grace
To suppliants, natives of the place?
VINCENT BOURNE, translated by WILLIAM COWPER

The waiters at Trinity must have been shuffling china plates like
cards, from the clatter that could be heard in the Great Court.
Jacob's rooms, however, were in Neville's Court; at the top; so
that reaching his door one went in a little out of breath; but he
wasn't there. Dining in Hall, presumably. It will be quite dark in
Neville's Court long before midnight, only the pillars opposite
will always be white, and the fountains. A curious effect the gate
has, like lace upon pale green. Even in the window you hear the
plates; a hum of talk, too, from the diners; the Hall lit up, and the
swing-doors opening and shutting with a soft thud. Some are late.

Jacob's room had a round table and two low chairs, There were
yellow flags in a jar on the mantelpiece – a photograph of his
mother; cards from societies with little raised crescents, coats of
arms, and initials; notes and pipes; on the table lay paper ruled
with a red margin – an essay, no doubt – 'Does History consist of
the Biographies of Great Men ?'...

VIRGINIA WOOLF, *Jacob's Room*, 1922

*François Roubiliac's statue of Newton in the Chapel – Pevsner calls it 'a
masterpiece of quiet characterisation' – impressed Wordsworth, as it did the
severe William Gilpin at about the same time: not much else did.*

Trinity-library is a well proportioned room. In the anti-chappel,
the statue of Newton is a master-piece. The character is rather

boyish: but the attitude, the expression, the management of the drapery, and indeed the *whole*, and every *part*, are excellent. A fine Statue I have often thought one of the greater efforts of human art ...

WILLIAM GILPIN, *Observations on several parts of the Counties of Cambridge, Norfolk, Suffolk and Essex. Also on several parts of North Wales; relative chiefly to picturesque beauty. In two tours,* 1809

❋

The appeal of Clare College, less glamorous perhaps, is no less palpable:

King's College, April 18, 1844

It is very true that if a body wants to see the amenity of spring and of outward college life he should stand on Clare Bridge on such a day as yesterday, and look at the chestnut tree. Italian bridge and building most graceful, garden most serene, trees out a good bit further than in London, ... sweet smells rife, and birds besides, with the sun and weeping willow, and clean water below, and no gownsmen within sight (at least when I was there). It is the best part of Cambridge.

WILLIAM JOHNSON (CORY), *Letters and Journals,* 1897

❋

Arthur Sale's influence has worked like a yeast in the minds of many who encountered him while reading for the English Tripos in the decades from the 1950s to the 1990s. During the Second World War, when centuries of European civilisation collapsed into barbarism, Clare Bridge became for him a sustaining emblem of permanence and continuity.

THE BRIDGE IN MOTION

The bridge is always moving moving under arches over levels bevels in
the sunlight from and over itself sliding.
Sometimes the flow pleats to a crest, slants, slats
down like an unwilling Venetian blind,
but mostly as in a print by Hokusai
lazy easy corrugation of flame.

A microscopic core now of disturbance
where final shadows intersect the water
blows billions of bright arcs off, like a whirring
watch spring, with intact centre but with sides
elongating in rising aggrandisement
out of penumbra up the open courses
(shining put in shade and shorn by sunlight)
with concentricity and contact with
the shaping impulse lost, like flimsy fairings
of concertina lattice, shilly shally,
dancing amorphously advance retreat,
a tribal tomtom dart recoil repeat.

Punts chocking by, the bridge plots radiant cables
to check them, vainly, dwindling in the washes
lithe and sly enough for slithery fishes.
Or as the mesh tightens towards adherence
thin spinning parallels like silver birches
come floating free, then sliver, cakewalk, crinkle,
into the quickest craziest graphlines ever
charted the minute fevers of the river.

At any instant in each arch the dance is
different in time, in movement, in direction,
but on all sunwards vertical surfaces
tempos designs and sizes all collapse
into the shapeless routine leap and lapse,
the disa- reappearing repeated
unchanging childish joggle on the wall,
the insubstantial rock bottom of things,
monstrous reflections flickering on stone
of atoms in the stone, montonous
continuous performance of their newsless
spectral collisions: – impossible campaigns
where all are enemies and none allies
and random bombardment never slackens
and the fight is not for freedom but for bonds.

And yet, bewildering reversal of our
world wars, from those intestine jars emerges
not chaos but communicating stone,
a compact bridge is heeled from their loose scrimmage
(Some catspaw comfort accelerates the ripples)
– in what primordial grove does this arch vista
rocking like a bridge of rattan arrive,
where a frail culture of translucent mistletoe
crystals a myth of healing, not of murder?

For now from a world washed flat by total war,
and assenting to the judgement of its flood,
and quite innocent of hope for myself
or salvage, glimpsing in, though not on quest,
this play in air on stone of fire and water
(as if the bridge now made, not spanned, an abyss),
the vision of some pre-organic grail,
abstract, schematic, in-principial,
beyond colour, beyond mass, too calorescent
to transfuse in the crass warmth of the blood:
– half suffering, half blessing the unguessable
emblem, the baffling beating of the dance,
yes, I nod, yes, yes, though bungling the rhythm,
to the ripple under over through the bridge.

ARTHUR SALE, *The Bridge*, 1941

*One of the unsung beauties of Cambridge is Newnham College garden.
Designed by Gertrude Jekyll, its hidden art is the perfect complement to
Basil Champneys' 'Dutch domestic building – all red brick, white wood
and bow windows. Begun in 1875, Newnham was the second of the
women's colleges. The elusive femininity of the place was caught by Virginia
Woolf in her account of 'Fernham College, Oxbridge'.*

A wind blew, from what quarter I know not, but it lifted the half-
grown leaves so that there was a flash of silver grey in the air. It
was the time between the lights when colours undergo their
intensification and purples and golds burn in window panes like

the beat of an excitable heart … The gardens of Fernham lay before me in the spring twilight, wild and open, and in the long grass, sprinkled and carelessly flung, were daffodils and bluebells, not orderly perhaps at the best of times, and now windblown and waving as they tugged at their roots. The windows of the building curved like ships' windows among generous waves of red brick, changed from lemon to silver under the flight of the quick spring clouds. Somebody was in a hammock, somebody, but in this light they were phantoms only, half guessed, half seen, raced across the grass – would no one stop her? – and then on the terrace, as if popping out to breathe the air, to glance at the garden, came a bent figure, formidable yet humble, with her great forehead and her long shabby dress – could it be the famous scholar, could it be J. H. herself? All was dim, yet intense too, as if the scarf which the dusk had flung over the garden were torn asunder by star or sword. [*J. H. is Jane Harrison, the great archaeologist, one of the stars of Newnham.*]

VIRGINIA WOOLF, *A Room of One's Own*, 1928

The third of the women's Colleges – and, like Newnham, still single-sex – was built in the 1960s. New Hall was still bright and new when P. D. James placed some of her characters there:

New Hall, with its Byzantine air, its sunken court and its domed hall like a peeled orange, reminded Cordelia of a harem; admittedly one owned by a sultan with liberal views and an odd predilection for clever girls, but a harem nonetheless. The college was surely too distractingly pretty to be conducive to serious study. She wasn't sure, either, whether she approved of the obtrusive femininity of its white brick, the mannered prettiness of the shallow pools where the goldfish slipped like blood-red shadows between the water lilies, its artfully planted saplings. She concentrated on her criticism of the building; it helped prevent her being intimidated. … After two fruitless enquiries for Sophia Tilling's room, a hurrying student called back at her:

'She doesn't live in college but she's sitting on the grass with her brother.'

Cordelia walked out of the shadow of the court into light and over turf as soft as moss towards the little group. There were four of them, stretched out on the warm-smelling grass ...

Her first impression of the little group, influenced perhaps by the college architecture, had been of a young sultan taking his ease with two of his favourites and attended by the captain of the guard. But, meeting Davie Stevens's steady intelligent gaze, that impression faded. She suspected that, in this seraglio, it was the captain of the guard who was the dominant personality ...

P. D. JAMES, *An Unsuitable Job for a Woman*, 1972

❉

Magdalene College, as we see it now, owes much to the generosity and vision of A. C. Benson. In his diary for April 8, 1904, he wrote:

... Stuart Donaldson *is* Master of Magdalene! – I could really envy him this. I have thought very tenderly of the poor little College – so beautiful and stately and venerable, and yet so out of elbows and out of heart. I made a prayer that I might be perhaps allowed to raise her up.

The Diary of Arthur C. Benson

Later Fellow, President and Master, he got his wish. His love for the place is still apparent all around the college three-quarters of a century after he died.

The one room in my College which I always enter with a certain sense of desolation and sadness is the College library. There used to be a story in my days at Cambridge of a book-collecting Don who was fond of discoursing in public of the various crosses he had to bear. He was lamenting one day in Hall the unwieldy size of his library. 'I really don't know what to do with my books,' he said, and looked round for sympathy. 'Why not read them ?' said a brisk and caustic Fellow opposite. It may be thought that I am in need of the same advice, but it is not the case. There are, indeed, many books in our library; but most of them, as D. G. Rossetti used to say in his childhood of his father's learned volumes, are 'no good for reading'. The books of the College library are delightful, indeed, to look at; rows upon rows of big irregular volumes, with tarnished tooling and faded gilding on the sun-scorched backs. What are they? Old editions of classics, old volumes of controversial divinity, folios of the Fathers, topographical treatises, cumbrous philosophers, pamphlets from which, like dry ashes, the heat of the fire that warmed them once has fled. Take one down: it is an agreeable sight enough; there is a gentle scent of antiquity; the bumpy page crackles faintly; the big irregular print meets the eye with a pleasant and leisurely mellowness. But what do they tell one? Very little, alas! that one need know, very much which it would be a positive mistake to believe. That is the worst of erudition – that the next scholar sucks the few drops of honey that you have accumulated, sets right your blunders, and you are superseded. You have handed on the torch, perhaps, and even trimmed it. Your errors, your patient explanations, were a necessary step in the progress of knowledge; but even now the procession has turned the corner, and is out of sight.

Yet even here, it pleases me to think, some mute and unsuspected treasure may lurk unknown. In this very room, for over a couple of centuries, stood on one of the shelves an old rudely bound volume of blank paper, the pages covered with a curious straggling cipher; no one paid any heed to it, no one tried to spell its secrets. But the day came when a Fellow who was both inquisitive and leisurely took up the old volume, and formed a resolve to decipher it. Through many baffling delays, through many patient windings, he carried his purpose out; and the result was a celebrated day-book, which cast much light upon the social conditions of the age, as well as revealed one of the most simple and genial personalities that ever marched blithely through the pages of a Diary ...

A. C. BENSON, *From a College Window*, 1906

❊

The Diary was that of Samuel Pepys. William Empson, Fellow of Magdalene, recalls sleeping in the cloister under the Library where Pepys' books still repose. (The poem refers to the R. L. Stevenson of Travels with a Donkey *and to James Joyce's pun on the name of Alfred, Lord Tennyson.)*

SLEEPING OUT IN A COLLEGE CLOISTER

Stevenson says they wake at two o'clock
Who lie with Earth, when the birds wake, and sigh;
Turn over, as does she, once in the night;
Breathe and consider what this quiet is,
Conscious of sleep a moment, and the stars.
But it's about then one stamped on someone
And chose an animate basis for one's mattress,
It must be later you look round and notice
The ground plan has been narrowed and moved up;
How much more foliage appears by starlight;
That Hall shelters at night under the trees.
    Earth at a decent distance is the Globe
(One has seen them smaller); within a hundred miles
She's *terra firma*, you look down to her.
There is a nightmare period between
(As if it were a thing you had to swallow)
When it engulfs the sky, and remains alien,
When the full size of the thing coming upon you
Rapes the mind, and will not be unimagined.
The creepiness of Cambridge scenery,
In the same way, consists in having trees,
And never, from any view-point, looking 'wooded' —
What was once virgin forest, in safe hands.
    But here the opposite disorder charms;
What was planned as airy and wide open space
Grown cramped, seem stifled here under traditions,
(Traditor), their chosen proportions lost;
Here jungle re-engulfs palace and campus;
The '*high* hall garden' of Lawn-Tennyson
(This is the uncomfortable view of night)
Drowned under flounces and bell-calm of trees.

WILLIAM EMPSON, Poems, 1935

*Even more creepy must Cambridge scenery have seemed when, during the
two World Wars, most undergraduates were away in the Forces. In the First
World War, very few young men remained: most had volunteered for the*

carnage in Flanders. They returned (if lucky) to a town, university and world vastly changed – and the deepest changes were, as Conrad put it, 'inside'.

Trinity College,
Sunday Evening 19 Mar, '16

My Darling,

The melancholy of this place now-a-days is beyond endurance – the Colleges are dead, except for a few Indians and a few pale pacifists and bloodthirsty old men hobbling along victorious in the absence of youth. Soldiers are billeted in the courts and drill on the grass; bellicose parsons preach to them in stentorian tones from the steps of the Hall. The town at night is plunged in a darkness compared to which London is a blaze of light. All that one cared for is dead, at least for the present; and it is hard to believe that it will ever revive. No one thinks about learning or feels it is of any importance. And from the outer deadness my thoughts travel to the deadness in myself – I look round my shelves at the books of mathematics and philosophy that used to seem full of hope and interest, and now leave me utterly cold. The work I have done seems so little, so irrelevant to this world in which we find we are living. And in everything except work I have failed so utterly. All the hopes of five years ago come before me like ghosts ...

BERTRAND RUSSELL, *Autobiography*, Vol. 1 1967

A few months later the Council of Trinity College deprived Russell of his Fellowship because he was a conscientious objector.

Many dons, particularly in World War II, were engaged in war work of one sort or another, and one of the best kept communal secrets until the 1980s was just how many had played important roles at Bletchley Park, cracking the German Enigma codes and helping to win the crucial Battle of the Atlantic. Meanwhile, Cambridge had many refugees from the towns most vulnerable to bombing. Part of The Leys School became a military hospital, and the Colleges were used in different ways: as training centres, as hospitals, as billets – as they had been during the Civil War. Just a very few undergraduates continued their studies.

Sir James Beament, formerly Drapers' Professor of Agriculture, and Fellow of Queens', describes Queens' in Wartime.

By 1942 the College was a strange place with less than a dozen third year men, apart from those reading medicine. A quarter of the residents were St Bartholomew's Hospital students, and their relationship with Queensmen was occasionally somewhat volatile. Everyone had to parade at Grange Road at 8.50 on Sunday mornings, in what was euphemistically called the Home Guard, and undergo preliminary army training until 5 p.m., under the abusive orders of sergeants of the Irish Guards. One night in ten we also had to take our turn in the fire-watching rota, which meant sleeping fully-dressed in one of the two Air Raid Precautions rooms, after making tours of the College until 1 a.m. and bellowing our heads off at any window which was showing a chink of light. The then Senior Tutor, James Potts, was the College fire warden: a splendid sight with his red beard, white tin hat, and, usually, a pair of Bermuda shorts. The College found it so difficult to find firewatchers during vacations that I resided for most of the Christmas Vac. of 1942 entirely at College expense, theoretically firewatching every third night, although there was nothing to do except catch up on a large amount of academic work.

One of the impressive things about this period was the remarkably high level of honesty. Because of the risk, had there been an incendiary raid, we were not allowed to lock our rooms at any time whether we were in or out, but theft was almost unheard of. There were no smoke detectors or fire alarms. Compared with today's safety and security precautions, personal responsibility was taken for granted; *sic transit gloria mundi*.

Most of our rooms still had coal fires, but we only had a fire if we collected our ration – in sacks – from behind the old squash courts and hauled them up to our rooms. Throughout the winter the bedmaker came in at 7 a.m., lit the fire, and expected us to be up by 8 for breakfast in Hall. Indeed by 1941 all meals were in Hall because, with rationing, it was the only way one got any food, and in all the circumstances we were reasonably well fed. The only notable rebellion was against boiled potatoes in their skins for dinner after dinner, and when Archie Brown appeared on the gallery of Old Hall to make yet another announcement about food rationing, he was pelted with them. We were, however, issued with our tea and sugar rations. I collected sugar and packed four precious pounds in the bottom of my trunk. The paper bags did not survive the journey, but my mother salvaged it for a Christmas cake. Alas, she had also thoughtfully put moth balls in the bottom of the trunk. The cake, with all its other carefully hoarded ingredients, was ruined ...

Gates were locked at 10 p.m. with late passes after midnight. One of the oddest things was that, for a period, the door to the bridge from Cloister Court was locked at midnight, and, if one lived on the old side of the College, the only way to climb in and out was over the spikes at the end of Dokett, made more comfortable if one threw a Home Guard greatcoat over them. It seems surprising that, with clothes rationed, gowns were still made and had to be worn at night, but squares [mortar boards] were abandoned in 1942 because they became trophies grabbed in the black-out by US airmen with whom the streets of the City abounded. And, because gowns made us identifiable, a few of the pubs most frequented by the said airmen were put out-of-bounds to the University: there was, of course, no College bar ...

SIR JAMES BEAMENT, in *Queens' College Record*, 1996

COMING UP

———— ❀ ————

MICHAELMAS TERM, 1964

On gleaming flagstones
cold rain falls
     Young men walk
above the stores of vintage
   to the library
        CLIVE WILMER, *Selected Poems*, 1995

❀

*Many young men and women had their first sight of Cambridge in
December, at the time of the Examinations for Entrance Scholarships. Up
to a few years before they were abolished in 1985, the examinations were
held in Cambridge.*

Early December: an anniversary of some sort. Thirty-odd years
ago, a determined Headmaster had arranged to send me, with others from the Upper Sixth, to take the Scholarship examinations
for Entrance awards at the various Colleges of the University. (He
had said, encouragingly, 'Not that you stand much chance,
Moseley, but you might as well have a go ...') It was the time of
year when in the middle of the afternoon the dark huddled in
round the pools of warm gaslight in the Lancashire streets, when
the tarmac and the remaining granite setts glistened with winter
rain; and mornings broke grey and damp, with scudding cloud
chivvied off the Irish sea by the restless wind. I can remember
setting out, that first morning of the longest journey: I can feel still
the acute self-consciousness of the youth who desperately wanted
to start shaving, to cut a dash, but in a green shirt my frugal father
had said was 'big enough for me to grow into' and new shoes that
had not got the desired crepe soles. The others, I suppose, were of
like inelegance. We Lancashire lads knew little of Cambridge and
its ways, except for Walmsley, whose brother was already at

73

Queens' and who told us importantly that to play bridge was an essential accomplishment. (Partly so ...) For most of our little group that was our first journey away without our parents; we sat on the train to Bletchley and attempted to smoke sophisticatedly. We tried to read while the flat green of the Midlands, greying now into winter, went past the windows. Then Bletchley, and over the bridge to the train for Cambridge, calling at Woburn Sands, Lidlington, Kempston Hardwick, Potton, Longstowe, Lord's Bridge and other Adlestrops long gone to farmland and interestingly converted residences. The whole journey took nine hours: we arrived at Cambridge station's long platform when it was full dark. Walmsley, who knew the ropes and we believed him, insisted we avoid the expense of a taxi (half a crown, I remember) and get the bus. We stood: and as the bus paused at a stop I can recall the sudden glimpse, through the steamed bus windows, of Cintra House, ennobled by keystones which were portrait busts of those who had participated in that convention which I had read about because Wordsworth wrote a sonnet about it. The most interesting building, I thought, I had ever seen – indeed, very possibly my first waking up to the potential of beauty in architecture that was not ecclesiastical and *therefore* 'beautiful' – a word my father said in that context only with hushed awed voice and eyes narrowed. A walk down Downing Street in the damp evening; arrival at Queens' porter's lodge (then still in Queen's Lane) and direction by Pinner the Head Porter (who called us 'sir', and for some would become mentor and confidant in a few short months) to the room in Old Court I was to share with Abbott for the week of the exams. Neither of us had any idea what to expect. No staircase in Cambridge then had doors, of course; and we were unfamiliar with the two doors to our set, the outer oak to be sported whenever one went out or wanted privacy. ('Never knock on a sported oak' was one of the first conventions I was to learn.) There were other strangenesses: outside the doorway, a drain at the edge of the grass plot, into which after we had finished our ablutions we were to pour the hot shaving water our bedder tactfully brought us in the morning. The vast mediaeval room was heated by one gas fire; the little bedroom held two iron-framed beds with hair mattresses. The toilets were in the basement of another staircase across the court.

The college was very quiet, for it was after the end of Term, and most undergraduates were no longer in residence. Our room bore traces of those who had just gone down, whose places we temporarily filled: a brass ashtray with a couple of manly briar pipes, some books, magazines like the *Listener*, the *Spectator* and the *Field*. A pair of gumboots hinted at the sporting interests of one (which?) of the faceless people whose beds we occupied, whose names were painted, white on black, above the doorway and at the entrance to the staircase, whose (whose?) girlfriend's photo, with the face fashionably oblique, smiled at us from a silver frame on the mantelpiece. And along the mantel, above the gas fire, invitation cards from the previous term, held there by a string: 'Julian Clanmorris and Trevor Matthews request the pleasure of the company of ...' repeated with variations by other Julians and Simons and Davids and Edwards and Henrys and Richards whom, mostly, we would never know: and they suggested, even then, a social aplomb far from what the likes of us were used to ...

Memories of the next few days are piecemeal, fogged like fading photographs: the edges are dim. Finding the Latin exam ridiculously easy, and amusing myself with trying translation into different styles before walking out early. Outside, a foggy morning, and then going down a quiet, empty Trumpington Street, past the bulk of the Fitzwilliam, its cornices disappearing into the grey. Buying a postcard at the little Post Office to send home, warning my parents that the exams had gone badly. Above all, the evening mist by the river, and the trees' drip the loudest noise on Tennis Court Road as we walked to see one of our number who was trying for Downing; and alone, on the Backs, at dusk, the slow smoke of gardeners' bonfires tanging the nostrils and filling up the mist. There is, too, one curious and ineradicable memory: walking down the Grove of Queens' (then a quiet, secret place, behind one of the loveliest Fellows' Gardens in Cambridge) and finding a man with a gun: I saw him shoot a duck as it came gliding in to land on the water. 'That's how we get them, just at dusk,' he said. Now several people have told me that story is impossible: but it will not go away. And the Dean himself, now full of years, when asked about it, nodded, took his pipe from his mouth, and said, 'Yes, it was probably one of the porters.'

Tourists and undergraduates now take the tribes of duck on

the river for granted, and indeed, I have seen the Dean himself, in his room by the river, open his window and lean out as if from a pulpit to feed the large congregation of ducks which had assembled (for he is a regular man) beneath it, waiting for his bread to be cast upon the waters. *Esca viatorum*. But Henry [StJ.Hart] remembered the hard years of the Thirties, when food was short and there was real hunger in the town, and then – and for some years afterwards – there were few duck on the river. They were eaten if they settled for a moment. (It was alleged, by members of other colleges, that there were no deer in Peterhouse deer park because the Fellows of that House ate the last when meat was rationed during the war. *Se non è vero …*)

CHARLES MOSELEY, 1997

Bertrand Russell also recalls taking the Scholarship examinations:

My father had been at Cambridge, but my brother was at Oxford. I went to Cambridge because of my interest in mathematics. My first experience of the place was in December 1889 when I was examined for entrance scholarships. I stayed in rooms in the New Court, and I was too shy to enquire the way to the lavatory, so that I walked every morning to the station before the examination began. I saw the Backs through the gate of the New Court, but did not venture to go into them, feeling that they might be private … I was very anxious to do well in the scholarship examination, and nervousness somewhat interfered with my work. Nevertheless, I got a minor scholarship, which gave me extreme happiness, as it was the first time I had been able to compare myself with able contemporaries …

… other friends whom I acquired during my first term I owed chiefly to Whitehead's recommendation. I learned afterwards that in the scholarship examination another man had obtained more marks than I had, but Whitehead had the impression that I was the abler of the two. He therefore burned the marks before the examiners' meeting, and recommended me in preference .to the other man.

BERTRAND RUSSELL, *Autobiography*, Vol. 1, 1967

Not all aspiring undergraduates followed the strenuous route of examination and interview. Gaining admission in 1932 was, for one person at least, a game without rules.

As a student from the Middle East I came to England in the early thirties with the hope of reading law at Oxford or Cambridge. The Department of Education in Jerusalem had been unhelpful and discouraging: too late in the year to apply, they said. On arrival in July 1932 I stayed at Betty Nuttal's residential tennis club in Ealing and from there I wrote two letters of application to the Registrars of Oxford and Cambridge. The former was on holiday but the latter was willing to grant me an interview so I put on my best lounge suit and booked a room at the University Arms. Good impressions might do the trick, I thought.

At the interview the Registrary hardly looked at me and cared less about where I was staying. He did examine each of my papers thoroughly, however, among them a BA from the American University of Beirut. This was neatly written out in long hand, both in English and Arabic, the one from left to right and the other from right to left: neither script claiming precedence over the other. The Registrary examined it very closely (as though it was a Dead Sea Scroll) and kept on saying 'Extraordinary! Really extraordinary! I have never seen anything like this before!' All the time I was getting hotter and hotter. I presumed it was all hopeless. I would never be accepted

Finally, ignoring my BA completely, the Registrary pronounced that since I had already passed the London matriculation I would be accepted, but I should first proceed to find a college with a vacancy, which was unlikely; if I failed to find a vacancy I should try Fitzwilliam.

I walked out feeling happy but bewildered. A cabby outside persuaded me that I would not require his services to reach the colleges, and also explained the difference between Fitzwilliam and a traditional college. So I walked and walked for the rest of the day, in and out of colleges whose names I didn't even know, until finally I discovered that Queens' and Downing both had vacancies. But which to choose? Downing looked fine and new: Queens' was ancient by comparison. Who could advise me? As I walked in I noticed the elderly hall porter at the University Arms.

'Which should I choose,' I asked, 'Queens' or Downing?' 'If I had a son I should send him to Queens',' he replied without hesitation. 'Why is that?' I asked. 'Because Queens' is the older college by three hundred years,' he said, as if this was clearly self-evident.

I went directly to Queens' and was interviewed by that charming gentleman, Dr Venn, the President. The one and only subject he mentioned was games. Did I play cricket, football, row ... how keen was I? Fortunately this was the one subject I could discuss with some confidence. Having been educated at St George's in Jerusalem where most of the teachers were young Oxbridge graduates, games had already played an important part in my life.

Dr Venn seemed satisfied, but asked that I produce two letters of recommendation from notable persons in England. But I knew no one in England, notable or otherwise. I did remember however that as a boy my parents had been visited by an English writer. He had presented my father with a copy of his book, *The New Jerusalem*, but I couldn't remember his name. A bookshop in Shaftesbury Avenue advised me that the writer's name was G. K. Chesterton and he lived in Beaconsfield.

Having written and secured an invitation to tea. I duly went to visit the Chestertons. Mrs Chesterton welcomed me warmly, and took me into the garden where she showed me how well the cyclamen bulbs were doing which my mother had given her. When the enormous tea was ready Mr Chesterton emerged. The conversation centred on the help my father had given him with *The New Jerusalem*. I was overwhelmed by the genuine kindness of the Chestertons and left with a standing invitation to tea every fortnight and the letter for Dr Venn.

But how to obtain the second letter? In desperation I wrote to Sir Herbert Samuel who had been High Commissioner in Palestine and had therefore also known my father. I was very surprised when his letter arrived by return of post. Armed with the two letters I headed straight back to Cambridge and handed them to Dr Venn who read them and then broke out in laughter. I became very anxious. What could they have written about me that was so amusing, particularly as neither man knew me personally? Dr Venn explained that he had never received such a combination of letters before, one from a

Catholic convert and the other from a Jew recommending a student from Palestine!

FARID HANANIA, in *Queens' College Record*, 1996

Arrival: then what? All newcomers need advice: the Varsity Handbook *for 1955-6 – it was published year after year – counselled the undergraduates who arrived from the grammar schools set up under the 1944 Education Act. Some of the advice is simply practical; some more revealing of social and sexual attitudes unquestioned only a generation ago – for example, a snobbery (to which few then in Cambridge might have objected). On how to cut a dash:*

Throw those corduroys away; this is not Nottingham University. If you want to wear undergraduate uniform (which we don't particularly recommend, and which does *not* include any part of Army uniform!) it consists for lectures of sports jacket and flannels. Eminently preferable is cavalry twill trousers, and a blazer, but don't repeat don't wear a pullover with a blazer; it looks like Balham Tech. if you do. Otherwise suits on high days and holidays, and duffles any time at all. No macintoshes – this is NOT Balham Tech.

And on how to get a social life going: a now unrecallable mindset lies behind the simple remark,

If you want to take a girl out cheaply, take her to a Union Debate, held every Tuesday evening ...

Varsity Handbook, 1955–6

Notice the assumption that the reader is male – as the great majority of undergraduates were, even in the 1960s. The cause of higher education for women, argued passionately in the 1860s, attracted much – not always unguarded – support from Cambridge men, who sometimes damaged their own careers by providing it. A figure most influential in the establishment of Newnham, the second women's college, was Henry Sidgwick, whose desk, in the room of a Fellow of that College, is still pointed out as deserving of some reverence. The University did not allow women to proceed to degrees until 1947, when the first to hold a degree from Cambridge, Queen Elizabeth the Queen Mother, was given an honorary degree. But much earlier, academic distinction had been recognised. In 1890 a Miss Fawcett was placed above the Senior Wrangler – that is, came top of the list in the Mathematical Tripos. The men had something to say about the arrival of learned ladies:

BALLADE OF THE GIRTON GIRL

She has just 'put her gown on' at Girton,
    She is learned in Latin and Greek,
But lawn tennis she plays with a skirt on
    That the prudish remark with a shriek.
In her accents, perhaps, she is weak
    (Ladies *are*, one observes with a sigh),
But in Algebra – there she's unique,
    But her forte's to evaluate π.

She can talk about putting a 'spurt on'
    (I admit, an unmaidenly freak),
And she dearly delighteth to flirt on
    A punt in some shadowy creek;
Should her bark, by mischance, spring a leak,
    She can swim as a Swallow can fly;
She can fence, she can put with a cleek,
    But her forte's to evaluate π.

She has lectured on Scopas and Myrton,
    Coins, vases, mosaics, the antique,
Old tiles with the secular dirt on,
    Old marbles with noses to seek.
And her Cobet she quotes by the week,
    And she's written on Κεν and on Και,
And her service is swift and oblique,
    But her forte's to evaluate π.

ENVOY
Princess, like a rose is her cheek,
    And her eyes are as blue as the sky,

And I'd speak, had I courage to speak,
But – her forte's to evaluate π.

ANDREW LANG, 1890

❄

The distance between Girton and the town made bicycles, already the city's dominant mode of personal transport, inevitably associated with the blue-stocking. The erotic possibilities were not lost on a latter-day undergraduate Robert Herrick, who wrote this parody of 'Upon Julia's Clothes':

HERRICK ON THE TRUMPINGTON ROAD

When as on wheels my Julia goes,
Then, then (methinks) how sweetly shows
That piston-action of her toes.

Next when I cast mine eyes and see
That brave vibration each way free,
O how that waggling taketh me!

Cambridge Review, 3 December, 1896

❄

Gentle stuff, and miles away from the overt behaviour of modern Cambridge. A sort of bridge between the two eras is glimpsed in advice to arriving undergraduates ('undergraduettes', they were briefly and tastelessly called) in the indispensable Varsity Handbook *of 1958. Strange as it now feels, nobody then seemed offended by it:*

Yes, you are really quite a remarkable person, aren't you? You must have some academic ability, or you would not be here – and your school possibly thinks you are wonderful. As a woman you are in an enviable position; the men will outnumber you by ten to one. So what are you going to do about it? You can sit on your laurels and wait for the flies to swarm around the honey pot – men now, employers later. But why not try wearing those laurels for a change? The mention of Cambridge in itself is not an Open Sesame to all the best jobs when you go down, and there are quite a lot of other women in town ...

Work and sex are your immediate problems – especially if you have come straight from school. The first is the easier to solve. No one will force you to work, and you can get by on the bare minimum – although you will probably regret this in three years time.

Sex may be a more subtle difficulty. The shortage of women is such that again you may be able to get by on the bare minimum – but again you will probably regret it. Don't be blatantly sexy, but on the other hand remember that you are a woman first, then an undergraduate. Steer clear of the man who needs a mother substitute; you'll find yourself darning his socks and cooking his omelettes – and that's all. Afterwards he will probably go back to his mother – who can do it much better.

You need have no lack of escorts, but do treat them well. About 80% are on government grants, which were not provided with you in mind. You might offer to pay half, but, since most men here are gentlemen, this will probably be refused. The only alternative is payment in kind. Invitations to tea are usually acceptable (even as far afield as Girton) – but try to find something more inspired than toast and cakes. There is always your college ball at the end of the Michaelmas term to which you can invite the very special man. But above all, in return for that evening at the cinema, theatre, or what have you, do thank your host warmly and let him feel that you have enjoyed it – even if you haven't. This should not need saying. Too many Cambridge men, however, assure me that it does.

Marriage, or engagement at least, is likely to be your last problem. Be careful! The romantic atmosphere at your first May Ball may lead you to accept a proposal which you will spend most of your second year backing out of. At your last May Ball, before going down, there is just as much danger. You have probably been told that Cambridge is the best marriage mart in England – and this will be your last chance. Accept if you feel you really mean it – but try to imagine what he will be like away from his idealized setting, at breakfast in a two-roomed flat in Surbiton. So don't be dazzled by Personalities with a capital P – the Union Man, the Idol of the Cambridge Stage, or even the Editor of *Granta*.

Varsity Handbook, 1958

The poet Kathleen Raine went up to Cambridge (as increasing numbers of undergraduates did in the middle decades of the twentieth century) on a College Exhibition and a County Major scholarship:

I was admitted to Girton. My father was satisfied, my school was proud of me. That was to be the last moment, after childhood, when I was not at odds with the world ...

So little did I know of the world, so boundless were my dreams of what the realms of civilization had to offer, that I never doubted when, for the first time, I breathed the characteristic country-house scent of beeswax, lavender and chrysanthemums in the corridors of Girton that before me lay a future of unbroken happiness and freedom, leading to the realization of every hope ... Cambridge, because it was not Ilford, seemed to me paradise. I would henceforth spend my time among people of culture, in whose life of the mind, delightfully occupied with knowledge for its own sake, I would participate. These cultured companions would be mine; they would share my values and among them I would no longer be alone. Poets too I might meet – had not Milton and Gray and Wordsworth and Coleridge and many more gone up, as I was going now, as students to Cambridge? ...

With the same ease as that with which as a child I had entered the palaces and sat upon the golden thrones of some fairy-tale in the person of the Princess, and into a like unreality, I now stepped into the enchantment of Girton. From the lowest table in Hall I looked up at those great and learned ladies who, in lustrous Italian silks and velvets, with Victorian smooth-parted hair, seemed, at High Table, high indeed; as some of them really were. Tall, beautiful Miss Allen, then bursar of the College, had once, as a suffragette, been chained, so it was said, to the railings of Hyde Park. Now, as under the rule of some royal Abbess, she and her sister dons enjoyed the fruits of their triumph, that beautiful and happy College. There is a world of difference between the admitting of the sons or daughters of the obscure into court or monastery or college to live among an aristocracy (of learning, of religion, or of some other kind) and to learn its ways, and the looting of palace or abbey or college by the crowd, whose total possession can but be a total dispossession. For the looted palace is no longer a palace at all, nor colleges places of that learning which revolution sweeps away ... in those days revolution was the

83

last thing we wished for. We respected the inherited standards of excellence with no thought of changing them. The dons of Girton believed no less than did the Masters and Fellows of other colleges in the culture they had fought for women's right to share. We as students believed no less in the value of what they had won for us; perhaps even more, the known being limited, the unknown, boundless. Athens, Rome, Florence, all the glory of learning once contained in the word 'Renaissance', cast their magic on my expectation of what Cambridge would be. All knowledge, I thought, was there; as if knowledge and learning existed in a world of its own, in books and libraries. I did not understand that there is no such immortal being as 'civilization', only civilized people; and the continuance of a culture depends upon those who receive its inheritance.

At Girton, then, I first began to study my part ... Girton was itself the first building in which, by its proportions, its architecture (it was then the fashion to decry Victorian Gothic, but Girton, as an example of that style, is not without distinction) imposed certain intangible values and standards. On those lawns, in those cool corridors, I found myself conforming my behaviour to the architecture and the spacious scale of buildings and garden; walking with a prouder poise, with a sense of being visible to others of my own kind ...

Certainly I took too much for granted, even by the standards of those days. I felt no gratitude, so far as I remember, only delicious pride. I believed I had been admitted to Girton because of my deserts. During our first week the Mistress (a figure much like Queen Victoria in my eyes, and indeed her dumpy figure was of the same unqueenly cast) had told the 'freshers' assembled in the Stanley Library of the great privilege which was ours, of the many called and the few chosen. We were an elect, and of this we were well aware. Every woman admitted to the relatively few available places at the two women's colleges must have reached what was, in the men's colleges, scholarship standard. So it was said and so we willingly believed. It was for us, by our work, to justify our election ... We who in 1926 went up to our Cambridge colleges believed in the excellence both of the education and the culture transmitted by our University; we did not doubt the social value of an educated elite...

Mine was the Girton of Rosamond Lehmann's novel *Dusty Answer*; published the year I went up. I remember the Mistress asking a group of us (invited, as was the custom, in small batches to take coffee in that elegant sanctum, 'the Mistress's room') whether we thought *Dusty Answer* gave a true picture of life in College. I tactlessly said I thought it did; not an answer to meet with official approval. The Mistress could hardly have seen with Rosamond Lehmann's eyes (or with ours) the 'godlike young men' who in those days, when examination requirements were less stringent, adorned the Backs, the river, and the courts of Magdalene, Trinity and King's. The phrase 'godlike young men' was current in Girton; and only half in irony, after all. Neither in Florence nor in Athens, nor in Murasaki's Kyoto, could our young aristocracy have been surpassed in that wellbred grace of good looks enhanced by good manners, and by the possessors' own carefree assurance of their own godlikeness. We loved our lords. Innocent of politics, no sense of guilt clouded our enjoyment; a moment of civilized youth, whose joyous freedom will perhaps never come again.

KATHLEEN RAINE, The Land Unknown, 1975

Kathleen Raine was not well off, but her life was luxurious by the standards of the Poor Student: a hardy perennial of the past, and increasingly of the present.

October at length arrived; my little equipments were got together, and I started with a heart full of glee and joyous anticipation for the great seat of learning and science. The last sixty miles of my journey I performed on foot. I had been under the necessity of taking from Leeds a coach through the midland counties to London. I was accordingly set down at Woburn; it was about six o'clock on one of the finest October mornings on which the sun ever shone. The coach that runs through this beautiful village, between Oxford and Cambridge, had just passed, and I had only the alternative of waiting till the next morning, or travelling through to Cambridge on foot. I preferred the latter, and arrived within sight of King's Chapel spire, 'the Freshman's beacon', just as the shades of evening were setting in. As I approached I enquired the shortest way to Queen's College, and instead of passing through the town, was directed along that beautiful range of gardens, groves, and meadows, which fringe the banks of the Cam, as it rolls lazily along that picturesque line of Colleges which form the western suburbs. My strength seemed to be renewed as I strode with all the freshness of morning through the fine avenues of towering elms which intersect each other in every direction. Day-light was not quite gone; there was light sufficient to enable me to see faintly the beauty and magnificence by which I was surrounded, while yet the impending darkness threw an air of melancholy grandeur round a spot consecrated to my heart by every association that I loved, cherished, and venerated.

SOLOMON ATKINSON: 'Struggles of a Poor Student through Cambridge', in *London Magazine and Review*, April 1, 1825

Some more Varsity Handbook *advice, useful for the newcomer:*

The day-to-day administration of discipline is in the hands of the Proctors. These officials are elected by the Regent House from each college in turn. The office is held for one year, and four Pro-Proctors are elected for the same period to act as assistants. When on official business, a Proctor wears academical dress, the hood of his degree and bands. He is attended by two constables or 'bulldogs', who are University or college Servants selected, so tradition has it, for their sprinting abilities. These buffers wear full morning dress with top hats while on duty, and when attending the Proctors at the University sermon or at the Senate House they wear, in addition, long blue cloaks and may carry the Proctors' traditional weapons, a linstock and a partisan or short pike. Each of them carries a large book of University Statutes (which only go up to 1850, however), which he hands to the Proctor at the entrance to the church or the Senate House.

No meeting of the Senate is valid without the Proctors. They have the right to enter in the course of their duties any tavern or 'place of public assembly' in Cambridge, or any University lodging house. They may ask anyone if he is a member of the University, and require him to give his name and College if he is.

In general terms, the undergraduate must take care not to do anything 'cruel, dangerous, liable to produce gambling, inconsistent with gentlemanly behaviour, detrimental to good order, or violating the canons of morality and decorum'. In addition, he must show due respect and obedience to the Vice-Chancellor, Proctors and those in authority in the University. He must 'behave himself at all times becomingly and modestly' ...

DO

Wear a gown after dusk or when in the University Library or Church, or in the Senate House, also in lectures, and when paying calls on University officials. The gown must be worn 'in decent order and in the proper manner'. It is not worn thus ifworn over a sweater, or by ladies in trousers ...

Varsity Handbook, 1955

❀

Gowns were of course obligatory for Tennyson's generation:

On February 20th, 1828, my father and my uncle Charles matriculated at Trinity College, Cambridge, where their elder brother Frederick was already a distinguished scholar, and had won the University medal for the best Greek ode on the Pyramids.

Of their entrance into Cambridge, – my father told me that they had left the coach and were walking down Trumpington Street in the dusk of the evening, when a proctor addressed him, 'What are you doing without your cap and gown, sir, at this time of night?' To which, not being aware of the dignity of the personage who addressed him, he promptly retorted, 'I should like to know what business it can be of yours, sir.'

HALLAM, LORD TENNYSON: *Alfred, Lord Tennyson: A Memoir, by his Son*, 1897

❀

A hundred years after Tennyson, Peter Scott, the naturalist, went up:

In the autumn of 1927 I went up to Trinity College, Cambridge, to read Natural Sciences, Zoology, Botany, Physiology and, later, Geology ...

The Master of the college at that time was J. J. Thompson, the famous physicist. I remember having tea with him at the Lodge early in my first term and being miserable because my shoes were dirty. I had managed not only to get rooms in college but in Great Court, by dint of sharing them with Humphrey Trevelyan (son of the historian who was to be the next Master of the college and who was a close friend of my stepfather's). I have often wondered how Humphrey stuck it out for the whole academic year, because I must have been a tiresome room-mate. For a start there was the aviary which occupied half my bedroom, extended on to the roof and incorporated the sitting-room window. Then there was the Flying Phalanger ... But Humphrey remained good-natured all the time. My second year was spent in Neville's Court, and my third year back again in Great Court with another attic room.

Young years are formative years, and just as many of my contemporaries at Oundle must have gained a taste for Bach and Handel by singing choral works in chapel, so I believe that I am a better man for having lived for three years surrounded by the glorious architecture of Trinity College, Cambridge. Beautiful surroundings seep into one's system, and make one all the more aware of beauty later.

My career at Cambridge began quite respectably. I had no idea of the red herring I was soon to find myself following. I went to all my lectures and demonstrations, and worked away at my books. For exercise I went out beagling three times a week with the Trinity Foot Beagles. One day after trotting across the upland fields we ran down through a little marsh, and as we ran snipe jumped up on all sides of us. Running beside me was Francis Wayne, who was up at Magdalene, and between puffs he told me that he knew ... of a place ... where we could go ... snipe-shooting. This was a new and exciting idea to me and I sent home for my father's old Cogswell and Harrison gun. A week later (it was in November 1927) we found ourselves on the Washes at Erith. The Washes are not to be confused with the Wash into which they eventually run. They consist of a wide strip of grass-land, lying between two high banks, which can be flooded as a sort of safety valve for the drainage systems of the fens. There are Washes on three of the Fenland rivers – the Welland, the Nene and the Ouse, and those of the Ouse are also known as the Bedford Levels. Because the level of the flood-waters was affected by the tide, these Washes were long held to offer free shooting to the wildfowler ...

My enthusiasm for the wild marshes and the birds and the chase occupied too much of my time. We were, of course, entitled to be away from college on a limited number of nights during the term, but the restriction meant little, for it was not difficult to climb out of college. This, combined with a scheme by which the bedclothes on our beds were ruffled to indicate that we had slept in college, enabled us to spend as many moonlight nights down on the shores of the Wash as our consciences would allow, which was a great many more than our tutors or directors of studies could have approved.

Climbing out of college was only one aspect of climbing. Roof-climbing was a well-supported activity in the University in those days. I was one of the party which made the first complete circuit of Trinity Great Court but the climb that frightened me most was the ascent of St John's College Chapel. There was an overhanging cornice about sixty feet from the ground which required the most determined disregard of my indifferent head for heights. I never extended these activities to rocks and mountains perhaps because the call of the marshes was too insistent.

PETER SCOTT, *The Eye Of The Wind*, 1961

Donald Davie, the poet and critic, recalls coming up from Yorkshire in 1939, when Cambridge was host to other institutions evacuated from more vulnerable areas: the London School of Economics, several hospitals. The windows of King's had been dismantled and stored in a place of safety. But the place still challenged the young mind:

From that North – still literal, though already metaphorical also – I came in 1940 to Cambridge, on Scholarships and Exhibitions that I had won through fierce competition. It had been for too many years the pinpointed objective of my own and my parents' ambitions; it was impossible that Cambridge, or any other place, should have lived up to the hope that we had placed upon it ... Some time in that span of years I arrived at the diagnosis which I adhere to still: that the Cantabrigian ethos — is it Cromwellian? I persuade myself with some gratification that it is — leaves no margin for *caprice*, for that free-running, freely associating, arbitrary and gratuitous play of mind out of which, not exclusively but necessarily, art-works arise ...

To a Northerner such as I believed myself to be, or was determined on being – one moreover who, as it happened, had been reared a Baptist – a Cromwellian ethos should have had, and in some measure it did have, obvious attractions. It would certainly appear that Cambridge was more appropriately my university, than Oxford would have been ... Undoubtedly when, in my second term, I was supervised by Joan Bennett in her house at Church Rate Corner in Newnham, the somewhat self-applauding stringency of the Cambridge ethos, and its disputatiousness, were very much to my taste; I felt secure and at home with these fashions of intellectual life.

But already I go too fast, or I fly too high. 'Cromwellian', that 'ethos' ... what do they have to do, such words, with the timid and entranced schoolboy who first saw Cambridge at Easter 1940? Already timid, already entranced, I had changed trains at Peterborough or March, and had spun on, alone in the compartment, eyes wide and intent over the erstwhile undreamed-of fenlands. I was to sit the Scholarship examinations, and would sleep for three nights over one of the spick and span shops in King's Parade. Two or three others were there with me, and one was Arnold Edinborough. It must have been with Arnold and another that I sallied forth that first evening to wander, in the dank but luminous twilight, among college buildings of which I remember for certain only the Bridge of Sighs in St John's. That evening, if never since, Cambridge lived up to my expectations. And yet that is wrong too. For I had no preconceptions: the place was all a wonder, and I all wonderment before it – as I could not have been had I moved in my schooldays through medieval or Victorian cloisters.

DONALD DAVIE, *These the Companions: Recollections*, 1982

❊

Another poet, Thom Gunn, came up just after the War:

I almost didn't go to Cambridge. My headmaster thought I should, and I thought I should, but my father wasn't sure. I wasn't bright enough to get a college scholarship and my father wasn't poor enough for me to apply for a state scholarship. So while I did National Service there was the possibility that I might not actually get there: it was in any case dreadfully distant, an escape from the drudgery of the army into the bright and tranquil life of the mind. I wrote a poem addressed to Cambridge. 'Shall I ever rest on your learned lawns?' I enquired. That was my image of it, a lot of serene young men sitting around on the Backs reading serious books.

So when, during a first roll-call of freshmen in Great Hall at Trinity, a student answered his name with 'Here, Sergeant', and I joined the general titter, it was from relief. We were here at last in Cambridge, actually on the site of learned lawns. We had entered the tradition.

I certainly didn't perceive the snobbery involved. I would have warmly denied it indeed, because my expectation of the place was largely based on the picture given of it in E. M. Forster's *The Longest Journey*. I expected a lot of Ansells and Rickeys, and exciting talks about ideas.

And Cambridge itself collaborated with my expectations. The Master of the college, G. M. Trevelyan, who was by then a very small bent old man, had all the new boys to tea early in that first term, and told us sweetly and learnedly about the buildings and history that we were now the latest instalment of. He showed us an Elizabethan ceiling with great pendulous decorations like stalactites which had been discovered in this century above a false ceiling of a later date, put up when Tudor things had become unfashionable. And he described how one Master, Bentley, had locked all the Fellows in a room until they gave in to his requirements for palatial alterations to his Lodge.

Meanwhile for us there were bedmakers to bring up our shaving water, there were meals in the big shadowy Hall, there was the crisp beauty of the buildings – Neville's Court for perfection, Great Court for show, and Whewell's Court for living in. And even Whewell's Court, where I was for all three years, was a fine example of heavy Victorian Gothic.

One of my contemporaries arrived at Cambridge with a broad Yorkshire accent. But this was 1950, and he made it his business to reform it, so that by the end of the year he was talking through his teeth as affectedly as any of the young gents at the Pitt Club. I wonder if he has since changed it back again.

I was reading English, and shared supervisions with a wonderful Manxman called Seth Caine. We were studying *Piers Plowman* when we found that as members of Trinity all we had to do was ask the librarian and he would show us the fifteenth-century manuscripts in the Wren Library. So we went. He was kind to us and perhaps slightly amused, since we had come not so much to satisfy scholarly curiosity as to test our power.

But historic elegance, detached enlightenment and the life of the mind just about summed up my first year at Cambridge. I read Chaucer and discovered Donne. My supervisor, Helena Shire, worked me hard, and I liked her very much. I tried to smoke a pipe, but kept on coming across a residue of bitter juices from former attempts which was most unpleasant. This was in my first term, when I also toyed with the idea of buying a blazer, and wrote a series of poems about dejected old men walking through dead leaves. Then I became a pacifist. Then I read aloud from left-wing poetry of the thirties at meetings of CUSC, the socialist club, with John Mander, an Etonian Marxist two or three years younger than I, who was writing poetry that seems good to me even today. I couldn't help noticing that his poetry had a vigour somewhat lacking in mine. And as I got toward the end of the academic year I couldn't help feeling, also, that perhaps rather more might have happened to me than the life of the mind. It certainly did seem that there could be parties a bit more exciting than CUSC meetings: one saw dashing undergraduates hurrying *somewhere*, gowns flapping in the wind, and it was evidently toward parties one wasn't asked to. The truth was, I had the desire to be a social climber, but not the talent. I couldn't even find the bottom rung of the ladder, if there was one.

THOM GUNN, 'Cambridge in the Fifties', in *The Occasions of Poetry: Essays in Criticism and Autobiography*, 1982

❈

A different, White Russian, perspective – from the author of Lolita *and* Laughter in the Dark. *It would be nice to think the elegance of Nabokov's English owed something to his time in Cambridge:*

Late in the afternoon of a dull and damp October day, with the sense of indulging in some weird theatricals, I put on my newly acquired, dark-bluish academic gown and black square cap for my first formal visit to E. Harrison, my college tutor. I went up a flight of stairs and knocked on a massive door that stood slightly ajar. 'Come in,' said a distant voice with hollow abruptness. I crossed a waiting-room of sorts and entered my tutor's study. The brown dusk had forestalled me. There was no light in the study save for the glow of a large fireplace near which a dim figure sat in a dimmer chair. I advanced, saying: 'My name is –,' and stepped into the tea things that stood on the rug beside Mr. Harrison's low wicker armchair. With a grunt, he bent sideways from his seat to right the pot, and then scooped up and dumped back into it the wet black mess of tea leaves it had disgorged. Thus the college period of my life began on a note of embarrassment, a note that was to reoccur rather persistently during my three years of residence.

VLADIMIR NABOKOV, *Speak, Memory: A Memoir*, 1951

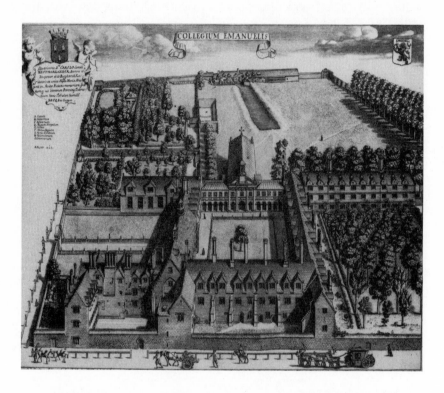

Collegium Emanuelis from Cantabrigia Illustrata, 1688
by David Loggan

ROOMS OF ONE'S OWN

❀

How can any boy fail to feel an ecstasy of pleasure on first finding himself in rooms which he knows for the next few years are to be his castle?

SAMUEL BUTLER, The Way of All Flesh, 1903

Not quite in those terms, but with palpable delight, Sylvia Plath wrote to her mother:

October 2, 1955
Sunday afternoon

I don't know how I can begin to tell you what it is like here in Cambridge! It is the most beautiful spot in the world, I think, and from my window in Whitstead [*students' residence*] on the third floor I can see out into the Whitstead garden to trees where large black rooks (ravens) fly over quaint red-tiled rooftops with their chimney pots.

My room is one of three on the third floor, and while it is at present bare of pictures and needs a bit of decorating, I love it dearly. The roof slants in an atticish way, and I have a gas fireplace which demands a shilling each time I want to warm up the room (wonderful for drying my washed hair by, which I did last night) and a gas ring on the hearth where I can warm up water for tea or coffee. I shall draw you a little map so you can see the layout. My books overflow everywhere and give me the feeling of color and being home ... Small, but capable of warmth and color after I buy a tea-set and a few prints for the bare walls. I love the window-sofa – just big enough for two to sit on, or for one (me) to curl up in and read with a fine view of treetops ...

I can't describe how lovely it is. I walked through countless green college courts where the lawns are elegantly groomed ... formal gardens, King's Chapel with the lacelike ceiling and intricate stained glass windows, the Bridge of Sighs, the Backs, where countless punts, canoes and scows were pushing up and down the narrow River Cam, and the shops on the narrowest streets imaginable where bikes and motorcycles tangled with the little cars. Best fun of all was the open marketplace in the square where fresh fruit, flowers, vegetables, books, clothes and antiques are sold side by side in open-air stalls ...

SYLVIA PLATH, *Letters Home*, 1975

Not long afterwards, Plath met her future husband, Ted Hughes. He had already graduated and was living in London, but, falling in love with her, he decided to re-establish himself in Cambridge. There were many young people in the 1950s and 60s living cheaply on the University's fringes, often in the barest of bare rooms. In those days, Petty Cury was a picturesque little street with many an ancient yard or alleyway leading off behind it.

It was somewhere to live. I was
Just hanging around, courting you,
Afloat on the morning tide and tipsy feelings
Of my twenty-fifth year. Gutted, restyled
À la mode, the Alexandra House
Became a soup-kitchen. Those were the days
Before the avant-garde of coffee bars.
The canteen clutter of the British Restaurant,
One of the war's utility leftovers,
Was still the place to repair the nights with breakfasts.
But Alexandra House was the place to be seen in.
The girls that helped to run it lived above it
With a retinue of loose-lifers, day-sleepers
Exhausted with night-owling. Somehow
I got a mattress up there in a top room,
Overlooking Petty Cury. A bare
Mattress, on bare boards, in a bare room.
All I had, my notebook and that mattress.
Under the opening, bud-sticky chestnuts,
On into June, my job chucked, I laboured
Only at you, squandering all I'd saved.
Free of University I dangled
In its liberties.

TED HUGHES, *Birthday Letters*, 1998

Others – including other Poets Laureate – have been more struck by the loneliness than the freedom. Tennyson, for instance:

[*Tennyson and his brother*] first occupied rooms at No. 12 Rose Crescent, moving afterwards to Trumpington Street, No. 57 Corpus Buildings. Although they knew but few men when beginning their University career, and were shy and reserved, they soon joined themselves to a set of friends who were all more or less remarkable. At first my father writes to his aunt, Mrs Russell: 'I am sitting owl-like and solitary in my rooms (nothing between me and the stars but a stratum of tiles). The hoof of the steed, the roll of the wheel, the shouts of drunken Gown, and drunken Town come up from below with a sea-like murmur. I wish to Heaven I had Prince Hussain's fairy carpet to transport me along the deeps of air to your coterie. Nay, I would even take up with his brother Aboul-something's glass for the mere pleasure of a peep. What a pity it is that the golden days of Faerie are over! What a misery not to be able to consolidate our gossamer dreams into reality ! When, my dearest Aunt, may I hope to see you again? I know not how it is, but I feel isolated here in the midst of society. The country is so disgustingly level, the revelry of the place so monotonous, the studies of the University so uninteresting, so much matter of fact. None but dry-headed, calculating, angular little gentlemen can take much delight in them ...'

HALLAM, LORD TENNYSON: *Alfred, Lord Tennyson: A Memoir, by his Son*, 1897

For some, arrival was a deeply unhappy, and very lonely, time. Rosamond Lehmann's novel Dusty Answer *was something of a* succès de scandale, *when it appeared: for her shy heroine, Cambridge provides an awakening into womanhood – but not yet:*

[Judith] surveyed the four walls in which her independence was to flower. They were papered in sage green with perpendicular garlands of white and yellow rosebuds. There was a desk, a kitchen chair, a cane table, a narrow iron bedstead behind a faded buff curtain; and a distinctive carpet. It was of a greenish brown shade, striped round the edge with yellow and tomato-colour, and patterned over with black liquorice-like wriggles.

'But I can't *live* in ugliness …'

A clamorous bell roused her from a state of apathetic despair; and she opened her door and crept along in the wake of the click of heels and the laughter of many voices.

This was Hall – huge, bare, full of echoes and hard light, whiteness and cold blue curtains … blue and high like twilight above ice and snow when the full moon is rising.

'I can always think of that and not mind if nobody talks to me …'

Down one wall, a row of black frocks and white aprons at attention; at the top of the room, High Table beginning to fill up: black garments, grey, close-brushed intellectual heads, serious thin faces looking down the room, one young one, drooping a little: piles of chestnut hair and a white Peter Pan collar. Crowds of dresses of all colours, shapes and sizes, all running about briskly, knowing where to go; a sea of faces bobbing and turning, chattering, bright-eyed, nodding and laughing to other faces, sure of themselves.

'Margaret, come and sit here … here … here! Next to me! Sylvia, next to me … Is there a place for Sylvia? …'

'I am lost, lost, abandoned, alone, lost,' thought Judith wildly and pounced for the nearest chair and clung to it. She was between two girls who stared at her, then looked away again. She bowed her head: the old terror of faces engulfed her.

There fell a silence. A voice like a bell went through the room, calling: *Benedictus benedicat*. And then came a roar, a scraping, an immense yelling that rose to the ceiling and there rolled, broke, swelled again without pause. Beneath its volumes she felt herself lost again; but nobody else appeared to have noticed it.

'Can I pass you the salt?' said her neighbour.

'After you,' said Judith earnestly.

ROSAMOND LEHMANN, *Dusty Answer*, 1927

Wordsworth does not invite you to visualise the room he had in St John's, but concentrates more on atmosphere, and the trains of thought it provoked:

The Evangelist St. John my Patron was,
Three gloomy Courts are his; and in the first
Was my abiding-place, a nook obscure;
Right underneath, the College kitchens made
A humming sound, less tuneable than bees,
But hardly less industrious; with shrill notes
Of sharp command and scolding intermix'd.
Near me hung Trinity's loquacious Clock,
Who never let the Quarters, night or day,
Slip by him unproclaim'd, and told the hours
Twice over with a male and female voice.
Her pealing organ was my neighbour too;
And, from my pillow, looking forth by light
Of moon or favouring stars, I could behold
The antechapel, where the statue stood
Of Newton, with his prism and silent Face,
The marble index of a mind for ever
Voyaging through strange seas of thought, alone.

WILLIAM WORDSWORTH, *The Prelude*, 1850

One of the most engaging impressions of undergraduate life at the end of the eighteenth century, for a man of modest means, is in Coleridge's letters to friends and relatives. A little later, Byron, with pride of title and a talent for running up debts, was able to play the Cambridge game with more panache and less hypochondria: but Coleridge first, writing to his brother, George Coleridge in 1791:

October 16th

Dear Brother
Here I am – videlicet – Jesus College …

I am very disagreeably situated on account of Mr B's plan of suspending the ten pound. I might daily by means of Middleton and his friends buy furniture, which will be necessary, at half the price, which I can have when the bills are sent in to [the] College

Tutor. If I had that money I could save near ten pound of the twenty allowed by the Hospital. Besides one feels cold and naked and shivering, and gelid, and chilly and such like synonimes – without a little money in one's pocket ...

A later letter (November 1791) to George suggests something of his routine, and it is one at which most moderns would quail. And there was still time to write letters that are even now worth reading ...

As I am now settled in my rooms, and as College Business is commenced, I shall be able to give you some little account of matters. We go to Chapel twice a day – every time we miss, we pay twopence, and fourpence on Surplice days – id est. Sundays, Saints' days, and the eves of Saints' Days. I am remarkably religious upon an economical plan.

We have Mathematical Lectures, once a day – Euclid and Algebra alternately. I read Mathematics three hours a day – by which means I am always considerably before the Lectures, which are very good ones. Classical Lectures we have had none yet – nor shall I be often *bored* with them. They are seldom given, and when given, very thinly attended.

After Tea – (N. b. Sugar is very dear) I read Classics till I go to bed – viz; eleven o'clock. If I were to read on as I do now — there is not the least doubt, that I should be Classical Medallist, and a very high Wrangler – but *Freshmen* always *begin* very *furiously*. I'm reading Pindar, and composing Greek verse, like a mad dog. I am very fond of Greek verse, and shall try hard for the Brown's Prize ode. At my Leisure hours I translate Anacreon – I have translated the first, the second, the 28th, the 32nd, the 43rd, and the 46th – Middleton thinks I have translated the 32nd ... very well – I think between us both, we might translate him entirely – You *have* translated 6 or 7, have you not?...

There is no such thing as *discipline* at our college – There was once, they say – but so long ago, that no one remembers it. Dr Pierce, if I am not very much misinformed, will introduce it with a vengeance this year. We have had so very large an admittance, that it will be absolutely necessary.

We do one declamation every term – two are spoken in a week, one English, one Latin. Consequently when the college was very thin, the men were pestered with two or three in a term. Themes and verses are in disuse at our College – whether the doctor intends to [restore] them [or] no, I cannot tell …

Those damp rooms (28 November, 1791):

Cambridge is a damp place – the very palace of winds: so without very great care one is sure to have a violent cold. I am not however certain, that I do not owe my Rheumatism [*he had complained of a violent head cold in the previous letter to George*] to the dampness of my rooms. Opium never used to have any disagreeable effects on me – but it has upon many.

And writing to Mary Evans:

Jes: Coll: – Cam: – Feb.: 7th 1793. I would to Heaven, my dear Miss Evans, that the God of Wit, or News, or Politics, would whisper in my ear something, that might be worth sending fifty four miles –; but – alas! I am so closely blocked up by an army of Misfortunes, that really there is no passage left open for Mirth or any thing else. – Now just to give you a few articles in the large Inventory of my Calamities. – Inprimis – A gloomy uncomfortable Morning. Item – My head akes – Item – The Dean has set me a swinging Imposition for missing Chapel – Item – of the two only coats, which I am worth in the world, both have holes in the elbows – Item – Mr Newton, our Mathematical Lecturer, has recovered from an Illness. – But the story is rather a laughable one – so I must tell it you. – Mr Newton (a very tall thin man, with a little tiny blushing Face) is a great Botanist – Last Sunday as he was strolling out with a friend of his, some curious plant suddenly caught his eye – he turned round his head with great eagerness to call his companion to a participation of the discovery and unfortunately continuing to walk forward he fell into a pool – deep – muddy – and full of Chick Weed. – I was lucky enough to meet him, as he was entering the College Gates on his return (a sight I would not have lost for the Indies!) His best black cloaths all green with duck weed – he shivering and dripping – in short, a perfect River God. – I went up to him (you must understand, we hate each other most cordially) and sympathized with him in all the tenderness of Condolence. – The consequence of his misadventure was a violent Cold attended with fever, which confined him to his room – prevented him from giving Lectures and freed me from the necessity of attending them – but this misfortune I supported with truly Christian Fortitude – however I constantly asked after his health with filial anxiety – and this morning making my usual enquiries, I was informed to my infinite astonishment and vexation, that he was perfectly recovered and intended to give Lectures this very day!!! – Verily I swear, that six of his duteous pupils, myself as their General, sallied forth to the Apothecary's house with a fixed determination to thrash him for having performed so speedy a cure – but luckily for himself the Rascal was not at home. But here comes my fidling Master – for – (but this is a secret –) I am learning to play on the Violin. – Twit twat – twat twit – pray, Mr De la peuche, do you think, I shall ever make any thing of this Violin? – do you think, I have an ear for Music? – 'Un Magnifique! Un superbe! / Par honeur, Sir, you be a ver great Genius in de music. Good morning, Monsieur !' – This Mr De la peuche is a better judge, than I thought for.—

This new whim of mine is partly a scheme of self defence – three neighbours have run Music-mad lately – two of them fiddlescrapers, the third a flute-tooter – and are perpetually annoying me with their vile performances, compared with which the gruntings of a whole herd of Sows would be seraphic Melody. Now I hope by frequently playing myself – to render my ear callous – as a lady of quality, being reprimanded by her husband for having eat onions, (or garlick) answered him – Why don't you eat onions yourself, my Dove, and then you would not smell them!

Valentine's Day, 1792, he writes playfully to the young Anne Evans:

My dear Anne, you are my VALENTINE. I dreamt of you this morning, and I have seen no female in the whole course of the day, except an old bedmaker belonging to the College – and I don't count her one, as the bristle of her beard makes me suspect her to be of the masculine gender. Some one of the Genii must have conveyed your image to me so opportunely – nor will you think this impossible, if you will read the little volumes, which contain their exploits, and crave the honor of your acceptance …

The quiet ugliness of Cambridge supplies me with very few communicables in the news way ... The Mutton and winter cabbage are confoundedly tough here, tho' very venerable for their old age. Were you ever at Cambridge, Anne ? The River Cam is a handsome stream of a muddy complexion, somewhat like Miss Yates, to whom you will present my Love – (if you like.) In Cambridge there are 16 Colleges, that look like work-houses, and 14 Churches, that look like little houses. The Town is very fertile in alleys, and mud, and cats, and dogs, besides men, women, ravens, clergy, proctors, Tutors, Owls, and other two legged cattle. It likewise —— but here I must interrupt my description to hurry to Mr. Costivebody's lectures on Euclid, who is as mathematical an Author, my dear Anne, as you would wish to read on a long summer's day.

Addio! God bless you, Ma chère Soeur, and your affectionate Frère,

S T Coleridge.

P.S. I add a postscript on purpose to communicate a joke to you. A party of us had been drinking wine together, and three or four freshmen were most deplorably intoxicated – (I have too great a respect for delicacy to say Drunk). As we were returning homewards two of them fell into the gutter (or kennel.) We ran to assist one of them – who very generously stuttered out, as he lay sprawling in the mud – Nnn no nn no ! – ssave my ffrfriend there – nnever mind me – *I* can swim.

SAMUEL TAYLOR COLERIDGE

Byron went up to Trinity on October 24, 1805 – three days after Trafalgar, and probably before the news of Nelson's victory arrived. First things first: on October 26, he writes to John Hanson, his lawyer:

Dear Sir – I will be obliged to you to order me down 4 Dozen of Wine, Port, Sherry – Claret, & Madeira, one Dozen of Each; I have got part of my Furniture in, & begin to *admire* a College Life. Yesterday my appearance in the Hall in my State Robes was *Superb*, but uncomfortable to my *Diffidence*. You may order the saddle & & for Oateater [*his horse*] as soon as you please & I will pay for them.

A month later, the wine having arrived:

Cambridge Novr. 23d. 1805
... I will settle with you for the Saddle and accoutrements *next* quarter. The Upholsterer's bill will not be sent in yet, as my Rooms are to be papered and painted at Xmas, when I will procure them; No Furniture has yet been got except what was absolutely necessary, including some decanters and wine Glasses ...

Those were the days when peers had their own special academical dress; until the mid twentieth century, undergraduates coming into residence were responsible (as Coleridge understood) for the furnishing of their own rooms.

[*To Augusta Byron*] *Trin. Coll.* Novr. 6th, 1805
My Dear Augusta – As might be supposed I like a College Life extremely, especially as I have escaped the Trammels or rather *Fetters* of my domestic Tyrant Mrs Byron, who continued to plague me during my visit in July and September. I am now most pleasantly situated in *Super*excellent Rooms, flanked on one side by my Tutor, on the other by an old Fellow, both of whom are rather checks upon my *vivacity*. I am allowed 500 a year, a Servant and Horse, so Feel as independent as a German Prince who coins his own Cash, or a Cherokee Chief who coins no Cash at all, but enjoys what is more precious, Liberty. I talk in raptures of that *Goddess* because my amiable Mama was so despotic ...

[*To Hargreaves Hanson*] *Trinity Coll. Novr. 12th. 1805*
College improves in every thing but Learning, nobody here seems to look into an author ancient or modern if they can avoid it. The Muses poor Devils, are totally neglected, except by a few Musty old *Sophs* and *Fellows*, who however agreeable they may be to *Minerva*, are perfect Antidotes to the *Graces*. Even I (great as is my *inclination* for *Knowledge*) am carried away by the Tide, having only supped at Home twice, since I saw your Father, and have more Engagements on my hands for A Week to come. Still my Tutor &

I go on extremely well, and for the 1st three weeks of my Life, I have not involved myself in any Scrape of Consequence ...

GEORGE GORDON, LORD BYRON

A century later, Frances Partridge recalls her life in Newnham in 1918. Much, obviously, had changed: but here too is the sense of youthful excitement at new-found independence:

My memories of those three exciting years shift and change pattern like the pieces in a kaleidoscope whose colours clash at one moment and are in ravishing harmony the next. What more perfect setting for the euphoria of youth could there be than Cambridge, with its idyllic beauty, surprising inhabitants, and a mental climate in which ideas sprouted, grew and changed shape? The place itself has not altered much since then, except that there are now, alas, no shiny brown hansom-cabs, nor ancient, learned-looking individuals traversing the streets on tricycles. Newnham College was never beautiful, its austere cream-washed corridors and common-room had a conventual air, yet, spinning downhill to lectures on our bicycles we felt we were members of the University, as we were sure the Girton girls – coming in by 'bus from their gloomy fastness – could not. Moreover, we had a charming garden where lilac and roses bloomed in profusion, and nightingales sang all night. So greatly did their exotic music thrill me that one fine summer I rigged up an uncomfortable species of chair-bed, on which it was impossible to do more than half lie, half sit, on a tiny balcony overlooking the garden, and slept there every night.

At weekends we often walked across the fens, past the sliding river, or down the footpath to Grantchester to pick bunches of red berries and leaves to decorate our rooms – that path, too, seems still unchanged except that it is no longer haunted by the disquieting presence of the village idiot. In Spring there were the famous displays of crocuses on the Backs, and soon afterwards the cherry trees spread their flowery arms over long grass full of scarlet tulips and martagon lilies, in faithful imitation of an Impressionist painting. And there was the Cam itself. Narrow and often muddy though it might be, there were many ways of possessing it. One could swim in it; take a canoe up to Byron's Pool and beyond, join a punt party with a picnic, or moor oneself alone in a secluded backwater with a book, enjoying the calm that comes from that perfect horizontality which is the keynote of the Cambridge landscape.

Did we discuss the good, the true and the beautiful, as undergraduates are supposed to do? Yes, certainly, but a great many much more frivolous subjects as well; and a new set of rather naive political or moral topics swam into our ken – egalitarianism versus individualism, for instance; free love versus marriage; whether there should be inherited wealth (this worried me a good deal), and even whether it was right to breed and kill animals for our food. For a short while Dot and I were registered as vegetarians, but our resolve soon crumbled before the starvation diet the college chef allowed us – one stuffed tomato does not make a dinner.

In October 1918 the propriety of the women's colleges and the virtue of their inmates were protected by a system of regulations as prehistoric as the walls topped with broken glass which used to enclose great estates. And, of course, for four years there had been few marauders. But in my very first term the War ended and young men flooded back, many of whom had been in the forces and were anxious to make up for lost time, and more interested in dancing and taking girls out than in swotting for their degrees ... What was to be done about the antiquated rules which decreed that no female undergraduate could visit a male one in his room, or entertain him in hers, unless a married lady was present as chaperone? It seems quite incredible now, but so it was. For my part I was reduced to inventing an imaginary duenna called Mrs Kenyon, whose services I called on quite often. Of course Pernel Strachey [*Principal of Peile Hall, where Frances Partridge resided*] didn't believe in her; she must have been well acquainted with all the Cambridge ladies, so I think it was mainly to tease me that she suddenly said to me one day, when I was lunching at the high table: 'And what is this Mrs Kenyon like? Do you find her charming?' Goodness knows what nonsense I mumbled.

But there was gunpowder in the air, and it finally exploded at a meeting between students and dons, convened to consider the question of chaperonage, when a brave girl stood up and asked why it was that an exception was made for those girls rich enough to have a sitting-room as well as a bedroom. In a dead silence she enquired: 'Is this because it is thought that the sight of the beds in our bed-sitting-rooms would be too much of a temptation?' This occasion, if not this actual remark, sounded the death-knell of chaperones. After this we met the men freely, played tennis with them, went punting and on picnics, and above all danced with them. All England had gone dancing mad and so had Cambridge. A University dance club called the Quinquaginta was formed, meeting weekly and admirably supplied with music by a jazz band of undergraduates. Dot and I were original members, and immodesty compels me to admit that we were among the stars, and our programmes filled up a week ahead. Lord Louis Mountbatten was one of the early members and I used to have a dance with him every week, though too shy to make much headway into friendship. But money for clothes was hard to come by. I had only one evening dress (an old one of Ray's), and Dot not very many more, yet we were so ashamed of always looking exactly the same that we bought or begged lengths of stuff to make one or two variations on our monotonous themes. I had neither skill nor knowledge of dressmaking, and being impatient by nature I cut and stitched away at random, adding a bit of ribbon for a belt, elastic in the hem to give the fashionable 'Turkish trouser' look and heaven knows what beside. I must have looked a perfect fright and was lucky not to come to pieces in mid-tango, yet no-one seemed surprised. Finally I got so sick of Ray's old dress that I dyed it black (an 'unsuitable' colour for girls at the time), and removed most of the front and all the back down to the waist, so as to give a startling decolletage which I vaguely shrouded in some pieces of gauze rather like wings. In this getup I was reported to look very 'fast' indeed – and that I certainly was not.

The difficulty about this obsessional dancing life was that all we cared about in our partners was their technical ability – they must be first-rate performers – and such young men were often great bores to talk to. We finally got paired off with two good dancers with whom we invariably went to May Week Balls. We always behaved with impeccable decorum and chastity and our conversations were of the most superficial sort, but I believe my partner must have had a great deal more in him than I credited him with, as he ended up Lord Chief Justice, and Lord Parker of Waddington.

FRANCES PARTRIDGE, *Memories*, 1981

Christopher Isherwood found less to enjoy:

The college authorities, considerate as always in such matters, had arranged to give me rooms on the same staircase as Chalmers: his were on the ground floor, mine the second. I disliked my sitting-room from the first moment I saw it. It was chilly, bare and high; and the walls had been newly papered and painted, a bright unfriendly brown. My few books huddled together, quite lost in the tall bookcase; and I had no photographs or menu-cards to break the long bleak black line of the mantelpiece. The grate did-n't draw properly: the fire was difficult to keep alight and the chimney smoked. There were eight hard, leather, brown chairs, none of which I ever used. They had to be ranged along the wall or grouped round the table; making you feel, in either case, that you were surrounded by stiff invisible presences. Altogether, the place was like an old-fashioned dentist's waiting-room.

We preferred to sit downstairs in Chalmers' room, which was low-ceilinged and snug. It seemed to me that Chalmers had strongly impressed his personality upon it; though more by accident than by design, and with a minimum of properties. There were lots of books, of course; the old favourites and the latest acquisitions of his first year – Baudelaire, Poe, Whitman, Owen, Sir Thomas Browne, Donne, Katherine Mansfield, Flaubert, Villon, Tchekhov, Dunbar and the Elizabethans. There were only three pictures: the Dürer engravings – 'Melencolia', 'St. Jerome' and 'The Knight, Death and the Devil'. On the mantelpiece were a pair of long-stemmed clay pipes and a little china skull, which Chalmers had seen one day in one of the many curiosity shops of the town. A big inverted lamp-shade, like a half-pumpkin, filled the room with warm red light. Chalmers hadn't many personal belongings; but, such as they were, they lay scattered about in the most unlikely places. His untidiness made his two rooms seem homely and inhabited; I recognized this, with admiration and occasional irritation – in my sitting-room even the matchbox had its proper position, a position which Chalmers never failed to disturb. With an absent-mindedness which was too consistent to be entirely unintentional, he would knock out his pipe on to my hearth-rug, catch my pained glance (for I hated to check the flow of our conversation), smile guiltily, mumble an apology, and make the feeblest of efforts to sweep up the mess with his hand. In the end, of course, I had to get out of my chair and tidy things up with my little hearth-brush under Chalmers' ironical, mock-apologetic eyes. And by the time I had finished, we had both forgotten what it was that we had been talking about ...

Throughout their first year, those four, [*Chalmers and three friends*] surrounded by a group of hearties from the [*rugby*] fifteen and the college boat, had spent most of their time together. During the winter, they played poker, dashed round the country-side in Sargent's car, assisted at all the more violent rags and did some dangerous climbs along the neighbouring roofs. In summer, they had taken shopgirls up the river in punts, returned after mid-night without their gowns and scrambled back into college over a private garden wall. Chalmers, whatever he tried to pretend to the contrary, had enjoyed these adventures. His noisy hearty friends accepted him without question; he was old Al, our Al, who played soccer and got drunk and ran after the girls; he was one of the gang. Nobody minded his being a poet – that sort of thing was quite usual up here; even Anderson, the left back, had contributed a sonnet about rose gardens to the College magazine. Literature had its recognized place as long as you weren't highbrow about it and could play some game as well. Black and his friends rather made fun of the colleges which tried to be spartan and tough. Even if Al did know which end of the pen Shakespeare used, he was all right – aren't you, Al old boy? And Al grinned at them faintly as they slapped his back ...

CHRISTOPHER ISHERWOOD, *Lions and Shadows: An Education in the Twenties*, 1938

Contrast this with Kathleen Raine:

... how I loved my College room of my own – two rooms, in fact, a small bedroom and a little sitting-room in 'Top Old'... In the morning, our 'gyp' brought to each of us a can of hot water, set it in our wash-basin, and covered it with a towel. And we each had a coal-fire (also laid for us daily) and a graceful oval copper kettle, polished on top (the kettles of the dons were polished all over). Each of us had our own desk, writing-chair, arm-chair, and book-shelves with curtains and covers of fresh clean linen; in many of the rooms still of the original William Morris designs, very old fashioned it was fashionable to think, in those days when Heal's furniture and the rectilinear style were new. We added, of course, our own touches. We had our toasting forks, from which we dropped our Matthews' crumpets into the fire; I bought some handwoven blue material, and put up two rhyme-sheets, one, of William Allingham's 'Four ducks in a pond', the other Blake's 'Never seek to tell thy love'. Some of us had Byron's 'We'll go no more a roving / So late into the night'. The choice of rhyme-sheets was restricted.

We considered ourselves emancipated, for the chaperon rules had recently been relaxed; and now two or more students might entertain young men in their rooms, to tea, if permission was obtained in writing, from the Mistress, the names and colleges of all students present being given. We dropped our neatly folded notes into the Mistress's letter box the previous day, and as a matter of course received our permission. This was seen as a great advance. A friend some ten years my senior remembers permission being refused to a friend who had been invited to accompany her father and herself on the river; the friend was a daughter of one of her father's fellow Ministers in Asquith's Cabinet. Yet another relaxation, new in my year, allowed students to carry their own parcels from Cambridge; mostly, even so, we had our orders from Matthews cake-shop, or Heffers' book-shop, delivered at the College. No more than we felt guilt as a privileged elite (words with no anti-social connotations in those days) did we feel ourselves 'victimized' by the strict rules under which we lived and worked. If a few habitually, and most of us once or twice, broke the rule of being in College by 10 p.m., and climbed in through a window into a ground-floor room, that was at our own risk, and for the sake of the adventure. We were only too glad to live in that College, the very realization of Tennyson's *The Princess*; to visit one another's rooms, like schoolgirls, for sophisticated coffee, or homely 'jug' (cocoa at 9 p.m.). Most were still virgins at the end of our three years; nor was it the virgins among us who were neurotic, restless, dissatisfied and liable to breakdowns, but the 'emancipated' minority who were not. As I remember it seems to me that living as a student in Girton was one of the few perfectly happy times of my life; but happy as a dream is happy, as something that had befallen me; not ... a time when the world, its hills and skies, its simple tasks and simple people were like a part of myself.

KATHLEEN RAINE, *The Land Unknown*, 1975

❀

The Russian-born novelist, Vladimir Nabokov, was rather less content than Kathleen Raine:

... at first, I shared an apartment in Trinity Lane with a puzzled [Russian] compatriot. After a few months he left college, and I remained sole occupant of those lodgings. They seemed intolerably squalid in comparison with my remote and by now non-existent home. Well do I remember the ornaments on the mantelpiece (a glass ashtray, with the Trinity crest, left by some former lodger; a seashell in which I found the imprisoned hum of one of my own seaside summers), and my landlady's old mechanical piano, a pathetic contraption, full of ruptured, crushed, knotted music, which one sampled once and no more. Narrow Trinity Lane was a staid and rather sad little street, with almost no traffic, but with a long, lurid past beginning in the sixteenth century, when it used to be Findsilver Lane, although commonly called at the time by a coarser name because of the then abominable state of its gutters. I suffered a good deal from the cold, but it is quite untrue, as some have it, that the polar temperature in Cambridge bedrooms caused the water to freeze solid in one's washstand jug. As a matter of fact, there would be hardly more than a thin layer of ice on the surface, and this was easily broken by means of one's toothbrush into tinkling bits, a sound which, in retrospect, has even a certain festive appeal to my Americanized ear. Otherwise, getting up was no fun at all. I still feel in my bones the bleakness of the morning walk up Trinity Lane to the baths, as one shuffled along, exuding pallid puffs of breath, in a thin dressing gown over one's pyjamas and a cold, fat sponge-bag under one's arm. Nothing in the world could induce me to wear next to my skin the 'woollies' that kept Englishmen secretly warm. Overcoats were considered sissy. The usual attire of the average Cambridge undergraduate, whether athlete or leftish poet, struck a sturdy and dingy note: his shoes had thick rubber soles, his flannel trousers were dark grey, and the buttoned sweater, called a 'jumper', under his Norfolk jacket was a conservative brown. What I suppose might be termed the gay set wore old pumps, very light grey flannel trousers, a bright-yellow 'jumper', and the coat part of a good suit ...

Suddenly, in the small hours of a November morning, I would become conscious of the silence and chill (my second winter in Cambridge seems to have been the coldest, and most prolific one). The red and blue flames wherein I had been seeing a fabled battle [*he had been reading the Russian epic of Prince Igor*] had sunk to the lugubrious glow of an arctic sunset among hoary firs. Still I could not force myself to go to bed, dreading not so much insomnia as the inevitable double systole, abetted by the cold of the sheets, and also the curious affliction called *anxietas tibiarum*, a painful condition of unrest, an excruciating increase of muscular sense, which leads to a continual change in the position of one's limbs. So I would heap on more coals and help revive the flames by spreading a sheet of the London *Times* over the smoking black jaws of the fire-place, thus screening completely its open recess. A humming noise would start behind the taut paper, which would acquire the smoothness of a drum-skin and the beauty of luminous parchment. Presently as the hum turned into a roar, an orange-coloured spot would appear in the middle of the sheet, and whatever patch of print happened to be there (for example, 'The League does not command a guinea or a gun', or '... the revenges that Nemesis has had upon Allied hesitation and indecision in Eastern and Central Europe ...') stood out with ominous clarity – until suddenly the orange spot burst. Then the flaming sheet, with the whirr of a liberated phoenix, would fly up the chimney to join the stars. It cost one a fine of twelve shillings if that firebird was observed.

VLADIMIR NABOKOV, *Speak, Memory: A Memoir*, 1951

SCENES
FROM ACADEMIC LIFE

Nearly every undergraduate gets a degree eventually, but it's really so much nicer to have a reasonably good one if you can manage it.

Varsity Handbook, 1958 (and many other years)

Some encouragement. In the 1950s, the Dean of Queens' College, Rev. Henry StJ. Hart, had two small framed inscriptions, in his beautiful italic script, on his mantelpiece. In that room he generously entertained year upon year of undergraduates of varying states of house-training, and many a young man has become thoughtful on looking up from toasting crumpets at the fire to see 'Leisure is well spent in reading for a degree'. On that other side, 'You can also read for a degree at home'. Recognising that they were quotations from adverts for a correspondence college (Wolsey Hall, Oxford) made the point, if anything, sharper.

✵

Thomas Gray answers Horace Walpole's request for a description of University life:

Oct. 31, 1734.

For Gods sake send me your Quaere's, & I'll do my best to get information upon those Points, you don't understand: I warrant, you imagine that People in one College, know the Customs of others; but you mistake, they are quite little Societies by themselves; ye Dresses, Language, Customs &c are quite different in different Colledges: what passes for Wit in one, would not be understood if it were carried to another: thus the Men of Peter-house, Pembroke & Clare-hall of course must be Tories; those of Trinity, Rakes; of Kings, Scholars; of Sidney, Wigs; of St Johns, Wirthy men & so on: now what to say about this Terra Incognita, I don't know; First then it is a great old Town, shaped

113

like a Spider, with a nasty lump in the middle of it, & half a dozen scambling long legs: it has 14 Parishes, 12 Colledges, & 4 Halls, these Halls only entertain Students, who after a term of years, are elected into the Colledges: there are 5 ranks in the University, subordinate to the Vice-chancellour, who is chose annually: these are Masters, Fellows, Fellow-Commoners, Pensioners, & Sizers; The Masters of Colledges are twelve grey-hair'd Gentlefolks, who are all mad with Pride; the Fellows are sleepy, drunken, dull, illiterate Things; the Fellow-Com[moners] are imitatours of the Fellows, or else Beaux, or else nothing; the Pension[ers] grave, formal Sots, who would be thought old; or else drink Ale, & sing Songs against ye Excise. The Sizers are Graziers Eldest Sons, who come to get good Learning, that they may all be Archbishops of Canterbury: these 2 last Orders are qualified to take Scholarships, one of which, your humble Servt has had given him: first they led me into the hall, & there I swore Allegiance to ye King; then I went to a room, where I took 50000 Latin Oaths, such as, to wear a Square Cap, to make 6 verses upon the Epistle or Gospel every Sunday morning, to chant very loud in Chappel, to wear a clean Surplice, &c: &c: Now as to eating: the Fellow-Com[moners] dine at the Fellows Table, their Commons is worth 6s-4d a-week, the Pensioners pay but 2s-4d; if any body don't like their Commons, they send down into the Kitchen to know, what's for Sizing: the Cook sends up a Catalogue of what there is; & they chuse, what they please: they are obliged to pay for Commons, whither they eat it, or no: there is always Plenty enough: the Sizers feast upon the leavings of the rest; as to dress, the Fell: Commoners usually wear a Prunella Gown with Sleeves, a hat & no band; but their proper habit has its Sleeves trimmed with Gold-lace, this they only wear at publick Ceremonies; neither do the Noblemen use their pr[oper] Habit commonly, but wear only a black Padesoy Gown: the Men of Kings are a sort of University by themselves; & differ in Customs from all the rest; every body hates 'em & when Almanzor comes to me, our Peoples stare at him, like a Lord-mayors Show, & wonder to see a human Creature among them: if I tell you, I never stirr out, perhaps you won't believe me; especially when you know, there's a Club of Wits kept at the Mitre, all such as come from Eton; where Alm[anzor] would introduce me, if I so pleased: – yet you will not think it strange, that I don't go abroad when I tell you, that I am got into a room; such [a] hugeous one, that little i is quite lost in it ...

THOMAS GRAY, *The Letters of Thomas Gray*

Sylvia Plath writes to her mother just after arrival from America:

October 9, 1955

... For the first time I'm taking a program which should slowly spread pathways and bridges over the whistling voids of my ignorance. My lecture schedule is about 11 hours (morning) during the week with men whose books are beginning to fill my shelves: F. R. Leavis on criticism: a magnificent, acid, malevolently humorous little man who looks exactly like a bandy-legged leprechaun; Basil Willey on the moralists (he's written enormous, readable books on the 17th, 18th, and 19th century background); and, if I have time next term, David Daiches on the Modern English Novel ...

SYLVIA PLATH, *Letters Home*, 1975

In this place one is constantly nudged by the past and consideration of how others remembered their time of study here. As Coleridge put it:

Surely, if the Religio Loci ['spirit of place'] dwell anywhere, it must be within these courts, every spot of which is hallowed by the feet of Piety and Genius. While passing under the gateway, the form of Newton seemed to rise before me, and I turned around to look at that window where he so often stood, decomposing the rays of morning. There was something inexpressibly delightful in the fancy.

SAMUEL TAYLOR COLERIDGE, *Table Talk: Conversations At Cambridge*, 1836

Earlier, William Pattison (like Abraham Cowley before him) felt the same awe:

115

Thus, dearest Florio thus, my faithful Friend,
In learned Luxury my Time I spend;
Till length'ning Shades the setting Sun display,
And falling Dews lament the falling Day:
Then, lost in Thought, where aged Cam divides
Those verdant Groves that paint his Azure Tides,
With musing Pleasure I reflect around,
And stand inchanted in Poetic Ground.
Straight to my glancing Thought those Bards appear,
That fill'd the World with Fame, and charm'd us here:
Here Spenser, Cowley, and that awful Name
Of mighty Milton, flourish'd into Fame;
From these amusing Groves, his copious Mind,
The blooming Shades of Paradise design'd.
In these Retirements, Dryden fann'd his Fire,
And gentle Waller tun'd his tender Lyre;
Hail! happy Bards, whilst thus I think, I hear
Your Tuneful Melody improve my Ear,
With Rev'rence I approach each sacred Shade,
Perhaps by Your creating Numbers made ...

WILLIAM PATTISON, *Epistle to a Friend*, 1724

J. A. Venn in Alumni Cantabrigienses, *comments:* 'Like most poets, [Pattison] did not fit in with college life. Went to London, where he died in great poverty, July 11, 1727.'

Wordsworth, too, described how aware he was of the heritage of 'illustrious Men' – Chaucer, Spenser, Milton:

Such was the tenor of the opening act
In this new life. Imagination slept,
And yet not utterly. I could not print
Ground where the grass had yielded to the steps
Of generations of illustrious Men,
Unmov'd; I could not always lightly pass
Through the same gateways; sleep where they had slept,

Wake where they wak'd, range that enclosure old,
That garden of great intellects, undisturb'd.
Place also by the side of this dark sense
Of nobler feeling, that those spiritual Men,
Even the great Newton's own ethereal Self,
Seem'd humbled in these precincts; thence to be
The more belov'd; invested here with tasks
Of life's plain business, as a daily garb;
Dictators at the plough, a change that left
All genuine admiration unimpaired.

Even so, as an undergraduate, Wordsworth did not work particularly hard.
Indeed, he came as near as a Wordsworth could to elegant dissipation, and
once got drunk in Milton's rooms:

Among the band of my compeers was one
Whom chance had stationed in the very room
Honour'd by Milton's name. O temperate Bard !
Be it confessed that, for the first time , seated
Within thy innocent lodge and oratory,
One of a festive circle, I poured out
Libations, to thy memory drank, till pride
And gratitude grew dizzy in a brain
Never excited by the fumes of wine
Before that hour, or since. Then, forth I ran
From that assembly; through a length of streets,
Ran, ostrich-like, to reach our chapel door
In not a desperate or opprobrious time,
Albeit long after the importunate bell
Had stopp'd, with wearisome Cassandra voice
No longer haunting the dark winter night.
Call back, O Friend ! a moment to thy mind,
The place itself and fashion of the rites.
With careless ostentation shouldering up
My Surplice, through the inferior throng I clove
Of the plain Burghers, who in audience stood
On the last skirts of their permitted ground,
Beneath the pealing Organ. Empty thoughts!
I am ashamed of them ...

WILLIAM WORDSWORTH, *The Prelude*, 1850

But one can look at Cambridge Past in more than one way:

Cambridge, the mother of poets, received him [Coleridge] with the kindness she had so often shown to her children. We – I speak as a Cambridge man – we flogged (or nearly flogged) Milton into republicanism; we disgusted Dryden into an anomalous and monstrous preference for Oxford; we bored Gray, till half stifled with academic dulness, he sought more cheerful surroundings in a country churchyard; we left Byron to the congenial society of his bear; we did nothing for Wordsworth, except, indeed, that we took him to Milton's rooms, and there for once (it must really have done him some good) induced him to take a glass too much; and we, as nearly as possible, converted Coleridge into a heavy dragoon.

SIR LESLIE STEPHEN, Hours in A Library, 1874

✸

Sometimes the weight of memory elicits whimsy: Frank Sidgwick's Thoughts on a Spoon *deliberately recall Jonathan Swift's* Meditation upon a Broomstick, *itself a parody of the moral essays of Lord Bolingbroke:*

> Spoon of Trinity College Hall,
>   Dated seventeen-ninety-eight!
> Stars may wane, and kingdoms fall,
>   Thou hast touched the lips of the great!
>
> Mayn't Macaulay have munched his meat,
>   Masticated meringues at noon, –
> Tennyson taken a toothsome sweet,
>   Out of thy bowl, O silver Spoon?
>
> Thirlwall's throttle, and Thackeray's throat
>   Knew, it may be, thy curving lip;
> Praed may have dropped thee over his coat,
>   Hallam, perhaps, hath kissed thy tip.

Spoon of seventeen-ninety-eight,
　　Years have sped, – a hundred and two;
Lo! I am linked with the century's great,
　　I have used thee, Spoon, I too!
　　　　　　FRANK SIDGWICK, *Granta*, 10 March, 1900

❈

From the moment I got to Cambridge, nothing did I hear from my teachers but 'tradition'. It was represented as something problematical, hard to get hold of, easily confounded with impostures. In particular it was supposed that I began with a prejudice against it, against the cloudiest concept of what it might be. But had Marlowe not lived in Corpus, James Shirley in St Catharine's, Wordsworth in St John's? Did I, then and there among the colleges, having won my way there out of the benighted provinces, need T. S. Eliot or F. R. Leavis or later Richard Hoggart to tell me on what terms to accept incorporation in the tradition there offered me, physically extant in the disposition of buildings and in book-stacks? Preaching at me, these authorities preached to the converted; and the long-converted grew to resent them. Now, in retrospect, I recognize how I must thank my parents for having saved me from the sterile class rancour that got in the way of so many of my contemporaries, and impedes their successors to the present day. Since disputatiousness was in Cambridge a sign of 'integrity', and since it came happily and naturally to my cast of mind, I indulged it – to good and profitable effect. But it never truly mirrored my temperament or my sensibility, by which I knew that the tradition was *there*, in Cambridge; and that the custodians of it were not pedagogues and critics, but poets, libraries, and the builders of libraries.

DONALD DAVIE, *These the Companions: Recollections*, 1982

❈

John Milton wrote Lycidas *for a volume of poems by members of the University commemorating the death of Edward King. He was not a close friend of King's, but in this poem recreates an undergraduate idyll, a pastoral trope, which is as true, and not, as many memories of time spent near libraries on the banks of the Cam:*

> Begin, then, Sisters of the sacred well
> That from beneath the seat of Jove doth spring,
> Begin, and somewhat loudly sweep the string:
> Hence with denial vain, and coy excuse.
> So may som gentle Muse
> With lucky words favour my destind Urn,
> And as he passes, turn
> And bid fair peace be to my sable shroud.
> For we were nurst upon the self-same hill,
> Fed the same flock, by fountain, shade, and rill.
>   Together both, ere the high Lawns appear'd
> Under the opening eyelids of the morn,
> We drove a-field, and both together heard
> What time the Gray-fly winds her sultry horn,
> Batt'ning our flocks with the fresh dews of night,
> Oft till the Star that rose, at Ev'ning, bright
> Toward Heav'ns descent had slop'd his westering wheel.
> Mean while the Rural ditties were not mute,
> Temperd to th'Oaten Flute,
> Rough Satyrs danc'd, and Fauns with cloven heel
> From the glad sound would not be absent long,
> And old Damoetas lov'd to hear our song.
>   JOHN MILTON, *Lycidas*, 1637

But old Damoetas could, and can, be jolly awkward – justifiably so, perhaps, when faced with adolescent cant. Christopher Isherwood describes a Difficult Supervision.

… Here I was, gowned, seated uneasily on the edge of the chair, reading my first essay aloud to my history tutor, the dreaded Mr. Gorse. The subject of the essay was: 'Better England Free than England Sober.' I had finished it with some pride: it exactly suited my idea of Mr. Gorse's requirements – snappy, epigrammatic, a bit daring in its language, sprinkled with witticisms

120

borrowed unacknowledged from Mr Holmes. Only now, for some reason, all my effects seemed to have gone wrong: the verbal fireworks were damp; the epigrams weren't epigrams but platitudes, pompous, painfully naïve, inept, and priggish. It was positive misery to have to utter them. I writhed with embarrassment, coughed, made spoonerisms, gabbled through the worst bits with my face averted: 'Apart from this consideration, there is no doubt that our own liquor restrictions are demoralizing ... The places where it is sold are unpleasant, and the upper classes, disdaining them, repair to their own homes, where they are no longer under the restraining eye of the world, and often fare badly in consequence ...' (Heavens, did I really write that? The sweat began to break out on my forehead.) 'The French café, with its refinement, its high social status and its atmosphere of harmless gaiety' (Phew) 'is as far removed from the English pub as the hotel is from the brothel ...'

'How do *you* know,' snapped Mr. Gorse, 'how far an hotel is removed from a brothel? Very often it *is* a brothel. Go on.'

I grinned nervously, and faltered through to the end. The last paragraph was particularly heavy going, because Mr Gorse had begun to drum with his fingers on the mantelpiece. 'Yes, yes ...' he kept muttering: 'Yes, yes ...' as though his impatience were increasing with every word. 'Well,' he told me, when, at last, I had finished: 'I'll say this for you – it's not the work of an entirely uneducated fool.' He paused. I grinned hopelessly, regarding him like a poodle which is going to be kicked. 'Look here, Isherwood,' he appealed to me abruptly, 'don't you yourself agree that it's all tripe?'.

CHRISTOPHER ISHERWOOD, *Lions and Shadows: An Education in the Twenties*, 1938

Charles Darwin (1809–82) was hardly a model undergraduate:

Although as we shall presently see, there were some redeeming features in my life at Cambridge, my time was sadly wasted there, and worse than wasted. From my passion for shooting and for hunting, and, when this failed, for riding across country, I got into a sporting set, including some dissipated, low-minded young men. We used often to dine together in the evening, though these dinners often included men of a higher stamp, and we sometimes drank too much, with jolly singing and playing at cards afterwards. I know that I ought to feel ashamed of days and evenings thus spent, but as some of my friends were very pleasant, and we were all in the highest spirits, I cannot help looking back to these times with much pleasure ...

I also got into a musical set ... From associating with these men, and hearing them play, I acquired a strong taste for music, and used very often to time my walks so as to hear on week days the anthem in King's College Chapel. This gave me intense pleasure, so that my backbone would sometimes shiver. I am sure that there was no affectation or mere imitation in this taste, for I used generally to go by myself to King's College, and I sometimes hired the chorister boys to sing in my rooms. Nevertheless I am so utterly destitute of an ear, that I cannot perceive a discord, or keep time and hum a tune correctly; and it is a mystery how I could possibly have derived pleasure from music ...

But no pursuit at Cambridge was followed with nearly so much eagerness or gave me so much pleasure as collecting beetles.

CHARLES DARWIN, Life and Letters, 1887

One of Lord Lytton's characters recalls Cambridge at the time of Darwin's residence at Christ's:

I do not exactly remember how I spent my time at Cambridge. I had a pianoforte in my room, and a private billiard-room at a village two miles off; and, between these resources, I managed to improve my mind more than could reasonably have been expected. To say truth, the whole place reeked with vulgarity. The men drank beer by the gallon, and ate cheese by the hundred-weight – wore jockey-cut coats, and talked slang – rode for wagers, and swore when they lost – smoked in your face, and expectorated on the floor. Their proudest glory was to drive the mail – their mightiest exploit to box with the coachman – their most delicate amour to leer at the barmaid.

It will be believed, that I felt little regret in quitting companions of this description. I went to take leave of our college tutor. 'Mr. Pelham,' said he, affectionately squeezing me by the hand, 'your conduct has been most exemplary; you have not walked wantonly over the college grassplats, nor set your dog at the proctor – nor driven tandems by day, nor broken lamps by night – nor entered the chapel in order to display your intoxication – nor the lecture-room in order to caricature the professors. This is the general behaviour of young men of family and fortune; but it has not been yours. Sir, you have been an honour to your college.'

Thus closed my academic career. He who does not allow that it passed creditably to my teachers, profitably to myself, and beneficially to the world, is a narrowminded and illiterate man, who knows nothing about the advantages of modern education.

LORD LYTTON, Pelham, 1828

By contrast, model behaviour (perhaps idealised), and a Model Undergraduate, an example to us all:

There be dyuers ther whych ryse dayly betwixte foure and fyue of the clocke in the mornynge, and from fyue vntyll syxe of the clocke, vse common prayer wyth an exhortacion of gods worde in a commune chappel, and from sixe vnto ten of the clocke vse euer eyther pryuate study or commune lectures. At ten of the clocke they go to dynner, whereas they be contente wyth a penye pyece of byefe amongest iiii. hauyng a fewe porage made of the brothe of the same byefe, wyth salte and otemell, and nothynge els.

After thys slender dinner they be either teachynge or learnynge vntyll v. of the clocke in the euenyng, when as they haue a supper not much better than theyr dyner. Immedyatelye after the whyche, they go eyther to reasonyng in problemes or vnto some other studye, vntyll it be nyne or tenne of the clocke, and there beyng wythout fyre are fayne to walk or runne vp and downe halfe an houre, to gette a heate on their feete whan they go to bed ... These be the lyuyng sayntes whyche serue god takyng greate paynes in abstinence, studye, laboure and dylygence, wyth watching and prayer.

THOMAS LEVER, *A Sermon preached at Paul's Cross,*
December 14, 1550

Lever was Master of St John's for two years (1551–3) under Protestant Edward VI, but the whirligig of Time made him a fugitive in Zürich under Catholic Mary I.

❊

And a first-hand account of student life from Ambrose Bonwicke (1691–1714) writing to his father:

Tho' I could not but be perfectly satisfied with, and very happy in many kindnesses I received from my mother and you in the country, for which I return many and hearty thanks; yet methinks I receive more than ordinary satisfaction in being returned to this pleasant seat of the muses, where I find my books and all things in a very good condition, and myself happy at the ethic-table at morning lectures in the hall. And I think myself duty bound on this day (Nov. 6) on which I was elected scholar, to give annual thanks to the Almighty for having most graciously afforded me so comfortable a subsistence, and such powerful patronage to enable me so happily to promote, not only my temporal but eternal welfare, in this learned and religious foundation. The hopes of being someways assisting to the preservation of your health, (added to the great satisfaction I always receive in seeing my dear relations) for the continuing of which I earnestly beg of you to listen to the frequent good motions of my dear mother, will be the only allurement to draw me hence.

AMBROSE BONWICKE, *A Pattern for Young Students in the*
University, 1729

More were (and are) like Bonwicke than the good copy that rogues and reprobates generate might suggest. Scandal is always more glamorous than virtue.

❊

The Rev. T. Pitcairn Campbell wrote to Frances Kingsley, describing the undergraduate occupations of one less decorous than Ambrose Bonwicke, but who made more noise in the world. Her husband was the Rev. Charles Kingsley, Professor of Modern History, naturalist, novelist, sportsman, opponent of John Henry Newman; simply to have elicited from Newman his Apologia Pro Vita Sua *is some distinction, indeed.*

Aston Lodge, November, 1875

My first acquaintance with your husband was formed sometime in the year 1840. We happened to be sitting together one night on the top of one of those coaches which in our time were subscribed for by a number of men 10s. or £1 each for various expeditions into the Fens – for instance, when Whittlesea lay broadly under water – Sir Colman Rashliegh, the Dykes of Cornwall or other driving men taking the management, wearing wonderful coats and hats, and providing the horses. I remember the drive very well. The moon was high, and the air was frosty, and we talked about sport and natural history, whilst the cornopean [the horn-blowing postilion] professor astonished the natives with what he called Mr. Straw's (!) walzes.

At last we got upon fishing, and I invited your husband to come to my rooms to view some very superior tackle which had been left me by a relative. He came at once, inviting me to join him in some of his haunts up the Granta and the Cam, where he had friends dwelling, and hospitable houses open to him.

I never shall forget our first expedition. I was to call him, and for this purpose I had to climb over the wall of Magdalene College. This I did at two a.m. and about three we were both climbing back into the stonemason's yard, and off through Trumpington, in pouring rain all the way, nine miles to Duxford.

We reached [Duxford] about 6.30. The water was clouded by rain, and I in courtesy to your husband yielded my heavier rod in order that he might try the lower water with the minnow.

He was, however, scarcely out of sight, before I spied, under the alders, some glorious trout rising to caterpillars dropping from the bushes. In ten minutes I had three of these fine fellows on the bank – one of them weighed three pounds, others two pounds each. We caught nothing after the rain had ceased ...

Besides these expeditions we made others on horseback, and I think at times we followed the great Professor Sedgwick in his adventurous rides, which the livery stablekeepers called jolly-gizing. The old professor was generally mounted on a bony giant, whose trot kept most of us at a hand-gallop. Gaunt and grim, the brave old Northern man seemed to enjoy the fun as much as we did – his was not a hunting seat – neither his hands nor his feet ever seemed exactly in the right place. But when we surrounded him at the trysting-place, even the silliest among us acknowledged that his lectures were glorious. It is too true that our method of reaching those trysting-places was not legitimate, the greater number preferring the field to the road, so that the unhappy owners of the horses found it necessary to charge more for a day's jolly-gizing than they did for a day's hunting.

There was another professor whose lectures we attended together, but he was of a different type and character – one who taught the gentle art of self-defence – a negro of pure blood, who appeared to have more joints in his back than are usually allotted to humanity. In carrying out the science which he taught we occasionally discoloured each other's countenances, but we thought that we benefited by these lectures in more senses than one. We had our tempers braced, yea, even our Christian charity; for instance, when we learnt to feel as we knew we ought for those who had just punished us.

As Dr Bateson, Master of St John's, said to Mrs Kingsley, from one point of view he

... made but indifferent use of the opportunities which his residence at Cambridge afforded him ...
    Charles Kingsley: His Letters and Memories of His Life, 1877

John Strype (1643–1737), a Freshman at Jesus, writes home in 1662. The University had just come through one of the most desperate and disturbing decades in its existence, but, like his successors and – one doubts not – his predecessors, Strype's major preoccupation is his food:

Good Mother, – Yours of the 24th instant I gladly received, expecting indeed one a Week before, but I understand both by Waterson and yourselfe of your indisposednesse then to write.

The reason you receive this no sooner is, because I had a mind (hearing of this honest woman's setting out so suddenly for London from hence, and her businesse laying so neer to Petticoate lane,) that shee should deliver it into your hands, that so you may better & more fully heare of me, and know how it fareth with me …

Do not wonder so much at our Commons [meals]: they are more than many Colledges have. Trinity itselfe (where Herring and Davies are), which is the famousest Coll. in the University, have but 3 half pence. We have roast meat, dinner and supper, throughout the whole weeke; and such meate as you know I do not use to care for; and that is Veal: but now I have learnt to eat it. Sometimes, neverthelesse, we have boyled meat, with pottage; and beef and mutton, which I am glad of: except Frydays and Saturdays, and sometimes Wednesdays; which days we have Fish at dinner, and tansy or puddings for supper. Our parts then are slender enough. But there is the remedie; wee may retire unto the butteries, and there take a half penny loafe and butter or cheese; or else to the Kitchin and take there what wee will that the Cook hath. But for my part I am sure I never visited the Kitchin yet since I have been here, and the butteries but seldom after meals; unlesse for a Cize, that is for a Farthingworth of small-beer: so that lesse than a Penny in Beer doth serve me a whole Day. Neverthelesse sometimes we have exceedings: then we have 2 or 3 Dishes (but that is very rare): otherwise never but one: so that a cake and a cheese would (as they have been) be very welcome to me: and a neat's tongue, or some such thing; if it would not require too much mony. If you do intend to send me any thing, do not send it yet, until you may hear further of me: for I have many things to send for which may all I hope be put into that box you have at home: but what they are, I shall give you an account here-after, when I would have them sent: And that is when I have got me a Chamber; for as yet, I am in a Chamber that doth not at all please me. I have thoughts of one, which is a very handsome one, and one pair of stairs high, and that looketh into the Master's garden. The price is but 20 shill[ings] per annum, so whereof a Knight's son, and lately admitted into this Coll. doth pay: though he doth not come till about Midsummer, so that I shall have but 10 shi[llings] to pay a yeare besides my income, which may be about 40 shill[ings] or thereabouts. Mother I kindly thank you for your Orange pills you sent me. If you are not to[o] straight of mony send me some such thing by the Woman, and a pound or two of Almonds and Raisons. But first ask her if she will carry them, or if they will not be too much trouble to her. I do much approve of your agreeing with the Carrier quarterly; he was indeed telling me of it, that you had agreed with him for it: and I think he means both yours and mine. Make your bargaines sure with him. I understand by your Letter that you are very inquisitive to know how things stand with me here. I believe you may be well satisfied by the Woman. My breakings out are now all gone, indeed I was affraid at my first coming it would have proved the Itch: but I am fairly rid of it: But I fear I shall get it let me do what I can: for there are many here that have it cruelly. Some of them take strong purges that would kill a horse, weeks together for it, to get it away, & yet are hardly rid of it. At my first coming I laid alone: but since, my Tutour desired me to let a very clean lad lay with me and an Alderman's son of Colchester, which I could not deny, being newly come: he hath laid with me now for almost a fortnight, and will do till he can provide himselfe with a Chamber.

Wee go twice a day to Chappell; in the morning about 7, and in the evening about 5. After we come from Chappell in the morning which is towards 8, we go to the Butteries for our breakfast, which usually is 5 farthings; an halfpeny loafe and butter, & a cize of beer. But sometimes I go to an honest House neere the Coll., and have a pint of milk boyled for my breakfast.

Quoted in CHRISTOPHER WORDSWORTH, *Scholae Academicae: Some Account of the Studies at the English Universities in the Eighteenth Century*, 1877

Despite (or because of) the (not always justified) legends about the quality of food at High Table, undergraduates have always complained about College food. Gunning, in his Reminiscences of Cambridge, *records Coleridge's remark about the dinners in Jesus:*

He described the veal which was served to them (and which

was large and coarse) in the following words – 'We have veal, Sir, tottering on the edge of beef!'.

The prodigious walks an earlier generation took as a matter of course would now be thought extraordinary, even without the Wordsworthian rhythms of recollection:

> We walked and walked
> As chance directed – by the river side
> To Grantchester – along the lanes which led
> To Cherry Hinton – out by Trumpington –
> And Madingley, sole village from the plague
> Of ugliness, in that drear land, exempt:
> The Gogmagogs were conscious of our talk;
> And I may say that seldom I came home
> No wiser than I went. – But in the days
> Of early spring, when even those treeless fields
> Look'd pleasant in the sunshine, and the lanes
> With constellations of bright primrose tufts
> Were here and there bestudded, – when the scent
> Of the cinque-spotted cowslip was exhaled
> From the low meadow-grass, – and in the woods
> The nightingale (more fitly heard by night)
> Sang lustily all day – with what a bound
> Of vernal exultation forth we sprang
> Into the clear, fresh air! – with what dispatch
> Of keen and craving hunger, we assail'd
> Our mid-day luncheon in the village inn,
> Served haply by the fair domestic hands
> Of her, the maid of Quy – that saint whose shrine
> By many a Cantabrigian pilgrimage,
> (By none more zealous or more pure than ours)
> Was, in those days, frequented ! – then at eve,
> As, homeward bound, through the suburban streets
> We wended in grotesque and careless guise –
> The very tassels of our trencher caps
> With cowslips interlaced, – how cheap we held

The laughter of the mob! – how little fear'd
The frown of Dean or Proctor ! – then our meal
Together shared, – the savoury steak sent hot
From the cook's shop – the amber-flowing ale
Of Trinity, – the spare desert, – the wine,
With olives relish'd – and our day's discourse
Prolong'd till midnight ! – College life alone
Can boast such joys as these.

JOHN MOULTRIE, *The Dream of Life*, 1843

Byron, we have seen, had mixed feelings about the place. From this letter to Elizabeth Pigot we can guess that Cambridge might have had rather negative views of him:

October 26th. 1807

My dear Elizabeth, –

… This place is wretched enough, a villainous Chaos of Dice and Drunkenness, nothing but Hazard and Burgundy, Hunting, Mathematics and Newmarket, Riot and Racing, yet it is a Paradise compared with the eternal dullness of Southwell, oh! the misery of doing nothing, but make *Love, enemies,* and *Verses* … I have got a new friend, the finest in the world, a *tame Bear,* when I brought him here, they asked me what I meant to do with him, and my reply was 'he should *sit* for a *Fellowship*'. – *Sherard* will explain the meaning of the sentence if it is ambiguous. – This answer delighted them not, – we have eternal parties here, and this evening a large assortment of *Jockies, Gamblers, Boaters, Authors, parsons,* and *poets,* sup with me. – A precious Mixture, but they go on well together, and for me, I am a *spice* of every thing except a Jockey, by the bye, I was dismounted again the other day.

Yet he was not exactly idle:

Thank your Brother in my name, for his Treatise. I have written 214 pages of a novel, one poem of 380 Lines, [which became *English Bards and Scotch Reviewers*] to be published (without my name) in a few weeks, with notes, 560 Lines of Bosworth Field, and 250 Lines of another poem in rhyme, besides half a dozen smaller pieces, the poem to be published is a Satire, apropos, I have been praised to the Skies in the Critical Review, and abused equally in another publication, so much the Better, they tell me, for the sale of the Book, it keeps up controversy, and prevents it from being forgotten ...

GEORGE GORDON, LORD BYRON

Alexander Pope (1688–1744), like many in his period, saw the two universities as places of irrelevant pedantry and stultifying dullness. As a Roman Catholic, he was debarred from being a member of either. In Book IV of his mock-epic, The Dunciad *(1742), the Goddess Dulness summons her devotees:*

> Prompt at the call, around the Goddess roll
> Broad hats, and hoods, and caps, a sable shoal ...
> Oxonians in droves, and ...
> As many quit the streams that murm'ring fall
> To lull the sons of Marg'ret and Clare-hall,   [St John's]
> Where Bentley late tempestuous wont to sport
> In troubled waters, but now sleeps in Port.
> Before them march'd that awful Aristarch!   [Bentley]
> Plough'd was his front with many a deep remark:
> His hat, which never vail'd to human pride,
> Walker[1] with reverence took, and laid aside.
> Low bow'd the rest: he, kingly, did but nod;
> So upright Quakers please both man and God.
> 'Mistress! dismiss that rabble from your throne:
> Avaunt! is Aristarchus yet unknown ?
> Thy mighty scholiast, whose unwearied pains
> Made Horace dull, and humbled Milton's strains.
> Turn what they will to verse, their toil is vain,
> Critics like me shall make it prose again.
> Roman and Greek grammarians! know your better,
> Author of something yet more great than letter;
> While towering o'er your alphabet, like Saul
> Stands our digamma, and o'ertops them all.'

ALEXANDER POPE, *The Dunciad*, 1742

---

[1]John Walker, 1692?-1747, Fellow of Trinity and, later, chaplain to George II; he was a supporter of Bentley

✾

Thomas Gray, too, had ambivalent feelings about the university where he spent most of his adult life. Widely regarded as the most learned man of his age, he never wrote a single scholarly book; he became Professor of History and Modern Languages in 1768. He expressed his mixed feelings in language and verse that recall Pope's fiercer satire:

HYMN TO IGNORANCE: A FRAGMENT

Hail, horrors, hail! ye ever gloomy bowers,
Ye Gothic fanes, and antiquated towers,
Where rushy Camus' slowly-winding flood
Perpetual draws his humid train of mud:
Glad I revisit thy neglected reign,
Oh take me to thy peaceful shade again.
But chiefly thee, whose influence breathed from high
Augments the native darkness of the sky;
Ah, ignorance! soft salutary power!
Prostrate with filial reverence I adore.
Thrice hath Hyperion roll'd his annual race,
Since weeping I forsook thy fond embrace.
Oh say, successful dost thou still oppose
Thy leaden aegis 'gainst our ancient foes;
Still stretch, tenacious of thy right divine,
The massy sceptre o'er thy slumb'ring line?
And dews Lethean through the land dispense
To steep in slumbers each benighted sense?
If any spark of wit's delusive ray
Break out, and flash a momentary day,
With damp, cold touch forbid it to aspire,
And huddle up in fogs the dang'rous fire ?
    Oh say – she hears me not, but, careless grown,
Lethargic nods upon her ebon throne.
Goddess! awake, arise! alas, my fears!
Can powers immortal feel the force of years?
Not thus of old, with ensigns wide unfurl'd,
She rode triumphant o'er the vanquish'd world;

Fierce nations own'd her unresisted might,
And all was ignorance, and all was night.

THOMAS GRAY, 1742

*Writing to Richard West in December 1736, Gray (still tongue-in cheek)
comments:*

Surely it was of this place, now Cambridge, but formerly known
by the name of Babylon, that the prophet spoke when he said, 'the
wild beasts of the desert shall dwell there, and their houses shall
be full of doleful creatures, and owls shall build there, and satyrs
shall dance there; their forts and towers shall be a den for ever, a
joy of wild asses; there shall the great owl make her nest, and lay
and hatch and gather under her shadow; it shall be a court of
dragons; the screech owl also shall rest there, and find for herself
a place of rest.' You see here is a pretty collection of desolate
animals, which is verified in this town to a tittle, and perhaps it
may also allude to your habitation, for you know all types may be
taken by abundance of handles; however, I defy your owls to
match mine.

Letters of Thomas Gray

*Tennyson (1809–92) could be pretty scathing about the Cambridge system
as he had known it in his undergraduate years:*

> …Therefore your Halls, your ancient Colleges,
> Your portals statued with old kings and queens,
> Your gardens, myriad-volumed libraries,
> Wax-lighted chapels, and rich carven screens,
> Your doctors, and your proctors, and your deans,
> Shall not avail you, when the day-beam sports
> New-risen o'er awaken'd Albion. No!
> Nor yet your solemn organ-pipes that blow
> Melodious thunders through your vacant courts
> At noon and eve, because your manner sorts

133

Not with this age wherefrom ye stand apart,
Because the lips of little children preach
Against you, you that do profess to teach
And teach us nothing, feeding not the heart.

ALFRED, LORD TENNYSON,
Lines on Cambridge in 1830

*But when he went back decades later, things had changed: the beginning
of the modern supervision system, which has benefited generation upon
generation, and which the new utilitarian barbarism wants to scrap:*

He honoured the University for the way it had adapted itself to
modern requirements; and he especially approved of the
University Extension movement, for spreading higher education
throughout local centres in Great Britain. Every vacation after his
marriage University men visited him, so that he kept level with
such movements.

What impressed him most, when he went to Cambridge in
1872, was the change in the relations between don and undergraduate. While he was keeping his terms (1828–1831) there was
'a great gulf fixed' between the teacher and the taught, but in 1872
he found a constant personal intercourse and interchange of ideas
between them. And, as the 'living word' is to each man more than
the mere lecture-room exposition, this change, he thought, could
not fail to have the best influence on the enlargement of the views,
sympathies and aspirations of the generations to come.

HALLAM, LORD TENNYSON: *Alfred, Lord Tennyson:
A Memoir, by his Son, 1897*

*George Herbert, of Trinity, had a distinguished career in the University, and
as Public Orator was its official spokesman. He was to leave his hopes of
worldly advancement behind him and settle for the modest life of a country
parson, at Bemerton. From that perspective, he wrote this devotional poem,
looking back on the pleasures, and hopes, of Cambridge life with some
desolation:*

AFFLICTION

Whereas my birth and spirits rather took
    The way that takes the town,
Thou didst betray me to a lingering book,
    And wrap me in a gown.
I was entangled in a world of strife,
Before I had the power to change my life.

Yet, for I threaten'd oft the siege to raise,
    Not simp'ring all mine age, –
Thou often didst, with academic praise,
    Melt and dissolve my rage.
I took thy sweeten'd pill; till I came where
I could not go away, or persevere.

Yet, lest perchance I should too happy be
    In my unhappiness,
Turning my purge to food: thou throwest me
    Into more sicknesses.
Thus doth thy power crossbias me; not making
Thine own gift good, yet me from my ways taking.

Now I am here, what thou wilt do with me
    None of my books will show.
I read, and sigh, and wish I were a tree:
    For sure then I should grow
To fruit, or shade; at least some bird would trust
Her household to me, and I should be just.
                     GEORGE HERBERT, *The Temple*, 1633

*Thomas Gray, famously the butt of some rowdy students who teased him
with his fear of fire in his first College, Peterhouse, moved across the road to
Pembroke:*

Mr Gray, our elegant Poet, and delicate Fellow Commoner of
Peterhouse, has just removed to Pembroke-hall, in resentment of

135

some usage he met with at the former place. The case is much talked of, and is this. He is much afraid of fire, and was a great sufferer in Cornhill; he has ever since kept a ladder of ropes by him, soft as the silky cords by which Romeo ascended to his Juliet, and has had an iron machine fixed to his bedroom window. The other morning, Lord Percival and some Petreuchians, going a-hunting, were determined to have a little sport before they set out, and thought it would be no bad diversion to make Gray bolt, as they called it, so ordered their man Joe Draper to roar out fire. A delicate white night-cap is said to have appeared at the window: but finding the mistake, retired again to the couch. The young fellows, had he descended, were determined, they said, to have whipped the butterfly up again.

REV. JOHN SHARP, Letter of 12 March, 1756

Gossipy Henry Gunning recounts the fall from virtue of Magdalene:

Among the persons whom I was in the habit of meeting at the rooms of my friend Banks was Hare Townsend, a Fellow-commoner of Trinity Hall, and the only son of Alderman Townsend, of Bruce Castle. By relating an anecdote concerning him, I can best illustrate the manners of the University at that particular period. Entering the hall of Magdalene College one evening, much intoxicated, when the Society were at supper, he went to the Pensioners' table, laughed at the paltry fare with which they were regaling themselves, and said, if they would sup with him the following evening, he would show them how gentlemen ought to live. The Fellows were at supper at the upper table, but though he was in his cap and gown, and made a great noise, they took no notice whatever of the intrusion. Strange and almost incredible as it may appear, it is a positive fact that all the members of the Pensioners' table (with the exception of two or three) accepted the invitation thus given from a man they had never seen before. The next evening the undergraduates went in a body to Townsend's room; he had ordered a magnificent supper to be prepared, and desired the butler to buy a new pail in which the punch was to be served up. As the butler was carrying the pail across the court in the dark, a magpie belonging to the college, whose conversational talents had rendered him a great favourite with the whole Society, perched upon the edge of the pail. The butler attempted to brush him off, but unfortunately brushed him into it. This was not discovered until the pail was set upon the table, when the magpie was irrecoverably dead. The evening was passed in a convivial manner perfectly new to the undergraduates of Magdalene, whose temperate habits and devotion to tea were quite proverbial.

HENRY GUNNING, *Reminiscences of the University, Town and County of Cambridge*, 1854

Yes, indeed: such was the tea-drinking earnestness of Magdalene under-graduates, many of whom, like the Fellows, were of the Evangelical persuasion, that another member of a University much given to tippling claimed that the river below the College was rendered 'absolutely ... unnavigable with tea-leaves'. Even in 1828, long after the heyday of these temperate habits recorded by Gunning, the Magdalene First Boat was christened 'The Tea Kettle'.

❁

Even after the foundation of the women's colleges of Newnham, Girton, and later New Hall, the population in Term was overwhelmingly young and male. Cambridge girls, until women students were admitted by the men's colleges in the 1970s and afterwards, had an enviable amount of male attention, and besides the many who made liaisons with the young gentlemen, not a few made 'very good' marriages. The pretty bar-keeper of the Mitre in Christopher Smart's poem had many descendants: undergraduates in the late 1950s, as always, frequented pubs where a pretty and talented barmaid drew the pints.

THE PRETTY BAR-KEEPER OF THE MITRE

'Relax, sweet girl, your wearied hand,
    And to hear the poet talk,
Gentlest creature of your kind,
    Lay aside your sponge and chalk;

Cease, cease the bar-bell, nor refuse
To hear the jingle of the Muse,

'Hear your num'rous Vot'ries prayers,
    Come, O come, and bring with thee
Giddy whimsies, wanton airs,
    And all love's soft artillery;
Smiles, and throbs, and frowns, and tears,
With all thy little hopes and fears.'

She heard – she came – and 'ere she spoke,
    Not unravished you might see
Her wanton eyes that wink'd the joke,
    'Ere her tongue could set it free.
While a forc'd blush her cheeks inflam'd,
And seem'd to say she was asham'd.

No handkerchief her bosom hid,
    No tippet from our sight debars
Her heaving breast with moles o'erspread,
    Mark'd little hemispheres, with stars;
While on them all our eyes we move,
Our eyes that meant immoderate love.

In every gesture, every air,
    Th' imperfect lisp, the languid eye,
In every motion of the fair
    We awkward imitators vie;
And forming our own from her face,
Strive to look pretty, as we gaze.

If e'er she sneer'd the mimic crowd
    Sneer'd too, and all their pipes laid down;
If she but stoop'd, we lowly bow'd,
    And sullen, if she 'gan to frown,
In solemn silence sat profound –
But did she laugh! the laugh went round.

Her snuff-box if the nymph pull'd out,
    Each Johnian in responsive airs
Fed with the tickling dust his snout,[1]
    With all the politesse of bears.
Dropt she her fan beneath her hoop,
E'en stake-stuck Clarians strove to stoop.

The sons of culinary Kays   [Caius]
    Smoking from the eternal treat,
Lost in extatic transport, gaze
    As tho' the fair were good to eat;
E'en gloomiest King's men, pleased awhile,
'Grin horribly a ghastly smile.'

'But hark,' she cries, 'my mamma calls,'
    And straight she's vanish'd from our sight,
'Twas then we saw the empty bowls,
    'Twas then we first perceived it night;
While all, sad synod, silent moan,
Both that she went – and went alone.
CHRISTOPHER SMART, ca. 1740

And the aftermath?

THE DOUBLE TRANSFORMATION

Secluded from domestic strife,
Jack Book-worm led a college life;
A fellowship at twenty-five
Made him the happiest man alive;
He drank his glass, and crack'd his joke,
And freshmen wonder'd as he spoke.
Such pleasures, unalloy'd with care,
Could any accident impair ?
Could Cupid's shaft at length transfix
Our swain, arrived at thirty-six?
O! had the Archer ne'er come down
To ravage in a country town!
Or Flavia been content to stop

---

[1]Johnians were sometimes nicknamed hogs.

At triumphs in a Fleet-street shop!
O had her eyes forgot to blaze !
Or Jack had wanted eyes to gaze;
O! – But let exclamations cease,
Her presence banished all his peace.
So with decorum all things carried,
Miss frown'd, and blush'd and then was – married.

OLIVER GOLDSMITH, ca.1752

Lucy Boston, the writer of the remarkable Green Knowe series of novels, spent part of the First World War nursing at Addenbrooke's Hospital in Cambridge. The man who became her husband was in Army camp nearby:

Throughout the Summer while the war grew ever less imaginable, I stayed on in Cambridge. I took to sleeping out in a punt up by Byron's pool, where Harold could slip out of camp and join me for an hour or two. Once waking up alone in the dawn I saw a kingfisher perched on my wrist, a portent surely. Or, I went by canoe along the rapidly diminishing upper river until even a canoe could be forced no further. Canoes are not good for sleeping in, but if they are well mud-grounded it is possible. Coming back into Cambridge in the early morning still full of wonder, I was amused to hear an early riser on the bank say to his companion, 'Gawd! She's come from the mountains!'

LUCY BOSTON, *Perverse and Foolish: A Memoir of Childhood and Youth*, 1979

Margot Fonteyn used to go with the Sadlers Wells Ballet to dance in Cambridge in the Easter Term in the years just before the Second World War. It was the time when work ought to have been uppermost in the men's minds; but

… with fortitude and gallantry, the undergraduates entertained the dancers in a sort of permanent, floating party that, breaking out in different locations, never quite died down during the entire week.

She shared rooms with two friends in King's Parade: near where Lucy Boston had had rooms a war before.

On a particular night in 1937 there was a party in our rooms. Two dark-haired brothers were dancing the new rumba rhythm to a recording made by the Lecuona Cuban Band. The music invaded my mind, overwhelming any conscious thought as I stared at their dance – which resembled nothing I had seen before. I wonder now if the younger boy looked at me or spoke to me that night. I just don't remember; but the next morning something very strange occurred – and this is absolutely true. After I woke up I stepped out of bed to find the floor was not as usual. My feet did not touch it as I moved across the room, so I returned and sat on the edge of the bed to think the matter out. I could not understand what was happening to me. The phrase 'walking on air' came to my mind, and suddenly I remembered the dark-haired boy dancing the rumba the night before. That was it! I must be in love! I did not even know his name, except that they called him Tito.

MARGOT FONTEYN, Autobiography, 1975

Sylvia Plath, just arrived, writes (October, 1955) to her mother about first friendships:

I have been going to lectures and enjoying them immensely and am quite loving wearing my black gown, which makes me feel so wonderfully part of this magnificent place! Sort of like sacramental robes! …

A tall, skinny, rather sweet chap came over yesterday and took me on an exquisite walk to Grantchester for tea. I can't describe how beautiful it was to go down the little cobbled streets in the pink twilight with the mists rising from the willows along the river and white horses and black cows grazing in the pastures. Remember Rupert Brooke's poem? Well, we had tea by a roaring fire at 'the orchard' where they serve tea under flowering trees in spring) and the 'clock was set at ten of three' and there were the most delectable dark clover honey and scones!

SYLVIA PLATH, Letters Home, 1975

As academic life settles into routine, eyes get lifted from books, to contemplate other pleasures, other excitements:

The weeks drifted on. College became a pleasant habit. Lecturers ceased to be oracles. Work ceased to be important. Young men stared in lecture rooms and streets. There grew the consciousness of fundamental masculine apartness: of the other Sex mysteriously calling to and avoiding it across an impassable gulf. Bookshops became places in which to wander and browse whole mornings ...

ROSAMOND LEHMANN, Dusty Answer, 1927

And there is drama: many of the most distinguished actors of the twentieth century made their first public début through the Cambridge Amateur Dramatic Club or the Marlowe Society. Plays have always been a part of university life: they were important parts of festivities for Queen Elizabeth's visit in 1564 and for James I's. John Chamberlyn (1553–1627) writing to Sir Dudley Carleton, then Ambassador to Venice, March 16, 1614:

My very good Lord – I am newly returned from Cambridge ... The King and Prince lay at Trinity College, where the plays were represented; and the hall so well ordered for room, that above 2000 persons were conveniently placed. The first night's entertainment was a comedy, and acted by St. John's men, the chief part consisting of a counterfeit Sir Edward Ratcliffe, a foolish tutor of physic, which proved but a lean argument; and though it were larded with pretty shews at the beginning and end, and with somewhat too broad speech for such a presence, yet it was still dry. The second night was a comedy of Clare Hall, with the help of two or three good actors from other houses, wherein David Drummond in a hobby horse, and Brakin the recorder of the town [*see pp. 13–14*], under the name of Ignoramus, a common lawyer, bare great parts. The thing was full of mirth and variety, with many excellent actors (among whom the Lord Compton's son, though least, was not worst), but more than half marred with extreme length. The third night was an English comedy, called Albumazar of Trinity College's station and invention; but there was no great matter in it more than one good clown's part. The last night was a Latin pastoral of the same house, excellently written, and as well acted, which gave great contentment, as well to the King as to the rest.

JOHN CHAMBERLYN, 1614

❊

But undergraduate theatricals did not meet with universal approval, least of all from Puritans. John Milton remembers his reaction to plays at Cambridge, acted by young men who mostly were destined for the Church:

... in the colleges so many of the young divines and those in next aptitude to divinity, have been seen so often upon the stage, writhing and unboning their clergy limbs to all the antics and dishonest gestures of trinculoes, buffoons, and bawds; prostituting the shame of that ministry, which either they had, or were nigh having, to the eyes of courtiers and court ladies with their grooms and mademoiselles. There, while they acted and overacted, among other young scholars I was a spectator, they thought themselves gallant men, and I thought them fools, they made sport, and I laughed; they mispronounced, and I misliked; and, to make up the atticism, they were out, and I hissed. ... if it be unlawful to sit and behold a mercenary comedian personating that which is least unseemly for a hireling to do, how much more blameful is it to endure the sight of as vile things acted by persons either entered, or presently to enter into the ministry; and how much more foul and ignominious for them to be the actors!

JOHN MILTON, *Apology for Smectymnuus*, 1642

One man who has had more influence on undergraduate drama this century than any other is George (Dadie) Rylands, Fellow of King's and one of the moving spirits behind the Arts Theatre Trust in the thirties. Benson describes him starting his theatrical career:

March 10.[*1924*] – G. Rylands arrived, looking very young, blooming and serene in spite of his efforts. He is acting the

Duchess in the *Duchess of Malfi*. We were gay at lunch, but I was rather dazed by the long morning. Then R. and I went off by taxi to Milton: a cold day, with some snow still lying, but a lovely sun, and the fields about Horningsea and the clear river very beautiful: saw many gulls, hawks, wild-duck, etc. ...

We talked of innumerable things, and came down to Clayhithe ... We drove back and he came to tea, but was tired and silent, liking to be with me, not wanting to go and act. But he went off. I wrote a little.

... To the A.D.C., where I never feel at ease. The play began with faint and sad music by Ferrabosco, very sweet and pathetic. W. said it was the sort of music he would like before his lectures – resignation to a bad job.

The play was, I thought, detestable. It was well staged, the actors well drilled. But the dresses were fantastic, and there was an air of pedantry – and still worse, a sense of deep unreality. A play where again and again in a tragic moment a man finds time and heart to spout similes and platitudes! Soon the Duchess [Rylands] appeared, very pale, moving with dignity – but I didn't like the painted eyes and the very stiff carriage of the head. Yet when the Duchess was there, there was always a sense of reality. The young husband Antonio was a handsome boy, and the Cardinal was natural; but the lunatic scene was grotesque – and then the murders began. To see Rylands strangled on the stage and put kicking and mewing in a great black coffin was grotesque. Then Wormald, very limp and faint, was strangled, expostulating, and the audience laughed. Then four people were stabbed. The whole thing was sickening, and not redeemed by any art or beauty – the very motive of all this crime obscure. I could hardly believe that this sad stately woman was the young man who had been walking with me in the fields all the afternoon. I got tired and even bored when the Duchess was dead. Ogilvy excused himself, and I came back out of tune with everything. But it was a delightful day.

The Diary of Arthur C. Benson

✤

AFTER THE BUMP SUPPER
A drawing by G. K. Chesterton from the 'Twenty-First
Celebration' Number of the *Granta*, December 1907

Above all, Cambridge is talk. What graduate does not remember, with affection, interminable, inconclusive conversations like this?

'The cow is there,' said Ansell, lighting a match and holding it out over the carpet. No one spoke. He waited till the end of the match fell off. Then he said again, 'She is there, the cow. There, now.'

'You have not proved it,' said a voice.

'I have proved it to myself.'

'I have proved it to myself that she isn't,' said the voice. 'The cow is *not* there.' Ansell frowned and lit another match.

'She's there for me,' he declared. 'I don't care whether she's there for you or not. Whether I'm in Cambridge or Iceland or dead, the cow will be there.'

It was philosophy. They were discussing the existence of objects. Do they exist only when there is someone to look at them? or have they a real existence of their own? It is all very interesting, but at the same time it is difficult. Hence the cow. She seemed to make things easier. She was so familiar, so solid, that surely the truths that she illustrated would in time become familiar and solid also. Is the cow there or not? This was better than deciding between objectivity and subjectivity. So at Oxford, just at the same time, one was asking, 'What do our rooms look like in the vac?'

'Look here, Ansell. I'm there – in the meadow – the cow's there. You're there – the cow's there. Do you agree so far?'

'Well ?'

'Well, if you go, the cow stops; but if I go, the cow goes. Then what will happen if you stop and I go?'

Several voices cried out that this was quibbling.

'I know it is,' said the speaker brightly, and silence descended again, while they tried honestly to think the matter out.

Rickie, on whose carpet the matches were being dropped, did not like to join in the discussion. It was too difficult for him. He could not even quibble. If he spoke, he should simply make himself a fool. He preferred to listen, and to watch the tobacco-smoke stealing out past the window-seat into the tranquil October air. He could see the court too, and the college cat teasing the college tortoise, and the kitchen-men with supper-trays upon their heads. Hot food for one – that must be for the geographical don, who never came into Hall; cold food for three, apparently at half a crown a head, for someone he did not know; hot food, *à la carte* – obviously for the ladies haunting the next staircase; cold food for two, at two shillings — going to Ansell's rooms for himself and Ansell, and as it passed under the lamp he saw that it was meringues again. Then the bed-makers began to arrive, chatting to each other pleasantly, and he could hear Ansell's bedmaker say, 'Oh dang!' when she found she had to lay Ansell's tablecloth; for there was not a breath stirring. The great elms were motionless, and seemed still in the glory of midsummer, for the darkness hid the yellow blotches on their leaves, and their outlines were still rounded against the tender sky. Those elms were Dryads – so Rickie believed or pretended, and the line between the two is subtler than we admit. At all events they were lady trees, and had for generations fooled the college statutes by their residence in the haunts of youth.

But what about the cow? He returned to her with a start, for this would never do. He also would try to think the matter out. Was she there or not? The cow. There or not. He strained his eyes into the night.

Either way it was attractive. If she was there, other cows were there too. The darkness of Europe was dotted with them, and in the far East their flanks were shining in the rising sun. Great herds of them stood browsing in pastures where no man came nor need ever come, or plashed knee-deep by the brink of impassable rivers. And this, moreover, was the view of Ansell. Yet Tilliard's view had a good deal in it. One might do worse than follow Tilliard, and suppose the cow not to be there unless oneself was there to see her. A cowless world, then, stretched round him on every side. Yet he had only to peep into a field, and click! It would at once become radiant with bovine life.

Suddenly he realised that this, again, would never do. As usual, he had missed the whole point, and was overlaying philosophy with gross and senseless details. For if the cow was not there, the world and the fields were not there either. And what would Ansell care about sunlit flanks or impassable streams? Rickie rebuked his own grovelling soul, and turned his eyes away from the night, which had led him to such absurd conclusions.

The fire was dancing, and the shadow of Ansell, who stood

close up to it, seemed to dominate the little room. He was still talking, or rather jerking, and he was still lighting matches and dropping their ends upon the carpet. Now and then he would make a motion with his feet as if he were running quickly backward upstairs, and would tread on the edge of the fender, so that the fire irons went flying and the buttered-bun dishes crashed against each other in the hearth. The other philosophers were crouched in odd shapes on the sofa and table and chairs, and one, who was a little bored, had crawled to the piano and was timidly trying the 'Prelude to Rheingold' with his knee upon the soft pedal. The air was heavy with good tobacco-smoke and the pleasant warmth of tea, and as Rickie became more sleepy the events of the day seemed to float one by one before his acquiescent eyes. In the morning he had read Theocritus, whom he believed to be the greatest of Greek poets; he had lunched with a merry don and had tasted Zwieback biscuits; then he had walked with people he liked, and had walked just long enough; and now his room was full of other people whom he liked, and when they left he would go and have supper with Ansell, whom he liked as well as anyone. A year ago he had known none of these joys. He had crept cold and friendless and ignorant out of a great public school, preparing for a silent and solitary journey, and praying as a highest favour that he might be left alone. Cambridge had not answered his prayer. She had taken and soothed him, and warmed him, and had laughed at him a little, saying he must not be so tragic yet awhile, for his boyhood had been but a dusty corridor that led to the spacious halls of youth. In one year he had made many friends and learnt much, and he might learn even more if he could but concentrate his attention on that cow.

E. M. FORSTER, The Longest Journey, 1907

Both Rylands and Forster were Fellows of King's, both of extraordinary longevity, both members of the Bloomsbury Group.

DONS' DELIGHTS

———— ✳ ————

The university has always drawn scholars from abroad — from Erasmus to Wittgenstein and Kapitza. Though it has not always been kind to them, few have had to share the fate of the German Martin Bucer, whose heretic corpse was dug up and ceremonially burned in the Market Square in the reign of Mary I. At the beginning of the sixteenth century, John Fisher, confessor of the Lady Margaret Beaufort (Henry VII's mother, foundress of St John's and Christ's) and friend of Erasmus, drew the great Dutch humanist to Queens'. John Holloway, Fellow of Queens' College, muses, in a lyric form that Erasmus would have enjoyed, on Erasmus' letter of between 1509–14 to his friend Andrea Ammonio.

'Cambridge University!' No one knows the
least bit how to write in a decent hand – still,
'all I want, a room with a crackling fire, not
    draughty and windy.'

Queens' was cold, and close to the water flowing
north to Ely, out in the wilder country;
only, there, the tiny room in the tower
    warmed with his body.

'Boorish crafty monsters in human form! The
cask of wine is come, but the wine is sour, my
crates of books all splintered at every corner,
    Andrea Ammonio!'

'Plagued by surgeons – scoundrels or harpies. Drinking
Cambridge beer, not malmsey, can cause the stone: and
plague is driving me to a school at Landbeach.'
    — schoolmaster Gonnell

Groomed his horses once. 'Will you come to see me?
We shall share a mouthful of foolish tales then.'

So he wrote to Whitford or Humphrey Walkden,
    rain never ending.

Poor Erasmus, sore in his throat, and waiting
Out at Landbeach. 'Life of a snail', he called it.
Mused on clear streams Greece had set flowing: gold, de-
    lighting the Muses.

JOHN HOLLOWAY, Civitatula, 1993

Erasmus' own voice can still be heard. Like Gray, he was a terrible complainer, but Gray stayed nearly all his life, and Erasmus looked back on his sojourn with some pleasure. He started with, and retained, mixed feelings: he was undoubtedly poor, and promises made to him of financial support had not been kept. On 24 August, 1511, he wrote to John Colet, from Queens':

Bullock, after studying the stars, says he sees Jupiter somewhat malign. Already I agree. I see traces of Christian poverty; and I have so little hope of any gain that I am sure that I realise I shall have to spend, in the end, everything I can squeeze from my patrons.

But on 2 November, 1511, in perhaps the last of those pleasant days of autumn, he writes to Andrea Ammonio, thanking him for the cask of Greek wine he had sent:

All the same, this place does not wholly displease me.

Ten days later, November blues have set in; and a cask of wine sent by Ammonio arriving half empty does not improve matters:

Clearly, we have here to deal with a sort of men who combine with extreme boorishness extreme bad faith; and there is absolutely no reason why you should congratulate me on my retreat down here: indeed, shame alone stops my complaints.

In the same month, to Roger Wentforth:

I am rich with golden promises only ... You can easily guess how the money runs away here ...

As Term draws to its close, things get worse: to Ammonio, 27 November 1511:

And here – what a University! – there's no one to be found who will write even moderately well at any price ...

And a few days later, 2 December, 1511, to Ammonio:

As for a room, I'd like some nest protected from draughts, with a good *fire.*

Two years later, 28 November, 1513, he is still not happy:

I have been living a snail's life for some months now, Ammonio; shut up, stuck at home, I brood over my studies. I am very much on my own: everything is very deserted here, most people being away for fear of the plague, though even when all of them are around, it is a lonely place for me. Expenses are insupportably high, and not a farthing to be made ...

To Servatius Rogerus, from Hammes, July, 1514: passages of ironic self-description complement ironic reports of success:

The King and Bishop of London, who is all-powerful with the king at present, are showering me with splendid promises ... There are colleges here in which there is so much devotion, such regularity of life, that you would reject any monastic rule in comparison, if you could see them.

But distance made the heart grow fonder: to John Watson, Fellow of Peterhouse, from Brussels, 13 January, 1517:

I remember our close companionship, and those most pleasant days, and nights, we spent in talk with never a dull moment.

DESIDERIUS ERASMUS

❄

Sometimes, undergraduates looked on the Senior Members, the dons, with a very critical eye. Byron, writing to John Hanson:

Trin. Coll. Cambridge Novr. 23d. 1805

Dear Sir. – Your advice was good but I have not determined whether I shall follow it, this place is the *Devil*, or at least his principal residence, they call it the University, but any other appellation would have suited it much better, for Study is the last pursuit of the Society; the Master [William Lort Mansel] eats, drinks, and Sleeps, the Fellows *drink, dispute* and *pun*, the *employments* of the under Graduates you will probably conjecture without my description. I sit down to write with a head confused with dissipation, which though I hate, I cannot avoid. I have only supped at home 3 times since my arrival, and my table is constantly covered with invitations, after all I am the most *steady* man in the College, nor have I got into *many* Scrapes, and none of consequence.

GEORGE GORDON, LORD BYRON

Bertrand Russell was equally uncharitable in describing dons of his day:

The dons contributed little to my enjoyment of Cambridge. The Master [of Trinity, Montague Butler] came straight out of Thackeray's *Book of Snobs*. He generally began his remarks with 'Just thirty years ago today ...' or with, 'Do you by any chance remember what Mr Pitt was doing one hundred years ago today?', and he would then proceed to relate some very tedious historical anecdote to show how great and good were all the statesmen mentioned in history ...

I remember once going to breakfast at the Lodge, and it happened that the day was his sister-in-law's birthday. After wishing her many happy returns, he continued: 'Now, my dear, you have lasted just as long as the Peloponnesian War.' She did not know how long this might be, but feared it was longer than she could wish. His wife took to Christian Science, which had the effect of prolonging his life for some twenty years beyond what might otherwise have been expected. This happened through her lack of sympathy with his ailments. When he was ill, she would send word to the Council Meeting that the Master was in bed and refused to get up. It must be said, however, that the Vice-Master, Aldous Wright, and the Senior Fellow, Joey Prior, lasted almost equally long without the help of Christian Science. I remember when I was an undergraduate watching the three of them standing bare-headed at the Great Gate to receive the Empress Frederick. They were already very old men, but fifteen years later they seemed no older. Aldous Wright was a very dignified figure, standing always as straight as a ramrod, and never appearing out-of-doors without a top hat. Even once when he was roused from sleep at three in the morning by a fire, the top hat was duly on his head. He stuck to the English pronunciation of Latin, while the Master adopted the Continental pronunciation. When they read grace in alternate verses, the effect was curious, especially as the Vice-Master gabbled it while the Master mouthed it with unction. While I was an undergraduate, I had regarded all these men merely as figures of fun, but when I became a Fellow and attended College meetings, I began to find that they were serious forces of evil. When the Junior Dean, a clergyman who raped his little daughter and became paralysed with syphilis, had to be got rid of in consequence, the Master went out of his way to state at College Meeting that those of us who did not attend chapel regularly had no idea how excellent this worthy's sermons had been. Next to these three the most important person in the College was the Senior Porter, a magnificent figure of a man, with such royal dignity that he was supposed by undergraduates to be a natural son of the future Edward the Seventh. After I was a Fellow I found that on one occasion the Council met on five successive days with the utmost secrecy. With great difficulty I discovered what their business had been. They had been engaged in establishing the painful fact that the Senior Porter had had improper relations with five bedmakers, in spite of the fact that all of them, by Statute, were '*nec juvenis, nec pulchra*' ['neither young nor lovely'].

As an undergraduate I was persuaded that the Dons were a wholly unnecessary part of the university. I derived no benefits from lectures, and I made a vow to myself that when in due course I became a lecturer I would not suppose that lecturing did any good. I have kept this vow.

BERTRAND RUSSELL, *Autobiography*, Vol 1, 1967

❊

Francis Coventry describes the traditionally imputed idleness of a don's life:

He was in the first Place a Man of the most exact and punctilious Neatness; his Shoes were always blacked in the nicest Manner, his Wigs powdered with the most finical Delicacy, and he would scold his Laundress for a whole Morning together, if he discovered a wry Plait in the Sleeve of his Shirt, or the least Speck of Dirt on any Part of his Linnen. He rose constantly to Chapel, and afterwards proceeded with great Importance to Breakfast, which moderately speaking took up two Hours of his Morning; for when he had done sipping his Tea, he used to wash up the Cups with the most orderly Exactness, and replace them with the utmost regularity in their Corner-cupboard. After this, he drew on his Boots, ordered his Horse, and rode out for the Air, having been told that a sedentary Life is destructive of the Constitution, and that too much Study impairs the Health. At his Return he had barely Time to wash his Hands, clean his Teeth, and put on a freshpowdered Wig, before the College-bell summoned him to Dinner in the public Hall. When this great Affair was ended, he spent an Hour with the rest of the Fellows in the Common-room to digest his Meal, and then went to the Coffee-house to read the News-papers; where he loitered away that heavy Interval, which passed between Dinner and the Hour appointed for Afternoon Tea: But as soon as the Clock struck Three, he tucked up his Gown, and flew with all imaginable Haste to some of the young ladies above-mentioned, who all esteemed him a prodigious Genius, and were ready to laugh at his Wit before he had opened his Mouth. In these agreeable Visits he remained till the Time of Evening Chapel; and when this was over, Supper succeeded next to find him fresh Employment; from whence he repaired again to the Coffee-House, and then to some Engagement he had made at a Friend's Room to spend the remaining Part of the Evening. By this Account of his Day's Transactions, the Reader will see how very impossible it was for him to find Leisure for Study in the midst of so many important Avocations; yet he made a shift sometimes to play half a Tune on the German Flute in the Morning, and once in a Quarter of a Year took the Pains to transcribe a Sermon out of various Authors.

FRANCIS COVENTRY, History of Pompey the Little, 1751

A few years later, Thomas Warton made a similar joke in The Idler, *December 2, 1758. The contemporary alumni magazine,* Cam, *runs a feature in each issue called 'Don's Diary', catering for the perennial question, 'What do dons do?'. Only the seriousness is new.*

In the middle years of the nineteenth century, Joseph Romilly, Fellow of Trinity, kept a very full diary of his busy life as Registrary of the University. His keen eye records some of the great occasions as well as of the minutiae of Cambridge life. First, an example of the variety in a busy don's day, even in unreformed Cambridge:

Fri. 26. [*April, 1839*] Whewell's 3ᵈ Lecture. He gave us an account of Hobbes – & his opponents, partic[ularly] a certain [Benjamin] Whichcote [the seventeenth century Platonist] who used to express himself in abstract terms, & who seeing 2 children fighting said 'What! Moral entities & yet pugnacious?' – The audience not at all fallen off …

Tu. 30. [*April, 1839*] Convention of one of our undergrad[uates] for resisting the Porter who wanted to turn his dog out: confined the youth to gates & hall for 3 weeks …

Disciplinary problems took up time:

Sat. 2. [June, 1838] Yesterday an insufferable trial in V[ice] C[hancellor]'s Court from 12 to 5½ (keeping the women & G. waiting for their dinner till that late hour) brought by a foolish M.A. (called Sharpe of Queens) against an underg[raduate] of Trin[ity] Hall (Fenwick) for moving a girl's gotch [*pitcher*] & refusing his name when collared: – Fenwick was reprimanded & Sharpe deserved the same.

Mon. 4. [June, 1838] Long Seniority – Rusticated Hawker & Slinger for firing pistols at 2 this mor[ning] in College: rusticated also a F[ellow] C[ommoner] (Craufurd) for non-attend[ance] at Lectures.

JOSEPH ROMILLY, *Diary, 1838-39*

A. C. Benson seems to express perfectly the late nineteenth- and early twentieth-century idea of a don.

I became [*on election to a Fellowship*] a member of a small and definite society ... I found myself at once at home in my small and beautiful college, rich with all kinds of ancient and venerable traditions, in buildings of humble and subtle grace. The little dark-roofed chapel, where I have a stall of my own; the galleried Hall, with its armorial glass; the low, book-lined library; the panelled combination-room, with its dim portraits of old worthies: how sweet a setting for a quiet life! Then, too, I have my own spacious rooms, with a peaceful outlook onto a big close, half orchard, half garden, with bird-haunted thickets and immemorial trees, bounded by a slow river ...

Well, today was a wet day, so I did what I particularly enjoy – I went off for a slow stroll, and poked about among some of the smaller colleges ... These sweet and beautiful little places, with a quiet, dignified history and tradition of their own, are very attractive and beautiful. I went and explored a little college I am ashamed to say I had never visited before. It shows a poor plastered front to the street, but the old place is there behind the plaster. I went into a tiny, dark chapel, with a high pillared pediment of carved wood behind the altar, a rich ceiling, and some fine columned alcoves where the dignitaries sit. Out of the gallery opens a venerable library, with a regretful air of the past about its faded volumes in their high presses, as though it sadly said, 'I am of yesterday'. Then we found ourselves in a spacious panelled Hall, with a great oriel looking out into a peaceful garden, embowered in great trees, with smiling lawns. All round the Hall hung portraits of old worthies peers, judges, and bishops, with some rubicund wigged Masters. I like to think of the obscure and yet dignified lives that have been lived in these quaint and stately chambers. I suppose that there used to be a great deal of tippling and low gossip in the old days of the vinous, idle Fellows, who hung on for life, forgetting their books, and just trying to dissipate boredom. One tends to think that it was all like that; and yet, doubtless there were quiet lives of study and meditation led here by wise and simple men who have long since mouldered into dust. And all that dull rioting is happily over. The whole place is

156

full of activity and happiness. There is, if anything, among the Dons, too much business, too many meetings, too much teaching, and the life of mere study is neglected. But it pleases me to think that even now there are men who live quietly among their books, unambitious, perhaps unproductive, but forgetting the flight of time, and looking out into a pleasant garden, with its rustling trees, among the sound of mellow bells. We are, most of us, too much in a fuss nowadays to live these gentle, innocent and beautiful lives; and yet the University is a place where a poor man, if he be virtuous, may lead a life of dignity and simplicity, and refined happiness. We make the mistake of thinking that all can be done by precept, when, as a matter of fact, example is no less potent a force. To make such quiet lives possible was to a great extent what these stately and beautiful places were founded for – that there should be in the busy world a corner where activities should not be so urgent, and where life should pass like an old dream, tinged with delicate colour and soft sound. I declare I do not know that it is more virtuous to be a clerk in a bank, toiling day by day that others should be rich, than to live in thought and meditation, with a heart open to sweet influences and pure hopes. And yet it seems to be held nowadays that virtue is bound up with practical life.

ARTHUR C. BENSON, *From a College Window*, 1906

In those days there were old Dons at Cambridge who rampaged like mad bulls, if you just waved red rags at them. If the Don was Mathematical, you waved the Method of Projections: if he was Classical, you waved Archaeology. With the Method of Projections a short proof was substituted for a long proof, and the short proof was exact; but the old men had always used the long proof, and were indignant that the same results should be obtained so easily; and they had influence enough to get the easy proof prohibited in the Mathematical Tripos. The old Classical men were just as cross with Archaeology. They had learned to understand the Ancient World by years of patient study of its literature; and here were upstarts who could understand the Ancient

World (perhaps better than they did) by merely looking at its statues, vases, coins and gems.

I remember two old Mathematicians dining with us; and after dinner they talked shop, and my father went to sleep in the middle of their talk. Recovering himself, he said, 'I beg pardon, Mr X, I fear I dropped asleep while you were speaking.' Mr X replied, 'Not at all, Mr Torr, not at all: it was Mr Y who was speaking when you went to sleep.'

On roads near Cambridge one often saw Dons walking steadily on till they came to a mile-stone, touching the stone with their hands, and then walking just as steadily back. They had found out by experience how many miles they needed for their afternoon walk, and they always walked that number of miles, neither more nor less. An undergraduate told me that he went out for a walk one Saturday afternoon with a foreign Jew, who was at Cambridge lecturing; and he wondered how the Sabbath Day's Journey would work in. Instead of turning back at a mile-stone, the pious man took out a biscuit, put it down, and then walked on; and he did the same at every mile-stone that they passed. On getting back, my friend inquired about the biscuits; and the answer was quite clear – a Sabbath Day's Journey is a certain distance from your home; and the Mishnah says that where your food is, there also is your home. The biscuits were his Food, and every mile-stone was his home.

CECIL TORR, *Small Talk at Wreyland*, 1918–23

❋

The great anthropologist J. G. Frazer (1854–1941) expresses gratitude:

Finally, I thank the members, present and past, of the Council of Trinity College, who, by thrice prolonging my Fellowship, have enabled me, free from sordid care, to pass my days in 'the calm and still air of delightful studies' amid surroundings of all others the most congenial to learning. The windows of my study look on the tranquil court of an ancient college, where the sundial marks the silent passage of the hours, and in the long summer days the fountain plashes drowsily amid flowers and grass; where, as the evening shadows deepen, the lights come out in the blazoned windows of the Elizabethan hall, and from the chapel the sweet voices of the choir, blent with the pealing music of the organ, float on the peaceful air, telling of man's eternal aspirations after truth and goodness and immortality. Here, if anywhere, remote from the tumult and bustle of the world with its pomps and vanities and ambitions, the student may hope to hear the still voice of truth, to penetrate through the little transitory questions of the hour to the realities which abide, or rather which we fondly think must abide, while the generations come and go. I cannot be too thankful that I have been allowed to spend so many quiet and happy years in this ancient home of learning and peace.

J. G. FRAZER, Preface to *Pausanias's Description of Greece*, 1898

In these Arcadian surroundings, he found The Golden Bough.

Frazer conjures up an image that many summer visitors still take away with them, of high endeavour amid tranquil beauty. But living in a College room was not always luxurious. In many older Colleges, large mediaeval rooms were heated by a single gas-fire, and the staircases were open to the wind of heaven. An overseas visitor in the hard winter of 1962–3, with wide experience but only an optimistic command of English, viewed a Fellow's rooms in one of the old Colleges, and made the memorable remark: 'You live like middle-aged monkeys here.'

Senior members of the University, in loco parentis *until the change in the age of majority in the late 1960s, were bound to come in for a lot of criticism, not all good natured. Relations with the young men who were their pupils could be bad, and there was a time when those who infringed College statutes could be publicly flogged by a Fellow of the College. But it is certain that many Fellows lived a sober, serious life, and won the affection and respect of those undergraduates who, in their turn, seriously sought knowledge and learning. Milton, no friend to the idle, gracefully records, in a major piece of polemic, his gratitude to the Fellows of Christ's – and this is at a time when criticism of the universities was very loud, and there would shortly be moves to abolish them altogether.*

[My opponent's libel] hath given me an apt occasion to acknowledge publicly with all grateful mind, that more than ordinary favour and respect, which I found above any of my equals at the hands of those courteous and learned men, the fellows of that college wherein I spent some years ... As to those ingenuous and friendly men, who were ever the countenances of virtuous and hopeful wits, I wish the best and happiest things, that friends in absence wish each other.

JOHN MILTON, *Apology for Smectymnuus*, 1642

Many kindly men, forbidden by University Statute to marry until 1882, without any family save their College, constantly seeing their young pupils disappear to the duties of the world outside Cambridge, were, simply, lonely.

But fix our Scholar, and suppose him crown'd
With all the glory gain'd on classic ground;
Suppose the world without a sigh resign'd,
And to his college all his care confined;
Give him all honours that such states allow,
The freshman's terror and the tradesman's bow;
Let his apartments with his taste agree,
And all his views be those he loves to see;
Let him each day behold the savoury treat,
For which he pays not, but is paid to eat;
These joys and glories soon delight no more,
Although, withheld, the mind is vex'd and sore;
The honour too is to the place confined,
Abroad they know not each superior mind:
Strangers no *wranglers* in those figures see,
Nor give they worship to a high degree;
Unlike the prophet's is the scholar's case,
His honour all is in his dwelling-place:
And there such honours are familiar things;
What is a monarch in a crowd of kings?
Like other sovereigns he's by forms address'd,
By statutes govern'd and with rules oppress'd.
When all these forms and duties die away,
And the day passes like the former day,
Then of exterior things at once bereft,
He's to himself and one attendant left;

Nay, John too goes; nor aught of service more
Remains for him; he gladly quits the door,
And, as he whistles to the college-gate,
He kindly pities his poor master's fate.
  GEORGE CRABBE, *The Borough: Letter xxiv*, 1810

Two fitful lamps in the silent court
    Scarce vigour enough can muster
To throw on the nearest ivy-leaves
    A faint and sickly lustre.
My voiceless books on their dusty shelves
    Hang drearily round and above me,
For I'm a poor wretch with a Fellowship
    And never a soul to love me. –
One or two friends, good fellows enough
    Still linger about the old College;
One or two bring me a noddle to stuff
    With scrapings of Classical knowledge;
One or two dons I don't care for a straw
    In years and in learning above me; –
Servants that live on me, cramming their maw, –
    But never a soul to love me!
Right it should be so; – why should it not?
    Love for the lovable only; –
Yet a tup put to graze by himself for the rot
    May be pardoned for saying he's lonely.
  JAMES ROBERTSON, *Arachnia*, 1859

Once dons were allowed to marry, however, it became possible to escape such loneliness. There was a sudden need, as in north Oxford, for substantial houses to accommodate the new married Fellows who moved out of their College rooms and set up establishments, with the usual complement of servants. Barton Road, Grange Road, Hills Road, West Road, Madingley Road – a vast expansion of the town into leafy suburbia – owe their present appearance to that change in the Statutes.

O Alma Mater, art thou too
    Translated in so short a space?
Ah me! Since eighteen-eighty-two
    Thou wear'st a worse, an altered face ...

Alas! thou art not [*Cambridge still*]! thou art made
    A land of villas – load by load
The waggons grumble past, and trade
    Is busy on the Barton Road.

★   ★   ★

The grudging tutor, who of late
    Lived on in celibate content,
Now meekly plans a nursery grate,
    And speeds the growing pediment.

The Cambridge Fortnightly, 1888

❋

Romilly describes a polite party: here, two generations before Benson, is genteel Cambridge society:

Fri. 8 June, 1838. Cold N.E. wind ... Went to a Déjeuner at Powers at Trin[ity] H[all] given in the open air under the Chestnuts: it was very cold & ungenial: however the company (about 100) was in high good humour & I never saw so much lovemaking: it was comical to see the fiancés (or lovers at least) walking together: – Heaviside & Miss Skrine (by the way H. was not over gallant, & turned over his love to his Lecturer Phelps), A. Thomas (a heavyish large & somewhat vulgar man tho[ugh] a member of Sir C[harles] Grandison club[1] (alias True Blue – consist[ing] of 9 members) & Miss Julia (by the way he produced a scene by letting her parasol fall into the water) Miss Helena Jermyn & her engaged A. Power; the handsome Miss Lee & her devoted J. Blow (Joh), &c – A Band lying perdue under the Chestnuts was playing at intervals. At 4½ [4.30] we had our cold dinner under the said trees. It was very handsome with profusion of champagne. – After dinner

[1]A Trinity dining club, still in existence.

2 madrigals were sung by the Miss Skrines, Miss Wilkins, M^r &
Miss Freres, Mr Stuart &c – The overshadowing branches something deadened the sound, but the effect was very pleasing. –
Then came Quadrilles, Walzes & Country dances: all mightily gay
… We then formed ourselves into 4 separate tea-parties in different parts of the garden: of course the Clarks & Humfreys were not
in the same set. – Abund[ance] of ice! – About 8 the company
went into the Hall & resumed their dancing with much vigour. –
Power deserves much praise for his arrangements: in the gardens
were abund[ance] of sofas: rugs were put on the grass before them
& the tables; books, cards, chessmen &c were placed on the tables.
– By the way Amun Bey was here & I challenged him to Chess; he
declined & said he saw 'that I was very clever' – That is more than
he thinks of Englishwomen for he declares their conversation to
be very *horizontal*; – meaning perhaps *flat*; – but he is a Turk & a
mathematician & knows no better. – I went & played Cards with
Mills.

JOSEPH ROMILLY, Diary, 1838

*Thomas Hardy, to his patent delight, was elected an Honorary Fellow of
Magdalene College:*

Magdalene, November 1 [1913] – Dined at the Lodge at 8.0: the only
guest Thomas Hardy, who was very simple, merry and comfortable. We discussed the ceremony of installation … The Master was
afraid that Hardy might dislike a religious service. But Hardy said
that he wasn't afraid of a service or a surplice; he used to go to
church three times on a Sunday; it turned out that he often went
to St. Paul's and other London churches, like Kilburn, and knew
a lot about ecclesiastical music and double chants. He had ordered
a complete set of robes, too – bonnet, gown and hood. This
restored the Master's confidence. We sate and talked and smoked;
and the old man wasn't a bit shy – he prattled away very pleasantly
about books and people. He looks a very tired man at times, with
his hook nose, his weary eyes, his wisps of hair; then he changes
and looks lively again. He rather spoiled the effect of his ecclesiastical knowledge by saying blithely, 'Of course it's only a sentiment

to me now!' He said something like 'I wish you had some name for the college to avoid confusion with Magdalen Oxford'. I corrected him and said, 'You ought not to say you, you must say *we.*' He chuckled at this and said, 'Very well, *we* and *our* college.'

November 2. I went into the library at 10.25 and found Hardy in a surplice, with a gown (scarlet) over it. [Sir Stephen]Gaselee was perturbed and said, 'We must try to think of it as a *cappa magna.*' The Archdeacon of Zanzibar was there, an odd mixture, in appearance, of a woman, a Chinaman, and a seminary priest. We formed a procession, and the Master asked me to join it. He and Hardy went up to the altar; the men stared at the little figure, all ablaze ... The Master admitted him in Latin, standing by the altar, walked down with him, and put him in my old stall. There was a temporary organist who played badly, and the music was horrible. The Archdeacon preached rather well, on God being a God of *desire,* who both hated and loved – not a mild or impersonal force.

When we came out I took Hardy to my house, and he, as a former architect, was amused at my devices. He sate for half an hour and talked. He said he was amazed at my output. He said he couldn't write now, only a bit of verse at intervals; he was ashamed of his little book of republished stories and surprised at its good reception. I said that I wasn't an artist, only an *improvisatore* – no quality in my work. He said, 'Oh, you must leave other people to say that, if they choose.' He looked tired, but bucked up, and I walked back to the Lodge with him ...

At the end of dinner the Master proposed Hardy's health in a few very nice words; we rose and drank it. Hardy sate there beaming, drank and nodded back, but didn't speak ... He said, 'I should like to think I should come here often, and I mean to – but the flesh is weak!' I liked the old man very much, so simple and confiding. He told me he had enough verses for a book, but he didn't know whether he ought to include in it some verses he wrote when his wife died – 'very intimate, of course – but the verses came; it was quite natural; one looked back through the years and saw some pictures; a loss like that just makes one's old brain vocal.'

ARTHUR C. BENSON, Diary, 1913

Magdalene has had several notable men of letters as Honorary Fellows besides Hardy — for example, T. S. Eliot and Rudyard Kipling. Kipling writes to his daughter, 31 May 1932:

Me Daughter,

Haven't written you in a longish time. There has been a certain amount of work to catch up with and, at last, I am almost level with it.

Likewise, I have been away for a week-end all by my lone to be made a Fellow of Magdalene. (By the way *both* Colleges – Oxford and Cambridge – are pronounced 'Maudlin'. So misinformed you). It rained of course, and Cambridge in rain is about as dreary as you could imagine. But they were all immensely kind, and as easy as an old shoe. The President of Magdalen (Oxford) most kindly came to assist and he and the Bishop of Derby, an ex-Mayor of Cambridge and the sanest and most worldly Bishop I've met in a long while, were the only two other guests in the house of the Master – of Magdalene, Cambridge. Had a real good time with them talking over things.

It was an entirely intimate function – in Chapel on a Sunday evening. And if you had seen your Dad in a fair white linen surplice (*most* becoming) with his red D.Litt. hood trailing down his back, you'd have been impressed. The Master took me by the hand and led me – inducted is, I think, the word – a pace or two up the aisle and handed me into my stall and then evening service began. After which, dinner with unbelievable plate and then (no speeches) an adjournment to Combination room – all ancient panelling, ancient plate and wondrous wines – where we sat about talking till ten.

But what I appreciated most was the Guest room which one can book when one is coming up on one's own. It, too, is panelled and lovely; has a sitting and bedroom which has a modern washand [*sic*] stand and a truly bath [*sic*] round the corner. The rest is sixteenth Century. One can use the suite when one chooses. It seems almost too good to be true.

My other privilege is to walk on the grass of the Quads and in the Fellows' Garden. Undergrads are crucified for doing this. But it opened a whole new world to me, and one in which I took great pleasure. But their kindness to me was best of all. I look very

beautiful at meals in a simple black gown with ample sleeves ...
Your lovingest Dad
RUDYARD KIPLING, in *Magdalene College Record*, 41, 1996–7

Thom Gunn, after nearly thirty years in the USA, associates the consolations of reading with Cambridge and the life of study:

HIS ROOMS IN COLLEGE

All through the damp morning he works, he reads.
The papers of his students are interrupted
Still by the raw fury, the awkward sadness
His marriage has become. The young serious voices
Are drowned by her remembered piteous wail
'Discovering' the one unfaithfulness
He never did commit.
                Be more specific.
What do they have ahead of them, poor dears,
This kind of thing ?
                Today no supervisions;
But though he meant these hours for his research
He takes a book, not even in his 'field',
And some note touches him, he goes on reading
Hours long into the afternoon from which
The same low river fog has never lifted.
If every now and then he raises his eyes
And stares at winter lawns below, each time
He sees their hard blurred slopes the less. He reads,
He reads, until the chapel clock strikes five,
And suddenly discovers that the book,
Unevenly, gradually, and with difficulty,
Has all along been showing him its mind
(Like no one ever met at a dinner party),
And his attention has become prolonged
To the quiet passion with which he in return
Has given himself completely to the book.
He looks out at the darkened lawns, surprised
Less by the loss of grief than by the trust.
                THOM GUNN, *The Passages of Joy*, 1982

And finally,

> I knew a man who lived upon the Past,
> The which he bolted with prodigious speed
> Until his mind would only move astern.
>
> Perceiving this, they told him he was great,
> And bade him write them theses; which he did,
> Until his mind had ceased to move at all.
>
> They gave him then a Fellowship for life,
> And called him learned; which, perhaps, he was.
> GEORGE STEWART BOWLES,
in Granta, 21 October 1899

CEREMONIES
AND OCCASIONS

———— ❈ ————

One of the fullest earlier accounts of a degree ceremony, then called a Commencement, is by Baron Waldstein. From Bohemia, he seems thoroughly to have enjoyed his tour in England in 1600. He was, of course, given the red carpet treatment, which may have helped. So one has to read his account of Cambridge recognising that perhaps he saw even the admission to degrees through rosy Bohemian spectacles. He called Cambridge,

... one of [England's] two eyes as it were ... known far and wide as a storehouse of religious learning and humane studies ...

By great good luck we happened to arrive at the very time when they celebrate the annual Promotions (they themselves call it Commencement). They have a number of different degrees: first they are made Sophist minors, and then Sophist majors; then come the Bachelors, who after their seventh year are considered fit to proceed to the degree of Master. (They make so much of this degree that they consider it an honour even for the noblest persons: they even have Masters in the place of noblemen, nor will they admit anyone who does not hold this degree to take part in their Congregations.)

After the Theological Candidates have completed 12 years from the taking of their Master's degree, they are awarded their Doctorates. The Promotor is called the 'father', the candidate is his 'son'. Two days are allotted to the Promotions: during the morning of the first day each Professor gives a special lecture to a selected audience on some brilliant and carefully worked out theme. The afternoon is allotted to the disputations and declamations of the candidates ... we did discover that there had been a tremendous dispute among the Professors, one of whom had hotly maintained that until Christ's Ascension the Patriarchs were not in Heaven but in some other place; on the following day another Moderator made a long speech and publicly refuted him ...

169

During the morning we saw 4 Doctors of Theology obtaining their degrees. They came forward into the middle of the assembly wearing scarlet gowns trimmed with white fur, and the Promotor – or 'father' – first of all told them to advance to the chair, which represents Licence to Teach. Then he placed upon each of their heads a flat cap, black and with four corners, symbolizing Theological Truth. Finally he embraced them with a kiss, which signifies Peace, Mutual Love, and Unity of Mind, and gave them the third gift: rings, which indicate the dignity of their appointment ...

When this had ended the disputations began. A very clever young man – one of those who were taking their Master's degrees that day – had undertaken to give replies to the propositions. He began with a brilliant little speech, first of all explaining the theological points at issue (there were two of these: the Presence of Christ in the Sacrament, and Justification by Faith) and then proving the chief objections of the adversaries to be unsound. His own opinions he gave to his audience in verse. After he had finished, first the Promotor or 'father', and then the newly created Doctors his 'sons', produced arguments on the other side. And if they were found to be overstepping the limits of the debate or were being in any way irrelevant, then the Moderator interposed his authority and brought them back to the matter in hand with a warning not to use the weapons of Rhetoric and not to beat the air.

This lasted from 10 until one o'clock, when the Moderator began to sum up the main arguments and to wind up the debate by supporting the correct opinion with a number of apt quotations. Then, just as he seemed about to bring the whole thing to a conclusion, he reintroduced the main points of yesterday's disputation and made a most violent attack upon his colleague (the one who had conferred degrees upon the new Doctors). He belittled his theory concerning the Patriarchs, he undermined his arguments, and then he pressed home his own point with so much animus that the other man went quite red with mortification and might perhaps have spoken to defend himself if time had allowed ...

When the whole ceremony was over we followed the Vice-Chancellor back to Peterhouse where a banquet had been prepared: they even had ladies present among the guests.

(Members of the colleges usually celebrate by feasting together when one of their number has a degree conferred, and since there was such a crowd of candidates nearly every college was having a banquet.) We were given a splendid welcome (this is usual with the English where foreigners are concerned) and were most courteously entertained; we then went back to our lodging.

The Diary of Baron Waldstein, a Traveller in
Elizabethan England, 1981

Conduct at the ceremony had changed somewhat when Henry Gunning took his degree in 1788:

On the 18th of January, we were admitted *ad respondendum quaestioni.* The admission of the Bachelors took place without the least interruption. Our University at that time prided itself that in this respite our parity was diametrically opposite to that of our sister University, at which on all public occasions the entrance of the University officers, and of persons distinguished by their rank and station, was greeted either by shouts of applause, or by hissings and hootings. Sorry am I to observe that for many years past the conduct of our undergraduates has become more outrageous than that of the Oxonians. It has not unfrequently happened that the Proctors have been obliged to clear the galleries entirely, and it has happened that the Vice-Chancellor has been under the necessity of adjourning the proceedings; for not only have the University authorities, whose conduct has been thought to be marked by harshness and severity, been hissed and hooted, but even private individuals whose supposed opinions (whether political or religious) were disagreeable to the majority, have been received with marked insult. On this account the election of Vice-Chancellor, which used to take place in the afternoon, is now constantly completed at an early hour in the morning. After admission to their degrees, the Bachelors generally assembled in large parties to dinner, when everybody was obliged to swallow a considerable quantity of bad wine. The same evening at our college, and I believe in many others in the University, the Bachelors invited the Fellows to meet them at supper in the combination room, which invitation all the Fellows made a point of accepting. A handsome supper was provided, immense bowls of punch were emptied, and every one was compelled to sing a song or to drink an enormous glass of liquor by way of penalty. These disgraceful proceedings were carried on to a very late hour; and it was generally understood that no man should be called to account for any thing he said or did on so joyful an occasion. On the following evening the Father of the college gave a similar treat to the same parties, which was conducted much in the same manner. I am happy to say that these disgraceful meetings have in our college, for some years, fallen into disuse.

HENRY GUNNING, *Reminiscences of the University, Town and County of Cambridge*, 1854

The university's ceremonies are, strictly, domestic to itself, but it has always been heavily involved in national politics. The grand occasions for the conferring of honorary degrees were always played on a national stage. Managing of grand occasions is often a difficult and delicate business. Joseph Romilly, as Registrary, had a good deal to do with the public occasions of the University, including the arrangements for the conferring of Honorary degrees on the Great and Good. He allocated tickets for the Congregations at which degrees were conferred, and the demand for space always exceeded supply. His diary records a busy occasion in July 1835, untypical only in the distinction of the honorands:

Mon. 6. [July, 1835] Much bothered this morning by applications for tickets ... At a little before 11 it was necessary for me to go to the Senate House ... so I dismissed the crowd (many unprovided) telling them I would distribute tickets for tomorrow in the Ev[ening] – The Sen[ate] H[ouse] calculated to hold 2000: I have already distributed several hundred tickets more for each day ... – There were 36 ordinary A.M.[M.As.] to take their degree today. – While in my office distributing tickets we heard certain little cannons fired off w[hich] announced the arrival of the D[uke] of Wellington: I told the people what an interesting procession was going on in the street & recommended them to rush out to see it: they laughed but kept their places till they were supplied with tickets. The Duke arrived from Lord De La Warrs at Bourn: – at Trumpington he was met by a cavalcade of about 500: when in Cambridge the Mob took off the horses & dragged the D[uke] in: ... – on reaching Trinity College they laid boards along the steps & drew the carriage up to the Master's Lodge. – The Duke as well as the M[arquess] Camden is the Master's Guest. – ... This morning at 9 the Ch[ancellor] held a Levee in Trin[ity] Lodge at w[hich] the Master acted as Chamberlain ... it was attended by almost everybody & I regretted my necessary absence ... – At noon L[or]d Camden, accompanied by Pr[ince] G[eorge] of Cambridge, Pozzo di Borgo, the D[ukes] of Wellington, North[umberland] & Grafton &c &c came into the Senate house with great shouts of applause & we proceeded immediately to the tedious business of the Hon[orary] Degrees ... At the Matriculations Potter was awful in the quantities, pronouncing tueberis, Christophorus, Arturus &c: ... L[ord] Camden seemed to enjoy reading the Graces & writing his ad[misi] on each. This done the Orator's task began: & he acquitted himself extremely well: besides 7 Hon. Degrees ... he had 26 Hon. LLD. & Hon. A.M. ...The Orator presented Pozzo di Borgo first: this of course was a mere comp[liment] to the Russian Embassador (like what was paid formerly to Blucher) as he owes allegiance to another Sovereign ... There is a defect in the arrangem[ent] of the S[enate] H[ouse] for such public occasions: the platform for the Chanc[ellor], his friends, the Heads of H[ouses] & Doctors was raised about 4 feet & ascended by a flight of steps: the Orator stood at the foot of these, & with the dense crowd it was impossible (except for the Platform & the Galleries) to see him & the subj[ect] of his eulogy. – Next the Orator eulogized the A[rchbisho]p of Canterbury rather fulsomely. Then came the D[uke] of Grafton: – each fresh person was walked from the Platform by [Henry] Gunning to the foot of the steps, & after having been thoroughly bepraised by the Orator walked up again. – Then followed the D[uke] of Wellington who was received with a round of applause & reiterated shouts w[hich] seemed absolutely interminable: the effect was certainly very fine; & it so much worked upon one's feelings that it produced a choking sensation in one's throat. The Orator's speech about the D[uke] of W[ellington] was much admired, especially the part about mingling the civic Ivy with the Military Laurels. – Then followed the M[arquess] of Bute, &c to the end of the Chapter: – The Orator spoke for the 1st hour & a half: after that he read his eulogies: in general he presented each person separately ... The poor Orator must have had a most wearisome & anxious task, of w[hich] he acquitted himself admirably: however one got tired before it was all over. – This 1st or mor[ning] Cong[rega-tion] lasted till 4½ [4.30] when the Chanc[ellor] &c went to the Déjeuner in Sidney Gardens: the V[ice] Ch[ancellor] remained for the afternoon congreg[ation] to admit the 36 ordinary A[rtium] M[agistri]. – Went ... to the Sidney breakfast: it was very elegant: when we went in we were the 635 & 636th: about 200 afterwards. The place was very tastefully fitted up: a great festoon of diff[erent] coloured flowers exhibited CAMDEN: the preparations for eating & drinking were most profuse, & the Master of S[idney] was rather proud that 24 Doz[en] of Champ[agne] was drunk. There was a band & lamps &c to make a sort of a Vauxhall at night & then the world danced ... – Dined with the V[ice]Ch[ancellor] at 6½ [6.30]. He is the only person who suffered by the rain of last night: the awning w[hich] he had prepared over the Cloister Court was so sopped that he gave up his favorite scheme of dining there: this was a sad pity as the effect would have been very beautiful & we should have had abundance of room. As it was we dined in the Hall & were rather crowded ... We assembled on the grass in the V[ice] Ch[ancellor]'s garden before dinner & all the new-created Doctors were in their red robes, & all other persons in full Academic dress: – we did not wear buckles: very few indeed Cassocks: & the few (I among them) who came with hoods contrived to part with them before we sat down to dinner. Dinner was announced by small cannons fired from the top of Jesus Chapel ...The V[ice] Ch[ancellor] gave the Toasts with great brevity & with most happy propriety of language & gracefulness of manner. – Pozzo di Borgo returned thanks very sensibly & fluently & paid comp[liments] to the great men with whom he had been diplomatically connected. – D[uke] of Cumberland took up his usual topic of his affection for the Church & the establishm[ents] of the land: he spoke cleverly as he always did. – P[rince] George of Camb[ridge] delighted me by his returning thanks, because it was good simple schoolboy English: 'I am much obliged & shall *try to behave* so as to deserve some of the praise you have been good enough to bestow on me.' – Then came the D[uke] of Wellington's health: he has clearly lost some of his teeth but spoke in a manly forcible stile that was heard by every body. Of course his health was received with shouts of applause that made the courts echo. – His speech was expressive of the regard he bore to the Univ[ersity] of Cambr[idge] & to its Chancellor. I should have said that the A[rchbishop] of Cant[erbury's] health preceded that of the D[uke] of Wellington: the Primate made most lame stammering work of his reply ... As soon as the D[uke] of Well[ington] had returned thanks I took my departure & posted away home to deliver tickets: it was rather more than 9½ [9.30] & I met a considerable crowd outside my door: one man (not a gentleman) said 'he thought it was very uncivil to keep them waiting so': – my blood was up, & I told him 'if there was incivility it was on his part: that I had left a party of the most distinguished people in the kingdom to render every assistance I could to those who were still unprovided with tickets, & that in my voluntary services I had hitherto met with courtesy & thanks': — This was extremely well received & so I hope the man was ashamed of his rudeness ... I satisfied all the applicants by about 11½ [11.30] ... There was a group of Bishops sitting together at the V[ice] Ch[ancellor]'s dinner who amused us by the fixt attention they paid to Cranmer's portrait.

JOSEPH ROMILLY, *Diary*, 1835

Two-thirds of a century later, one can still sense the same excitement of a grand occasion, the same popular acclaim of a great military leader:

King's [College. Cambridge]
Thursday. [24 November 1898]

Dear Mother,
... I have had a very exciting day. I could not get a ticket for the Senate House but stood outside in a place Mr. Cooke told me of, between King's Chapel and the Senate House, where I hung like a bear on a railing and saw beautifully without the slightest crowd. The Sirdar passed so close that I could have almost have touched

him through the bars. Just as he drove up King's Parade, the weight of the people pulling against the high iron fence that runs along by the Senate House Green opposite the University Church wrenched it out of its fastenings and for the length of about 50 feet fell backwards into the crowd. It is a very great miracle that no one was killed, as they were all flung down with the heavy iron on top of them. As it was, only about six were at all hurt, one having his Leg broken. I write this today in case you might see anything in Friday's paper, and think I or anyone you know was hurt. The Sirdar walked with a long procession into the Senate House. He wore his red doctor's gown over his uniform and had his helmet on so he looked very ridiculous. As soon as he was in I ran to the Union to find all the passages crammed. At 2 30 the doors of the debating hall were opened and we squeezed in and waited for an hour and a quarter. It reminded me of the school concerts; there were violent cheers when the electric light was turned on. At last the Sirdar appeared looking rather a chaw-bacon in a grey suit which even I knew was not a proper fit. He was proposed and seconded, and then made a little speech. This evening there was a grand bonfire in the market place. Mollison fetched me, and we stayed quite a long time. I have never seen such a night; they pulled up all the goalposts and railings and posts from the backs to feed the fire. It began in the middle of the square but gradually worked its away [*sic*] across till it embraced a gas lamp, which sent out a spout of flame, and there were quantities of squibs & crackers & roman candles which were thrown in at the windows. We all said How foolish, but enjoyed it very much. The chapel & senate house looked marvellous with the red light. …

Your loving
Morgan

The Sirdar (Commander of the Egyptian Army) was Kitchener of Khartoum; the date 1898; the irresponsible undergraduate E. M. Forster, writing to his mother.

❀

An honorary degree is conferred on John Ruskin, the art critic and social reformer:

Cambridge, *3rd May, 1867.*

My Dearest Mother,

All went well today – and pleasingly, if anybody had been there to please. But it is a great deal, yet, to have one's honour thought of ... The form of admission — is first that you put on a scarlet gown, furred with white: then the Latin orator takes you by the hand (right hand by right hand, which you reach across to him), and leads you up the middle of the Senate House, to the front of the Vice-Chancellor's seat. There, putting you to stand by yourself before the Vice-Chancellor, he himself stands aside, turns to the spectators, and delivers a Latin laudatory speech (recommendatory of you for the honour of degree), some ten minutes or fifteen minutes long; in my case, there being nothing particular to rehearse – except that I had written books 'exquisite in language and faultlessly pure in contention with evil principles', with much more to a similar effect, which, having been all said in Latin, I wished that the young ladies present could better understand that learned language than I fear even Cambridge young ladies may be expected to do ... The orator dwelt more on the *Crown of Wild Olive* than on any other of my books, which pleased me, as it was the last.

The Oration finished, he takes your hand again and gives it to the Vice-Chancellor ... The Vice-Chancellor stands up, and after a little bit more of Latin which I didn't understand, because I was looking him full in the face (having kept my eyes on the ground through the Oration, I thought it proper to show that I *could* look straight) and I was wondering if he would think it impudent, instead of minding what he was saying. But presently came 'I admit thee doctor of this University – in the name of the Father, and the Son, and the Holy Ghost.'

Which I heard, not inattentively, and retired backwards about six steps, and then turned and went down to join the rest of the Masters at the lower part of the Senate House. (The little bit of backing was said by one of the young ladies *here*, to have been very gracefully done.) One can hardly get any directions from anybody, and so I had to do what seemed to me fittest, out of my head.

After that, I had a walk of a mile and a half in the country, and thought over many things. I am to have a quite quiet evening here, with a little music and mineralogy, so I hope to be fresh for my lecture to-morrow. It is rather bright – but terribly cold. I have a very comfortable room, however, and hope that nothing is now likely to interfere with my success.

I will telegraph after lecture to-morrow, and then write to Joanna. Dear love to her ...

Ever, my dearest mother, your most affectionate son,

J. Ruskin, Ll.D.

The Works of John Ruskin, Vol. 36, 1909

Ruskin was a notable benefactor of the Fitzwilliam Museum. On being appointed Slade Professor of Fine Art at Oxford, he gave the Cambridge institution 25 watercolours by his hero, J. M. W. Turner. He was not even-handed, though: he gave 50 to the Ashmolean in Oxford.

The Universities of Oxford and Cambridge for centuries (until 1950) elected their own Members of Parliament. The last Members for the University were K. W. M. Pickthorn (Conservative) and H. W. Harris (Independent), who beat J. B. Priestley into third place. Some MPs for the Universities (like the Younger Pitt) made quite a noise in the world, and, many latterly being independent of party, contributed views that would otherwise not have been heard. Bonstetten gives a rare account of an election, in 1770:

My father knows, doubtless, of the change of ministry and the fall of the Duke of Grafton [Prime Minister] ... The other day an MP for the University of Cambridge was elected: I was there, and all the honours were done me that one could accord to a foreigner. The Vice-Chancellor presides in his scarlet robe and ermine tippet, the Masters of Arts write their votes and their name on little pieces of paper which they go and put on the table before the Vice-Chancellor. Mr de Grey, Attorney General, was elected; he had been recommended by the Duke of Grafton, and the University, which blindly follows the will of the court, was almost embarrassed to learn, the very eve of the election, of the fall of the Minister. The Heads of the Colleges entertained me in turn; one is served by students in long black gowns, with trailing sleeves, in huge gothic rooms. On Sunday I was invited to the [Vice] Chancellor's [William Richardson, of Emmanuel]; there is no nation in the world more hospitable. Mr [Thomas] Gray's friendship with me makes everyone eager to oblige me; he is surely the foremost writer and poet of England.

CHARLES VICTOR DE BONSTETTEN, from
The Letters of Thomas Gray

Royal visits are common, whether or not accompanied by presents of books. 5 August, 1564: the beginning of Queen Elizabeth I's visit. In the next few days she visited several Colleges. On 9 August, in Great Saint Mary's, she spoke, after considerable persuasion, to the university. This young woman, confronted by a collection of some of the toughest and most contentious divines that the preceding three reigns had been able to nurture, was understandably nervous: she wanted to speak in English but was told that statute forbade the University to be addressed in anything but Latin – she need speak 'three words only', she was assured. So she did: it was an elegant speech, showing that Master Ascham, one time Public Orator, had taught his pupil the conventions of rhetoric properly, and closed with a nicely modest: 'nunc tempus est, ut aures vestrae hoc barbaro orationis genere tam diu detentae, tedio liberentur. E. R. A. Dixi.' – [*'Now's the time for your ears, so long detained by this barbarous kind of speech, to be set free'.*] *All were* 'marvelously astonied', *and* '... spoke forth in open voice, "Vivat Regina". But the Queen's Majesty said on the other side, in respect of her oration, "Taceat regina" [*"may the queen be silent"*]. And wished, That all they that heard her oration had drunk of the flood of Lethe. And so her Majesty chearfully departed to her lodging.'

The visit began with a ceremonial entry into a town decorated to receive her:

First, at the corner of the Queen's College and Martin Gill's house, was set a great falling-gate, with a lock and staple. From that place, unto King's College Church west door, stoode, upon both sides, one by one, all the University. From the gate stood the Scholars; then the Batchellors of Arts; then the Batchellors of Law; then the Master Regents; then the Non-Regents and Batchellors of Divinity. Then, at last, the Doctors in their degree; and every one in [their] habits and hoods. The last Doctor and the Vice-chancellor stood upon the lowest greese [step] of the west door. And by him the three Bedells.

The whole lane, between King's College and the Queen's College, was strawed with rushes, and flags hanging in divers places, with coverlets, and boughes; and many verses fixed upon the walls ...

After a speech by the Mayor and several ceremonies, the Queen and company processed 'to the sound of trumpets' to King's College Chapel.

The Mayor of the Town, riding before her Majestie bare-headed, stayed himself at the King's College south-gate; as acknowledging that he had no authority or jurisdiction in that place. Of this he was advertised the day before by Mr. Secretary.

When the Queen's Majestie came to the west doors of the church, Sir William Cecyl kneeled downe and welcomed her Grace; shewing unto her the order of the doctors. And the Bedells, kneeling, kissed their staves; and so delivered them to Mr. Secretary; who likewise kissed the same, and so delivered them to the Queen's hands: who could not well hold them all. And her Grace gently and merrily redelivered them, 'willing him and other magistrates of the University, to minister Justice uprightly, as she trusted they did. Or she would take them into her own hands, and see to it.' Adding, 'that, although the Chancellor did hault' (for his leg was sore ...) 'yet she trusted that Justice did not hault.'

The public Orator then spoke for half an hour, praising the queen, to which she reacted somewhat impatiently; she settled down while he went through the same sort of claims for the antiquity and virtues of Cambridge and the University that Francis Brackyn would make to James I on a similar occasion (see pages 13–14). After that, she dismounted, and entered King's Chapel for the service. She was duly appreciative: as she left the Chapel,

... she thanked God that had sent her to this University, where she, altogether against her expectation, was so received, that she thought, she could not be better.

Nothing like frankness. She probably did enjoy herself, for 'if provision of beer and ale could have been made', she would have remained even longer than the five days she did.

On Sunday 6 August, the Queen was entertained again in King's Chapel:

At the said church door foure of the eldest Doctors carried a canopy over her Majestie to her travis [traverse]. Incontinently began the Letany. And, after that, Mr Andrew Perne, DD, ready in his Doctor's cope, was, by the Bedells, brought to the pulpit, which stood over against her travis. Which her Highness caused to be drawn open. And so, at the [e]nd of the stoole did sit down, and was seene of all the people at the time of the sermon.

The Preacher, after he had done his duty, in craving leave by his three curtesys, and, so kneeling, stood up, and began his matter, having for his theme, *Omnis anima subdita sit potestatibus supereminentibus* [let every soul be subject to the higher powers].

This text was strictly observed by Andrew Perne throughout his life (see page 199).

About the midst of his sermon, her Majestie sent the Lord Hunsdon to will him to put on his cap; which he did unto the end. At which time, or he could get out of the pulpit, by the Lord Chamberlayn she sent him word, that 'it was the first sermon that ever she heard in Latin; and, she thought, she should never hear a better.' And then the quire sung, in prick-song, a song. Which done, she departed to her palace by the secret way; the four Doctors bearing the canopy as before. Which the footmen as their fee claimed: and it was redeemed for 3£ 6s. 8d … [After evensong, she went] to the play 'Aulularia Plauti'. For the hearing and playing whereof, was made, by her Highness surveyor and at her own cost, in the body of the [King's College] Church, a great stage containing the breadth of the church from one side to the other, that the chappels might serve for houses. In the length it ran two of the lower chapels full, with the pillars on a side. Upon the south wall was hanged a cloth of state, with the appurtenances and half-path, for her Majesty. In the rood-loft, another stage for ladies and gentlewomen to stand on. And the two lower tables, under the said rood-loft, were greatly enlarged and rayled for the choyce offers of the Court …

When all things were ready for the plays, the Lord Chamberlayn with Mr. Secretary came in; bringing a multitude of the guard with them, having every man in his hand a torch staff (for no other lights were occupied); and would not suffer any to stand upon the stage, save a very few upon the north side. And the guard stood upon the ground, by the stage side, holding their lights. From the quire doore unto the stage was made as 'twere a bridge, rayled on both sides; for the Queen's Grace to go to the stage: which was straightly kept. At last her Highness came, with certain Lords, Ladies and Gentlewomen: all the Pensioners going on both sides, with torch staves. But the sword was not carried, nor the mace. And so took her seat, and heard the play fully. Which was played by certain selected persons, chosen out of all the Colleges of the town ...

J. NICHOLS, *The Progresses and Public Processions of Queen Elizabeth*, 1788

And so the celebrations went on. A better Latinist than many of the scholars and a better theologian than some of her bishops, Elizabeth seems to have listened to the debates and orations with pleasure. Two of the subjects debated before her were 'Is monarchy the best form of government?' and 'Is frequent changing of the laws dangerous?' Given the political and religious upheavals of the previous twenty years – by no means guaranteed to be over, indeed – and Her Grace's known hotness of temper, whether it can have been equally pleasurable to take part in the debates is open to question.

❇

Queen Victoria's Coronation was marked by a Banquet on Parker's Piece, given to the poorer people of the town. Romilly, of course, was there:

Th. 28 [June 1838]. ...Today was a glorious bright day & the more cheering from the 3 preceding wet days. A little before 1... I went to Parkers Piece: I had a carving knife & fork in my pocket as I was to preside at table 24. We had tickets for the Promenade (w[hi]ch cost 1/-) but did not go to the extrav[agance] of seats in the Rotunda (which cost 2/6) ...

Round the Promenade were tables in a circle for the Sunday scholars (about 3000): Radiating from these were 60 tables for the poor: – about 12,000 of these sat down. And round the extr[emit]y of these tables was an outer promenade where the serv[ants] &c walked with gratuitous tickets from the subscribers. The subscr[iption] amounted to £1758: the [pounds]of meat were 8120, the plum puddings 1650, the barrels of beer 99. – A little after 2 the Signal was given for dinner, & everything went off admirably: all the people seemed to enjoy themselves & those who came to eat performed their part with a good will. – The orchestra was not effective enough, & the singing God save the Queen was very feeble from being sung in parts ... We remained till 'God save the Q' had been sung & all the charity children & sunday scholars had retired & then (about 4 o'clock) went to Prof. Cumming's & had an excellent cold dinner: Lucy was amused with the ingenuousness of Harriet Cumming, who said to her (when she invited her to our house) 'No! I have no wish to' ... we came home soon after 5, the women less knocked-up than I expected. – George & I went to Jesus Piece to see the 'Rustic Sports' – they were said to be under the direction of Dr Woodhouse: – they consisted of donkey races, grinning thro' horse-collars, hunting soap-tailed pigs, climbing greased poles, eating biscuits against time, bobbing for cakes in treacle, & sixpences in meal &c &c. – they were rather a failure. – They concluded with Green and his wife going up in the Nassau balloon. – George & I drank tea with Mr Sherwood. – He & I & M went a little before 10 to Prof. Willis to see the fireworks: they not go off well & were not very remarkable. – The dinner however on Parker's P[iece] was eminently successful: everybody seemed happy; the day was brilliant, & Cambridge may be proud of her fête.

JOSEPH ROMILLY, Diary, 1838

✳

The Queen herself visited Cambridge. Adam Sedgwick, Fellow of Trinity and since 1818 Professor of Geology, describes the scene in Trinity as she arrived:

By one o'clock the members of the University were marshalled in our Great Court, to the number of more than 2000, in silent and solemn order. My windows commanded an excellent view, and were filled with ladies. At length, about two o'clock, the sound of distant voices, and the clattering of bells, produced a slight undulating sympathetic movement in our ranks, and before long the Royal Standard was seen to rise slowly and majestically over the great gateway. A few seconds more and the gates flew open; and down rushed the Guard followed by the Royal carriages. For a moment all was as silent as death; each man was drawing in his breath that he might with more energy send forth a shout of gratulation. I never heard such a shout before, reverberated as it was from every corner of our noble court. The most striking, order was still preserved, and the Royal carriage advanced to the centre of the court, where the Master and Seniors were met to do homage, and present to their sovereign the College keys. You never saw such an ample bunch of keys – large, ponderous, and rusty – and strapped together by an old greasy bit of leather – thick enough to have bound the limbs of unshaven Samson, and looking as if it had been cut from the flank of a rhinoceros. Her Majesty contemplated this phenomenon with eyes of wonder, and then gently waving her Royal hand signified thereby her will that the ponderous bunch should be restored to the keeping of the Bursar. On the carriage moved towards our Lodge door – order was at an end – the whole University moved like a great wave, and threatened some dire confusion; but the front rank halted at a respectful distance, so firmly that no act of disorder was committed. The very tumult, and sudden condensation of the Academic mass, only added to the heartiness and joyousness of the greeting.

Life and Letters of the Reverend Adam Sedgwick, 1890

Queen Victoria recorded in her journal her delight in this occasion:

Both on going and returning [*to Trinity*] the scholars threw down their gowns for us to walk over, like Sir Walter Raleigh.

She also wrote of her reception (31 October, 1843) to her uncle Leopold, King of the Belgians:

I seldom remember more enthusiasm than was shown at Cambridge, and in particular by the undergraduates. They received my dear Albert, too, with the greatest enthusiasm.

This was not the only visit Queen Victoria paid to Cambridge. Her husband, Prince Albert, became a notably energetic, active and far-sighted Chancellor. His installation in that office, to which the Queen accompanied him, was not without the distressing prelude of a bitterly contested election – Lord Powys was the favoured candidate of much of the University. Robert Rhodes James, formerly MP for Cambridge City, gives a charming vignette of the two young people:

In July 1847 Prince Albert and the Queen, in their roles as Chancellor and eminent Royal visitor, travelled to Cambridge, where the Prince read a formal address of welcome to his wife, which she described as 'almost absurd'. The Poet Laureate, Wordsworth, had composed an Ode [*now thought to be mainly by one E. Quillinan*] of such dismal banality that it gave clear evidence of failing powers or possibly – being a St. John's man and a Tory[1] – lack of personal commitment to his task. One evening the Royal couple walked together down the incomparable Backs – which the Queen, sadly, described as 'the waterside' – with Prince Albert in Chancellor's cap and a mackintosh over his formal clothes, with Queen Victoria in full evening dress but 'with a veil over my diadem'. Indeed, Cambridge had been astounded by her diamonds. Their only complaint, as they wandered together, quite alone and in deep happiness, was of the absence of music and singing.

ROBERT RHODES JAMES, Albert, Prince Consort, 1983

Stourbridge Fair's heyday lasted from the Middle Ages to the nineteenth century: it still happens, at the same time of year, but is now no more than an amusement fair. Modern street names – Garlick Row and Cheddars Lane, for example – recall where once the stalls of particular trades stood – in the latter case, cheesemongers. Once it was one of the great fairs of Europe: a place of exchange particularly for cloth, but locally also important as a hiring fair and a mart for general goods. In the Middle Ages, the right to hold the fair, and the right to the market dues from it, and the proceeds from

---

[1] Lord Powys, a Johnian, stood against the Prince, with the support of the Master of St John's. The Government, which leaned heavily towards Prince Albert, was Whig.

it of the administration of justice in its 'court of pie powder' (i.e. pieds poudrés – 'dusty feet', a court for travellers) had been given to the Mayor and Aldermen. Well into the railway age the fair was a major event of the year in the local economy.

First, Henry Gunning:

Stourbridge Fair was, at the time I am now speaking of, a place of considerable importance, not only on account of the various trades that were carried on there, but as furnishing sights and scenes rarely to be met with out of the metropolis. I will endeavour to describe it, and I trust my memory will enable me to do so pretty accurately. As soon as you left Barnwell, there was a small public-house on the right-hand side, called the Race-horse; here the cheese fair began; from thence till you came opposite the road leading to Chesterton Ferry, the ground was exclusively occupied by dealers in that article. It was the great mart at which all the dealers in cheese from Cottenham, Willingham, with other villages in the county and isle assembled; there were also traders from Leicestershire, Derbyshire, Cheshire, and Gloucestershire. Not only did the inhabitants of the neighbouring counties supply themselves with their annual stock of cheese, but great quantities were bought and sent up to London, the practice of employing travellers being at that time scarcely known. In the neighbourhood of the [Barnwell Leper] Chapel, which is still standing (1851), there were about a dozen booths, called 'Ironmongers Row': these, among a great variety of other articles, furnished the goods required by saddlers and harness-makers, together with every description of leather in great abundance ...

Another row of booths, reaching from the Chapel to Paper Mills turnpike[1] was called "The Duddery". These contained woollen cloths from Yorkshire and the western counties of England; but this part of the fair was beginning to be on the decline. There was also a very large piece of ground set apart for the sale of hops. A considerable part of the Common was occupied by earthenware and china from the Potteries, and by the coarser wares from Ely. On the left-hand side of the road, leading from the Newmarket

[1]The turnpike house is till there, just over Barnwell railway bridge, and the old paper mill is still standing next to the contemporary Globe public house.

road to the Ferry, was a row of booths extending to the Common; they consisted of silkmercers, linendrapers, furriers, stationers, an immense variety of toys, and also of musical instruments. At one of these booths, I recollect that if you bought an instrument, the proprietor undertook to give lessons upon it gratis. The most conspicuous person in the fair (and whose booth stood upon three times as much ground as the largest amongst them) was named Green; he came from Limehouse, and dealt in tea, sugar, soap, candles, and every other article in grocery that housekeepers could possibly require. His goods were of the first quality, and he sold them as cheap as they could be bought in London; so that any family in Cambridge, or within thirty miles of it (who could afford the money), laid in their annual stock at that season. He was also an extensive dealer in pickles. This man was a widower, with one daughter, who always accompanied her father. She was, at the age of fourteen, very pretty, and was called by the University men, who stopped to admire her father's pickles, 'Miss Gherkin'; she grew, however, so very large, that the name of Gherkin (or of 'Little Pickle') could no longer be applied to her with any propriety, and she was then styled 'Miss Mango'. There was not the slightest vulgarity in her manner or conversation, and it was remarked by an incorrigible punster (of St John's) that she was *Wapping* in nothing but her size. This young lady was a decided coquette, and many members of the University, of *various ages* and *various ranks*, were in the habit of paying her much attention. Her father was extremely proud of the admiration she excited, and wished it to be understood that 'the man of her choice would find he had not made a very bad bargain'. What became of her I know not, but it was to me rather unaccountable that so rich a prize (whose conduct was without reproach) should visit Cambridge for eight or ten years without getting a husband.

HENRY GUNNING, *Reminiscences of the University, Town and County of Cambridge*, 1854

And now for a racier voice: The London Spy, *again*:

I took a walk to Stir-Bitch-Fair … I had not walk'd above Half a

Mile from Cambridge towards the Fair, but I came to a renown'd Village which by all reports very deservedly has gain'd the Ignominious Epithet of Bawdy-Barnwel, so call'd from the Numerous Brothel-Houses it contains for the Health, Ease, and Pleasure of the Learned Vicinity, and has had so ancient a Reputation for Sacrificing it's Female Off-spring thro many Ages, to the Use and Service of the Neighbouring Societies, that there has not been a Maiden-head known in the Town at Sixteen years of Age, since the time of King Henry the first, in whose Reign Cambridge was new Model'd into an University.

From thence I march'd forward till I came to the Fair, where I beheld such a Number of Wooden Edifices, and such a Multitude of Gentry, Scholars, Tradesmen, Whores, Hawkers, Pedlars, and Pick-pockets, that it seem'd to me like an Abstract of all sorts of Mankind, drawn into a lesser Body, to show the World in Epitomy: At first I came to the Proctors' Booth, wherein he keeps an Arbitrary Court to Punish ... all Misdemeanors touching the Scholars, from whence there can be no Appeal; and near to this is held another Wooden Court of Justice on the Behalf of the Corporation, where his Worshipful Bulkiness the Mayor, sits to determine all such Matters as concern his authority, assisted with the cornuted Elders of the Town, who are ready to lend a Horn upon occasion, to help the Head of their Superiour in all cases of difficulty.

From thence I turn'd to the left, by the River side, where my Nostrils were Saluted with such a Saline Savoury Whiff, as if I had been walking in a dry Fishmongers shop in Thames-Street; at last I came into a Dutch Market of red and pickled Herrings, Salt-fish, Oysters, Pitch, Tar, Soap, &c ... Adjoyning to this place, stand about a Dozen of Sutlers boozing-Kens, distinguished by the Name of the Lyn-Booths [i.e. from King's Lynn]; the good People that keep 'em being Inhabitants of that Town, and have so fair a Reputation for the foul practice of Venery, that their sinful Hovels have always maintain'd the Character of being notorious Bawdy-Houses; the Scholars, to encourage the old Trade of Basket-making, have great resort to these Up-tail Accademies, where they are often presented with a Lyn Fairing, which brings 'em to thin Jaws, and a Month or two's spare diet, as pennance for a minutes Titilation ...

From these Booths I went strait up a Hill, and came into a very handsome Street call'd Garlick-Row, where the slit-deal Tenements were occupy'd by Sempstresses, Perfumers, Milleners, Toy-men, and Cabinet-makers; and is chiefly frequented by Powder'd Beau's, Bushy-Wig'd Blockheads, Country Belfa's, and Beautiful Bury Ladies ... This Place terminates in a Place call'd originally Cooks-Row, but now more properly Cuckolds-Row, from the great Number of Booksellers that are now crept into Possession of their Greasinesses Division; this Learned part of the Fair is the Scholars chief Rendezvous, where some that have Money come to buy Books, whilst others who want it, take 'em slily up, upon Condition to pay if they're catch'd, and think it a Pious piece of Generosity, to give St Austin or St Gregory Protection in a Gown Sleeve till they can better provide for 'em. Here the most famous Auctioneer of all Great as well as Little Britain, fells Books by the Hammer, and gives the Scholars as merry an Enertainment, as a Mountebank and his Andrew. 'Here's an Old Author for you, Gentlemen, you may Judge his Antiquity by the Fashion of his Leather-Jacket; herein is contain'd, for the Benefit of you Scholars, the Knowledge of every thing; written by that famous Author, who thro' his Profound Wisdom, very luckily discover'd that he knew nothing? For your Encouragement, Gentlemen, I'll put him up at two Shillings, advance 3 Pence; Two Shillings once: What no Body bid?' ...

On the other side the River there's a little Town, call'd Chesterton, in which there is the Sign of the Black Bull, where the Country Chapmen generally Lodg that come to the Fair, for the sake of rare strong humming Ale, for which 'tis famous; over which they get Drunk, Quarrel, and make Bargains, till the Fox brings 'em to Sleep; and Sleep, by the next Morning, to a Sober Repentance ...

EDWARD (NED) WARD, 'A Step to Stur-Bitch Fair, with Remarks upon the University of Cambridge', *The London Spy*, 1700

❊

Trinity Hall *by I. K. Baldrey*, 1808

The river trade was one of the reasons for the growth of Stourbridge Fair.
That trade is now gone. The Backs had already become a place of pleasure
when Baron Pierre de Coubertin visited in the 1880s; but below Jesus Lock
things get more serious: here is the course for the Races, the Lents and the
Mays:

It is four o'clock. Boats made of varnished wood glide in flotillas
over the river's surface; in the meadows there are dozens of young
people playing tennis. Here is the note of gaiety, the more modern
side of Cambridge. People are strolling up and down the long,
shady avenues. On this side of the river, behind the Colleges,
there are no houses: nothing but trees. The best way of enjoying
what are known here as 'The Backs'… is to get into a punt – one
of those charming little boats made comfortable with cushions –
and to go wherever the current leads between the grassy banks.
You will see, coming towards you through venerable trees, the

monumental facade of St. John's [*New Court*]. The river washes up against its walls and flows on under a 'Bridge of Sighs' that's delightfully moulded and pierced with barred windows. Before long, you are leaving the city, and the Cam as it sweeps to the right is just broadening when a lock suddenly brings you up short. Beyond that is the serious boating: this is the realm of the racing eights. In the opposite direction the landscape is much greener, the bridges hung with ivy and wistaria, and small channels off the river disappearing into the foliage. At the entrance to one of these, a friendly punter tells me that I am heading for a marshy bit where turning will be difficult.

'You are a stranger in Cambridge ?'

'Not only in Cambridge, but in England.'

'German, perhaps?'

'No, French.'

'Ah, French.' And raising his hat, he says 'Vive la république!' with a courteous grin.

'God save the Queen!' I reply, and we go our separate ways.

PIERRE DE COUBERTIN, *L'Education en Angleterre*, 1888

Coubertin was the founder of the modern Olympic Games. His noble ideal, of international understanding founded on sporting endeavour and excellence, looks pretty tattered now. But at the time, it would have appealed to Charles Kingsley, associated as he was with the ideals of 'Muscular Christianity'. He sent Alton Locke to the races, where he sees his beloved:

... there I stood, fascinated, gazing across the river, heedless of the racing-boats, and the crowd, and the roar that was rushing up to me at the rate of ten miles an hour, and in a moment more, had caught me, and swept me away with it, whether I would or not, along the towing-path, by the side of the foremost boats.

And yet, after a few moments, I ceased to wonder either at the Cambridge passion for boatracing, or at the excitement of the spectators. *Honi soit qui mal y pense.* It was a noble sport – a sight such as could only be seen in England – some hundred of young men, who might, if they had chosen, have been lounging effeminately about the streets, subjecting themselves voluntarily to that intense exertion, for the mere pleasure of toil. The true English stuff came out there; I felt that, in spite of all my prejudices – the stuff which has held Gibraltar and conquered at Waterloo – which has created a Birmingham and a Manchester, and colonised every quarter of the globe – that grim, earnest, stubborn energy, which, since the days of the old Romans, the English possess alone of all the nations of the earth. I was as proud of the gallant young fellows as if they had been my brothers – of their courage and endurance (for one could see that it was no child's play, from the pale faces and panting lips), their strength and activity, so fierce and yet so cultivated, smooth, harmonious, as oar kept time with oar, and every back rose and fell in concert – and felt my soul stirred up to a sort of sweet madness, not merely by the shouts and cheers of the mob around me, but by the loud fierce pulse of the rowlocks, the swift whispering rush of the long snake-like eight oars, the swirl and gurgle of the water in their wake, the grim, breathless silence of the straining rowers. My blood boiled over, and fierce tears welled into my eyes; for I, too, was a man, and an Englishman; and when I caught sight of my cousin, pulling stroke to the second boat in the long line, with set teeth and flashing eyes, the great muscles on his bare arms springing up into knots at every rapid stroke, I ran and shouted among the maddest and the foremost.

CHARLES KINGSLEY, Alton Locke, 1850

A tourist guide, designed for visitors whom the new railway brought to the town, recommends the Races:

It is a very interesting sight on a fine May evening, between six and seven o'clock, to see the population of Cambridge, pouring by several avenues across the broad Common between the town and the river. The racing-course extends about a mile and a furlong, being almost entirely embraced by two long reaches of the river, which make an elbow opposite the pretty church and vicarage gardens of Ditton, and form a boundary on the left Bank to a Common or fen, which extends far away into the distance. Along the edge of this Common runs the towing-path, which is occupied by the spectators. Boats of all sizes are drawn up along the banks, and on the opposite side of the river, which is impracticable for those who wish to keep up with the boats, are stationed groups of ladies and the less enthusiastic admirers of the sport. What situation can there be in life of such thrilling interest as the few minutes preceding a University Boat-race? Let the reader conceive from twenty to thirty boats arranged at short intervals along a straight reach of five or six hundred yards in length; their prows projecting into the middle of the stream in the very attitude of nautical impatience; the steerer of each boat holding the extremity of the rope by which his place is attained by the extremity of his fingers; in each are eight men learning eagerly forward with the corner of their blades just touching the water, to give the utmost advantage of time and sweep to their start; the dense crowd on the bank watching the signals in breathless silence, and a sympathetic suspense spreading along the chain of spectators, from the mass collected on the spot to the straggling groups at the extremity of the course. And then let him imagine the sudden contrast as soon as the gun has been fired; the instant dash of two hundred oars; the steady double knock of two hundred rowlocks; the rush; the whirl of the narrow stream, torn into ten thousand conflicting eddies; and high above all the universal uproar from the banks – the shouting, the screaming, the frenzy, the Niagara of the human voice! And now, stationed at a prudent distance, you see the black column which had fixed itself alongside the first boats dashing round the first corner scattering at its approach the smaller knots of spectators whose anxiety it is to keep ahead of the tumult, and spare themselves the whole length of the course. Off run the stragglers with averted faces, trying to get a glimpse of what is going on behind them, and yet to avoid the dangers of the whirlpool gathering on their heels. Opposite to the Ditton corner we are alongside Jesus; behind them is the Caius, within twenty yards, and will gain round the corner. There is no water for the bow oars within 10 feet of the bank and the steerer must have steady nerves to keep his course at the proper distance. And now numbers two and four, who have been pulling their hardest in company with the rest, must pull harder still to coax the boat round the corner. Not half the distance has yet been done – the men are still in full vigour – the turn of the river has brought them within a few feet of the crowd on the bank, and they are saluted by name or number by many familiar voices. All the attention they can spare from their work is to the rise and fall of the tumultuous shout. If it slacks, the popular opinion favours the escape of the Caius; if it thickens, prow and stern are nearing each other; and it is only a question of two, or three, or four more strokes. Now is the time to exercise that: a human individual voice has risen above the clang – 'Three strokes will do it!' But Jesus boat however still maintains its position.

The great evening connected with the boat-racing is at the close of the season, when the rival crews row in procession through the College walks, with each boat gaily ornamented with flowers and the crews in their Boating Costumes, and then all draw up alongside each other in King's and cheer the crew who are at the head of the river. Then may be seen that great multitude assembled on King's lawn and the bridge, and numbering perhaps some ten thousand human beings, all entering right heartily into the spirit of the scene. 'Tis then the flagging oarsman receives his well-earned laurels; and 'tis then when the shades of some soft May evening are falling around that he feels the first taste of that sweet flattery – the praise that meets success. It is pleasure once tasted never to be forgotten, and will form an incitement lasting as his life.

Railway Traveller's Walk Through Cambridge, 1871

FIGURES,
WITH LANDSCAPE

Memories of Cambridge are, above all, memories of people. But not all are of dons: some, mute and inglorious, have a place in memory as assured as that of any commentator on Aristotle.

CAMBRIDGE PAYS TRIBUTE TO TREVOR HUGHES

A remarkable Cross-section of the Cambridge community gathered in the church of St Mary the Less yesterday for a funeral service for a well-known Cambridge personality.

There was a former Dean of Jesus College, a police superintendent, booksellers, shopkeepers, a solicitor, market traders, college staff. They heard an address from the Rev James Owen, and they sang hymns.

Then they exchanged reminiscences about the man whose service they were attending, paid tribute to his memory, and went away.

A regular occurrence in a town like Cambridge, perhaps. A distinguished academic, or leading businessman, had died it might be thought.

But yesterday's service was not for this sort of personality, but for a man of no fixed address, who had some 113 convictions, mainly on drinking charges, and who was known to the congregation of 50 as the shabby old man with a beard who sat and drank in the city centre.

Some friends of Trevor Hughes, who died last week at the age of 66 after a heart attack, had not wished to see his death go unmarked and unnoticed by a community which had come to notice him. and even to love him, in all his years in Cambridge.

They approached Mr Owen, as Trevor Hughes used to visit the church in Trumpington Street, and he readily agreed to take the service, and to officiate at the cremation afterwards.

'He was a personality in an age when the powers-that-be would like everyone to conform', he told the congregation yesterday. 'Even if he could be awkward and difficult, Trevor Hughes was a warm personality who added a richness to Cambridge.

'This is not a sentimental occasion. It simply reminds us of the Christian message at Christmas, when God came to share our lives. And Trevor Hughes was a part of that.'

It was the sort of occasion that could only happen in Cambridge.

Cambridge Evening News, 1979

❋

EPITAPH FOR A DERELICT

Here lies an oldish man, whose late decay,
Early begun by drink, was held at bay
By will and great good humour: not quite sunk
In degradation; cussèd, feckless, drunk.
Now that his fellow-citizens have paid
Respects to one who lived beyond their aid,
Reader, judge only that they had been moved
Less by misfortune than the life it proved.

CLIVE WILMER, *Devotions*, 1982

In the early sixties there was another eccentric, well-beloved of all who frequented the Anchor pub. Jock was always cheerful, used to dance in the streets, and on occasion, particularly at the time of the full moon, good naturedly challenged cars to a fight. On him, too, be peace.

❋

Lady Margaret Beaufort, mother of Henry VII, foundress of Christ's and St John's, died on 29 June 1509. She was a devout and charitable lady. Her confessor John Fisher, of Queens', later Bishop of Rochester and then martyr, remembers her:

All Englonde for her dethe had cause of wepynge. The poor creatures that were wont to receyve her almes, to whom she was always pyteous and mercyfull; the students of both the Unyversytees, to whom she was a moder [mother]; all the learned men of England, to whom she was a veray patroness … generally the hole realm hathe cause to complayne and morne her dethe.

BISHOP JOHN FISHER

Fisher's eulogy (and there is more of it) is grudging compared to this effusion by Matthew Prior:

MANY DAUGHTERS HAVE DONE WELL, BUT THOU
EXCELLEST THEM ALL: Proverbs 31. 29.
As spoken in a Vision to the Lady Margaret Foundress of St: John's

> T'was night, the Drousy Diety began
> To chain with sleep the buisy thoughts of Man,
> When free from Noise and troubles of the Day
> Our … Poet in those flowery Meadows lay
> Where reverent Cham cuts out its famous way
> When loe! O strange, an unexpected light
> Dispers'd the Native darkness of the Night
> And rais'd at once his wonder and delight.
> But how, how welcome did that light appear
> Which usher'd in a form all Heav'nly fair
> A Form which lately left its Mansh'on there.
> A Woman proper, beautiful and fine
> Her garb was Noble and her Mein divine
> Majestick greatness Triumph'd in her face
> And every Limb had its peculiar grace.
> With sober Pace the lovely Ghost drew near,
> Her smiling seem'd to Chide His useless fear
> At length he knows the venerable Shade,
> Runs to meet that of which he was afraid.
> And thus with reverence Thrice bowing said
> Hail mighty Patroness! Hail great and Good!
> Hail doubly fam'd for Virtue and for blood!
> Hail Thou, whose Acts should I presume to show
> I shou'd blasphem by Epithets too low.
> Hail Saint or Princess royal or Divine
> Hail wonder of our Sex and Fame of Thine

Be Thou my Muse vouchsafe to look on me
The meanest of thy learned Progeny.
Inspire my Soul that I may sing Thy fame ...
... You gave us Learning too.
Then, then indulgently both paps you drew
And rais'd Two fabricks which shal ever be   [Christ's
Great Monuments of Piety and Thee.   and St John's]
    Fain wou'd the cheerful Poet have gon on
To Sing the Works her Charity had done
But She who did like Heav'n her Gifts dispence
Without the Hopes of any recompence
Seem'd by a frown to chide his saucy Eloquence ...
MATTHEW PRIOR, ca. 1700

Prior was a Johnian, of course.

Lancelot Andrewes, lord bishop of Winton [Winchester], was borne in London; went to schoole at Merchant Taylors schoole. Mr. Mulcaster was his schoolemaster, whose picture he hung in his studie ... Old Mr. Sutton, a very learned man of those dayes, of Blandford St. Maries, Dorset, was his school fellowe, and sayd that Lancelot Andrewes was a great long boy of 18 yeares old at least before he went to the university. He was a fellowe of Pembrokehall, in Cambridge (called *Collegium Episcoporum*, for that, at one time, in those dayes, there were of that house so many bishops).

The Puritan faction did begin to increase in those dayes, and especially at Emanuel College. That party had a great mind to drawe in this learned young man, whom if they could make theirs, they knew would be a great honour to them. They carried themselves outwardly with great sanctity and strictnesse, so that 'twas very hard matter to [fault them] as to their lives. They preached up very strict keeping and observing the Lord's day; made, upon the matter, damnation to breake it, and that 'twas lesse Sin to kill a man then [to do so] ... Yet these hypocrites did bowle in a private green at their colledge every Sunday after sermon; and one of the colledge (a loving friend to Mr. L. Andrewes) to satisfie him one time lent him the key of a private back dore to the bowling green, on a Sunday evening, which he opening, discovered these zealous preachers, with their gownes off, earnest at play. But they were strangely surprized to see the entrey of one that was not *of the brotherhood*.

There was then at Cambridge a good fatt alderman that was wont to sleep at church, which the alderman endeavoured to prevent but could not. Well! this was preached against as a signe of *reprobation*. The good man was exceedingly troubled at it, and went to Andrewes his chamber to be satisfied in point of conscience. Mr. Andrewes told him that it was an ill habit of body not of mind, and that it was against his will; advised him on Sundays to make a more sparing meale, and to mend it at supper. The alderman did so, but sleepe comes upon him again for all that, and was preached at. He comes againe to be resolved, with tears in his eies; Andrewes then told him he would have him make a good heartie meale as he was wont to doe, and presently take out his full sleep. He did so; came to St. Marie's, where the preacher was prepared with a sermon to damne all who slept at sermon, a certaine signe of *reprobation*. The good alderman having taken his full nap before, lookes on the preacher all sermon time, and spoyled the designe. – But I should have sayd that Andrewes was most extremely spoken against and preached against for offering to assoile or excuse a sleeper in sermon time. But he had learning and witt enough to defend himselfe.

JOHN AUBREY (1626–97), Brief Lives, 1813

It was for this Lancelot Andrewes that Milton wrote an obituary poem. Beloved of all for his sweet nature, he was a notable preacher and among the translators of the King James Version of the Bible. Patron of George Herbert, he also across the centuries had a huge influence on T. S. Eliot.

Andrew Perne, 1519?–1589 (see page 181) makes quite a contrast: yet he was a benefactor of the town, and the runnels of water that course down Trumpington Street in summer to this day are part of his legacy. For some reason, he also gives his name to one of the dullest of dull modern streets:

Dr Andrew Perne, then Master of Peterhouse College, [was] a divine of such accommodating breadth of view that he alone, amongst all the higher authorities of the University, succeeded in retaining his post and his emoluments throughout the horrible see-saw of the Reformation period.

We first hear of him in the reign of Edward the Sixth, as a Protestant of such stalwart calibre that he destroyed as 'idolatrous' almost every single book in the University Library. Under Mary he figures as no less ardent a Catholic, even to the degree of digging up and publicly burning (in default of living heretics) the corpses of the celebrated Protestant teachers Bucer and Fagius. Finally the accession of Elizabeth convinced him once more that Protestantism was the truest form of Christianity; and she lived long enough to keep him from again changing his principles. This amazing versatility naturally did not pass without comment. The wits of the University coined from his name the Latin verb *pernare*, 'to be a turncoat', and declared that the A.P. which showed on a new weathercock given by him to his College stood for A Protestant or A Papist indifferently.

It was this man who, in 1574, started the idea of bringing the Shelford water into Cambridge. The plan was carried out by 'Undertakers' (who hoped to make money by it), in 1610, and amongst these Hobson would seem to have been the predominant partner.

This pleasant feature [*the runlets of water down Trumpington Street*] is attributed to the benevolence of an ancient Cambridge worthy, Thomas Hobson, who dwelt here from the reign of Henry the Eighth to that of Charles the First. By trade he was a 'carrier', a profession which at that date included not merely the transport of goods but the provision of locomotion for passengers – then almost wholly equestrian. This Hobson not only himself travelled regularly to and from London with his stage-waggon, but kept a large stable of horses, not fewer than 'forty good cattle', ready for hire – even supplying his customers with boots and whips for their journey. But he was very autocratic in the matter, and would never allow any steed to be chosen except in accordance with his will. 'This or none' he would say to any hirer who dared to remonstrate. And his business was so prosperous that he could afford to say it, and thus give rise to the still current expression 'Hobson's Choice'. He rose to be Mayor of Cambridge, and his portrait still hangs in the Guildhall.

Finally when he died at the age of eighty-six, in 1630, he gained the honour of a serio-comic epitaph from Milton, then a student of Christ's College, 'on the University Carrier who sickened in the time of his Vacancy, on being forbid to go to London by reason of the Plague'.

> Here lieth one who did most truly prove
> That he could never die while he did move;
> So hung his destiny, never to rot
> While he might still jog on and keep his trot ...
> Rest, that gives all men life, gave him his death,
> And too much breathing put him out of breath;
> Nor were it contradiction to affirm,
> Too long Vacation hastened on his Term ...
> But had his doings lasted as they were
> He had been an immortal carrier.

The popular tradition (attested by an inscription on the fountain in the Market Place) [*now moved to the junction of Lensfield Road and Trumpington Road*] which gives this hero the whole credit of the street runlets seems, however, to go too far, though they were certainly first made during his lifetime. Their source is in some springs which issue from the chalk near Great Shelford, four miles south east of Cambridge, and which are called, as such sources are commonly called hereabouts, 'The Nine Wells' – nine being used as an indefinite number ... The ancient outfall of these springs seems to have been by what is now called 'Vicar's Brook', which is bridged by the London Road at the first milestone from Cambridge. Till the eighteenth century the bridge was a ford, known as Trumpington Ford ...

REV. EDWARD CONYBEARE, *Highways and Byways in Cambridge and the Isle of Ely*, 1910

❊

An equally well-known character in the University but of a far different stamp, was a bookseller, who was universally known by the name of Maps [1730–96], though his only son, to whom he left a handsome property, discovered he was entitled to the name of Nicholson. When he first began business, he was a seller of maps and pictures, which he exhibited in the streets on a small movable stall; but when I came to college he was living in an old-fashioned, but large and commodious house belonging to King's College, and adjoining to what was then the Provost's Lodge. He had a very large stock of books required at college lectures, both classical and mathematical; and I do not believe I expended, during my undergraduateship, twenty shillings in the purchase of books for the lecture-room. His terms of subscription were five shillings and threepence per quarter, but were afterwards increased to seven shillings and sixpence. When his house was pulled down to make way for the Screen which connects the Chapel of King's with the New Building, he built and removed to the house now occupied by [Daniel] Macmillan *[founder of the publishing firm]*. He was indefatigable in pursuit of business, and was to be seen most part of the day loaded with books, going from room to room in the different colleges, and announcing himself by shouting MAPS as he proceeded. Persons requiring themes, or declamations, or compositions on occasional subjects, were in the habit of applying to him, and if they had no objection to pay a high price, were furnished with articles of considerable literary merit. It was said that manuscript sermons might be obtained through him; but in every transaction of this kind he strictly concealed the names of the parties concerned. By the desire of Dr Farmer, his truly characteristic portrait was placed on the staircase of the Public Library, a distinction he was better entitled to, than a smirking Professor in scarlet robes, who hangs very near him.

HENRY GUNNING, *Reminiscences of the University, Town and County of Cambridge*, 1854

When the University Library moved to its present site, his portrait (see frontispiece) went with it, and, appropriately enough, hangs in the foyer. His eyes now overlook the simpering marble statue below of a laurel-wreathed George II in the wildly improbable habit of a Roman general.

❁

Richard Bentley, Master of Trinity, and one of the giants of modern textual scholarship in the Classics, had a long-standing quarrel with the Fellows of Trinity. He drew the fire of Pope and Swift, among others: yet stuck to his guns, and in the end had his way. Daniel Defoe comments:

The dispute between the university and the Master of Trinity College has been brought to a head, so as to employ the pens of the learned on both sides; but at last prosecuted in a judicial way, so as to deprive Dr Bentley of all his dignities and offices in the university; but the Dr flying to the royal protection *[The Mastership of Trinity is a Crown appointment]*, the university is under a writ of mandamus, to shew cause why they do not restore the doctor again, to which it seems they demur, and that demur has not, that we hear, been argued, at least when these sheets were sent to the press; what will be the issue time must show.

DANIEL DEFOE, *Tour Through the Whole Island of Great Britain*, 1724-27

After not attending chapel for many years, Bentley tried to open the lock of the Master's stall; and found it so rusty that it would not budge.

UPON DR BENTLEY, MASTER OF TRINITY COLLEGE, CAMBRIDGE

Zoilus,[1] tir'd with turning o'er
Dull indexes, a precious store,
For ease to chapel took his way,
Resolv'd to take a nap or pray.
Proceeding slow in solemn state,
Forward he marches to his seat.
But, oh! the lock, long since disus'd,
T'admit the holy man refus'd!
The virger tugs with fruitless pains;
The rust invincible remains.
Who can describe his woful plight,

[1]Bentley: so called, after the quarrelsome Cynic Philosopher of Amphipolis.

Plac'd thus in view, in fullest light,
A spectacle of mirth, expos'd
To sneering friends and giggling foes?
Then first as 'tis from fame receiv'd,
(But fame can't always be believ'd,)
A blush, the sign of newborn grace,
Gleamed through the horrors of his face.
He held it shameful to retreat,
And worse to take the lower seat.
The virger soon, with nimble bound,
At once vaults o'er the wooden mound,
And gives the door a furious knock,
Which forc'd the disobedient lock.
Then Zoilus ent'ring in confusion,
His elbows placing on a cushion,
Devoutly loll'd in musing deep,
Unable now to pray or sleep,
Some words imperfect mumbled o'er:
The wicked Sophs declare he swore,
That none should e'er for seven years' space
Again behold him in that place.
What then? 'tis plain, in strictest truth,
Religiously he kept his oath.

ANON, 1724

*Another great Classical Scholar, the equal of Bentley in crotchetiness if not
in polemic, was Richard Porson, here recalled by Byron in a letter to John
Murray:*

Venice. – February 20th, 1818
... I remember to have seen Porson at Cambridge, in the hall of
our college, and in private parties, but not frequently; and I never
can recollect him except as drunk or brutal, and generally both: I
mean in an evening, for in the hall he dined at the Dean's table,
and I at the Vice-master's, so that I was not near him; and he then
and there appeared sober in his demeanour, nor did I ever hear of

excess or outrage on his part in public, – Commons, college, or Chapel; but I have seen him in a private party of undergraduates, many of them freshmen and strangers, take up a poker to one of them, and heard him use language as blackguard as his action. I have seen [R. B.] Sheridan drunk, too, with all the world; but his intoxication was that of Bacchus, and Porson's that of Silenus. Of all the disgusting brutes, sulky, allusive, and intolerable, Porson was the most bestial, as far as the few times that I saw him went, which were only at William Bankes's (the Nubian Discoverer's) rooms. I saw him once go away in a rage, because nobody knew the name of the 'Cobbler of Messina', insulting their ignorance with the most vulgar terms of reprobation. He was tolerated in this state amongst the young men for his talents, as the Turks think a madman inspired, and bear with him. He used to recite, or rather vomit pages of all languages, and could hiccup Greek like a Helot; and certainly Sparta never shocked her children with a grosser exhibition than this man's intoxication.

GEORGE GORDON, LORD BYRON

Porson was nonetheless a very great scholar, whose work even today no Classicist can ignore. Another great Classicist a century later, A. E. Housman, once began a speech after a dinner with the words 'This hall has seen Wordsworth drunk and Porson sober, and here stand I, a better scholar than Wordsworth and a better poet than Porson, somewhat betwixt and between ...'

Frances Partridge, née Marshall, was born in 1900 and came up to Newnham in 1918. There were giants on the earth in those days ...

The Moral Science dons of my last year make a more impressive portrait gallery than those of the English faculty. G. E. Moore was still in residence but no longer lecturing, so that I was not subjected to the enormous influence his originality and personal charm had exerted on a previous generation; but the Bloomsbury bible, *Principia Ethica*, was still obligatory reading for Moral Science students. I duly read it and was impressed but not bowled over: J. S. Mill and Bentham were among my heroes and I didn't find his attempt to demolish their theories convincing. Greatly daring, I sometimes attended the Moral Sciences Club, an informal evening gathering in one of the men's rooms, where undergraduates and their betters argued in blue clouds of pipe smoke. Only once do I remember seeing Moore there – a middle-aged, middle-sized, grayish man, who sat on the hearthrug holding his ankles in both hands and tying himself in knots, while he endeavoured to pinpoint 'what one *exactly* meant when one said one was going to Madingley that afternoon'. It was amazing the way these great men could make such apparently trifling issues so important, but that they were important and led to profitable molelike tunnelling in all directions I never doubted. ('"All Cretans are liars," said the Cretan'; 'the present King of France is bald', or 'the case of the child who says, "Shan't say thank you!"' were other such.) Behind Moore stood a tall, cadaverous man, with a noble forehead, goggle glasses and an inconspicuous nose, who was the only one really brave enough to challenge the Master – and he spoke in 'the [Bloomsbury] voice'[1]. This was H.T.J. (Harry) Norton, a mathematician whose brilliant promise foundered under successive nervous breakdowns, and who had financed Lytton Strachey while he wrote *Eminent Victorians*.

If Mrs Partridge was not 'bowled over' by Moore, she was more nearly so by the 'outstanding' J. R. McTaggart,

… who expounded Hegel to us without, I fear, very much success. He certainly didn't talk down to us, but I got the impression he didn't greatly care whether he enlightened our incomprehensible ignorance or not. Sebastian Sprott was the sole exception, and with him McTaggart would hold a spirited dialogue at times. But he was, I'm sure, a kindly and certainly an engaging man. His tall, portly form used to float into the lecture-room like a barrage-balloon, and he held his big, round baby's head with its benign expression and spectacles so much on one side that he generally drifted after it. This one-sided trend kept him walking along close to any wall that he encountered as he crossed the quads or

[1]As Mrs Partridge describes it, 'starting low and soft, rising to a faint scream, stopping altogether, swallowing itself, and then sinking to the depths again'.

even a room, and I can quite believe the story that he once floated up to the fountain in Trinity Great Court, and continued circling round it deep in thought until some kind passer-by detached him. He had many interests and achieved the feat of believing in immortality but not in God.

FRANCES PARTRIDGE, *Memories*, 1981

Bertrand Russell also recalls McTaggart:

Another friend of my Cambridge years was McTaggart, the philosopher, who was even shyer than I was. I heard a knock on my door one day – a very gentle knock. I said: 'Come in', but nothing happened. I said, 'come in', louder. The door opened, and I saw McTaggart standing on the mat. He was already President of the Union, and about to become a Fellow, and inspired me with awe on account of his metaphysical reputation, but he was too shy to come in, and I was too shy to ask him to come in. I cannot remember how many minutes this situation lasted, but somehow or other he was at last in the room. After that I used frequently to go to his breakfasts, which were famous for their lack of food; in fact, anybody who had been once, brought an egg with him on every subsequent occasion. McTaggart was a Hegelian, and at that time still young and enthusiastic. He had a great intellectual influence upon my generation, though in retrospect I do not think it was a very good one. For two or three years, under his influence, I was a Hegelian. I remember the exact moment during my fourth year when I became one. I had gone out to buy a tin of tobacco, and was going back with it along Trinity Lane, when suddenly I threw it up in the air and exclaimed: 'Great God in boots! – the ontological argument is sound!' Although after 1898 I no longer accepted McTaggart's philosophy, I remained fond of him until an occasion during the first war, when he asked me no longer to come and see him because he could not bear my opinions. He followed this up by taking a leading part in having me turned out of my lectureship.

And also G. E. Moore:

For a long time I supposed that somewhere in the university there were really clever people whom I had not yet met, and whom I should at once recognize as my intellectual superiors, but during my second year, I discovered that I already knew all the cleverest people in the university. This was a disappointment to me, but at the same time gave me increased self-confidence. In my third year, however, I met G. E. Moore, who was then a freshman, and for some years he fulfilled my ideal of genius. He was in those days beautiful and slim, with a look almost of inspiration, and with an intellect as deeply passionate as Spinoza's. He had a kind of exquisite purity. I have never but once succeeded in making him tell a lie, and that was by a subterfuge. 'Moore,' I said, 'do you *always* speak the truth?' 'No', he replied. I believe this to be the only lie he had ever told.

BERTRAND RUSSELL, Autobiography, Vol. 1, 1967

Mrs Partridge describes the Sunday afternoon gatherings at the house of W. E. Johnson, where she sang to his accompaniment on the piano. A few years later, at just such a Sunday afternoon at that house, an interesting encounter took place: F. R. Leavis, one of the most influential teachers of the twentieth century, recalls his first meeting with Ludwig Wittgenstein.

I was helped, no doubt, by my having no philosophic qualifications, a fact that must have been plain to Wittgenstein, though I met him first (before I knew who he was) at the house of my old friend, W. E. Johnson, the logician, who had 'supervised' him long before – as he had supervised all the Cambridge philosophers from Russell onwards … It must have been in 1929, the year when Wittgenstein first came back to Cambridge after the outbreak of war in 1914. It was at Ramsey House, Barton Road, on a Sunday afternoon, when at tea-time Johnson and his sister, Miss Fanny, were 'at home' to lecturers for the Moral Sciences Tripos, distinguished old pupils, and visiting philosophers.

As I have indicated, I was not one of these, but it had become plain in the course of years that there was no tendency to regard me as an intrusive presence: I was, in fact, an established familiar in the little drawing-room, which was a quarter filled with the Broadwood grand piano on which the old logician used to take his exercise playing Bach. On this Sunday it was crowded, and I couldn't have named half the company. I wasn't, for instance, in a position, though I had heard of him, to identify the enlightened young viscount who (at his own request, I gathered) was known by his not uncommon surname, and was pledged to live – a matter of conscientious scruple – on an extremely small weekly expenditure. It was brought home to me that he was present, and that he was one of Johnson's pupils, when he was asked by name to sing something of Schubert's. What followed was the occasion of my first identifying Wittgenstein.

So far from the truth was the account old Johnson, with his benign sardonic twinkle, put into currency – 'When Wittgenstein and Leavis met they fell on one another's necks' – that it would be nearer to say that, moved to indignation, I offered to *fall on* Wittgenstein. It was what struck me as the cold brutality of his behaviour that provoked my anger. The young man, for whom the invitation was clearly an injunction, stood up – he seemed to me obviously very sensitive and very nice – and, looking across the room at the beautiful and stern face of (I assumed) the not so very much older man I had noticed as I came in, said nervously 'Er, Wittgenstein will correct my German'. Wittgenstein, in a manner I can neither describe nor imitate, replied 'How can I? How can I possibly?'

It was essentially meant to be routing. It had its effect, and when the unfortunate singer had finished, Wittgenstein triumph-antly – so I thought – got up and left. The front door had hardly shut behind him when I, who had followed him out of the packed drawing-room as fast as I could make my way, opened it again. I caught him up on the Barton Road, which, the Johnson house standing at the corner of Millington Road, flanked one side of it, and, with my hands on my lapels as if (I later realized) I was about to take my coat off, said: 'You behaved in a disgraceful way to that young man'. He looked at me in surprise: 'I thought he was a foolish young man.' To which I returned, emphatically containing myself: 'You may have done, you may have done, but you had no right to treat him like that. You've no right to treat anyone like that.' It was my turn to be surprised. Putting his hand on my shoulder he said: 'We must know one another.' Since he, we being at the bottom of the road, turned left towards the Backs and Cambridge, I, muttering 'I don't see the necessity', turned right towards the Grantchester footpath ...

However, the two soon became friends, and Leavis learnt that Wittgenstein had come to Cambridge to work with Bertrand Russell.

He communicated no hint of any sense he might have had of Russell other than as the distinguished mind that had collaborated on the *Principia Mathematica*. I noted this because I was already coming more and more to a full awareness that I disliked Russell, and profoundly – the Russell to be divined in his books and publicities. I recall it vividly now because of the way in which, in his memoirs, Russell refers to his relations with Wittgenstein. He had no glimmering of Wittgenstein's immense superiority to him as a person – as a centre of life, sentience and human responsibility. Of course one knew that, in the nature of Russell, that must be so. It came as a shock, however, to register the tone – the amused and blandly conscious superiority – in which he recounts how he asked a patently troubled young Wittgenstein who had come for an academic consultation whether he was worrying about his work or his sins. Russell clearly still had no suspicion that in the brief unepigrammatically intended reply he reports – 'Both'– we have the difference between pupil and supervisor: the difference to examine which entails the drastic critical commentary to which Russell is exposed.

Wittgenstein was a troubled soul, a fact that he neither advertised nor concealed. It became apparent to me in many ways, and was not less significant of the essential man than the assurance, the two being intimately related.

F. R. LEAVIS, *The Critic as Anti-philosopher: Essays and Papers*, 1982

A. S. Byatt, herself a Cambridge graduate, gives her character Professor Blackadder memories of Leavis:

[Blackadder's] father sent him to Downing College in Cambridge to study under F. R. Leavis. Leavis did to Blackadder what he did to serious students; he showed him the terrible, the magnificent importance and urgency of English literature and simultaneously deprived him of any confidence in his own capacity to contribute to, or to change it. The young Blackadder wrote poems, imagined Dr Leavis's comments on them, and burned them. He devised an essay style of Spartan brevity, equivocation and impenetrability. His fate was decided by a seminar on dating. The Cambridge room was crowded, the floor full, the chair-arms perched on. The lean and agile don, in his open-necked shirt, stood on the window-sill and tugged at the casement to let in fresh air, cold Cambridge light. The dating handout contained a troubadour lyric, a piece of dramatic Jacobean verse, some satirical couplets, a blank verse meditation on volcanic mud and a love-sonnet. Blackadder, schooled by his grandfather, saw immediately that all these poems were by Randolph Henry Ash [*a Victorian poet invented by Mrs Byatt*], examples of his ventriloquism, of his unwieldy range. He himself had two choices: to state his knowledge, or to allow the seminar to proceed, with Leavis enticing unfortunate undergraduates into making wrong identifications, and then proceeding to demonstrate his own analytic brilliance in distinguishing fake from authenticity, Victorian alienation from the voice of true feeling. Blackadder chose silence, and Ash was duly exposed and found wanting. Blackadder felt that he had somehow betrayed Randolph Henry Ash, though he might more justly have been thought to have betrayed himself, his grandfather, or possibly Dr Leavis.

A. S. Byatt, Possession, 1994

A. C. Benson, depressed by the late winter in Cambridge (and who can blame him?) and by the prospect of aging, seeks company:

18 February 1912: I went off to Trinity and dined with [A. N.] Whitehead, an undergraduate, in New Court – a cold dinner, on a nice blue-striped cloth. Two other young men there, so sensible and nice ... Then to Bevan's, where I read my paper to about twenty people. Bertrand Russell there, and a strange bearded man who turned out to be Lytton Strachey. It was rather a fiasco; I was tired and stupid. There was no discussion. The paper was on J. A. Symonds. Not worth the trouble – never mind, one must just go on.

The Diary of Arthur C. Benson

Benson's entry in his diary highlights something typical about this place: the importance of friendships, of talk and conversation with like-minded people.

One of the most unusual Cambridge Societies was The Apostles: secret, self-perpetuating and highly intellectual, it was founded in the 1820s by Frederick Denison Maurice, the Christian Socialist philosopher, and has continued right down to the present. In the interwar years it was associated particularly with Marxism, and, of course, several of the 'Cambridge Spies' were members – for example, Anthony Blunt. Tennyson was an early member:

[Thomas] Carlyle's account of [John] Sterling best describes, as far as I can gather, the typical intellectual undergraduate of my father's set: who hated the narrow and ignorant Toryism to be found in country districts: who loathed parties and sects: who reverenced the great traditions and the great men of past ages, and eagerly sympathized with the misfortunes and disabilities of his fellow-men.

He tells how Sterling, famous already for the brilliance of his talk, had at Cambridge 'a wide and rather genial circle of comrades'. They had among them a society called the 'Apostles': of which my father was an early member. 'On stated evenings,' Carlyle goes on, 'was much logic, and other spiritual fencing, and ingenuous collision – probably of a really superior quality in that kind; for not a few of the then disputants have since proved themselves men of parts, and attained distinction in the intellectual walks of life.'

It is of the 'Apostles' that Sterling writes to Trench [*later Archbishop of Dublin*]: 'Pray let me see you as soon as you reach London, and in the mean time commend me to the brethren, who, I trust, are waxing daily in religion and radicalism.'

Arthur Hallam, in a letter to Gladstone, says of Frederick

212

Maurice: 'The effects which he has produced on the minds of many at Cambridge by the single creation of that society of 'Apostles' (for the spirit though not the form was created by him) is far greater than I can dare to calculate, and will be felt, both directly and indirectly, in the age that is upon us.'

There were regular meetings of the society as distinguished from the almost daily gatherings in one or another man's rooms, at all of which much coffee was drunk and much tobacco smoked. The Apostle who proposed the subject for discussion, generally stood before the mantelpiece, and said his say. Douglas Heath writes that the image he has carried away of my father is of one 'sitting in front of the fire, smoking and meditating, and now and then mingling in the conversation.' With one short phrase he was wont to sum up the issue of the arguments. Heath continues: 'I cannot satisfy myself as to the time when I became an Apostle, or when I made acquaintance with A[lfred] T[ennyson]. My belief is that he had already become an honorary member extraordinary. In the usual course a member had to read essays in regular succession, or give a dinner in default during a certain period, after which he became honorary. But A.T. was, I suppose, bored by this, and the society was content to receive him, his poetry and wisdom unfettered.' 'Ghosts' was the subject of an essay written by my father for the Society, but he was too shy to deliver it. The preface alone has survived …

My father seems to have propounded in some College discussion the theory, that the 'development of the human body might possibly be traced from the radiated, vermicular, molluscous and vertebrate organisms.' The question of surprise put to him on this proposition was 'Do you mean that the human brain is at first like a madrepore's, then like a worm's, etc.? but this cannot be for they have no brain'.

HALLAM, LORD TENNYSON, *Alfred, Lord Tennyson: A Memoir, by his Son*, 1897

Interesting that Tennyson was concerned so early with ideas of evolution – they surface again in The Princess, *and in* In Memoriam.

❈

But the Apostles were not invariably high-serious. Some flavour of the interchanges, and the fun, in the group can be glimpsed from chance remarks in letters, such as this from Robert John Tennant to Tennyson, in October, 1834.

My dear Alfred,

... I expect great sport at Lushington's whereof you shall hear. Last Saturday, we had an Apostolic dinner, when we had the honour among other things of drinking your health, as having *once been* one of us. Edmund Lushington and I went away tolerably early, but most of them stayed till past two: John Heath volunteered a song, Kemble got into a passion about nothing but quickly jumped out again, Blakesley was afraid the Proctors might come in, and Thompson poured huge quantities of salt upon Douglas Heath's head. Kemble has just received a diploma from the Royal Society of Antiquaries at Copenhagen ...

R. J. TENNANT, *Letters of Alfred, Lord Tennyson*, 1982

❀

The Apostles have had many distinguished members, including Bertrand Russell:

The greatest happiness of my time at Cambridge was connected with a body whom its members knew as 'The Society', but which outsiders, if they knew of it, called 'The Apostles'. This was a small discussion society, containing one or two people from each year on the average, which met every Saturday night. It has existed since 1820, and has had as members most of the people of any intellectual eminence who have been at Cambridge since then. It is by way of being secret, in order that those who are being considered for election may be unaware of the fact.

It was owing to the existence of The Society that I so soon got to know the people best worth knowing, for Whitehead was a member, and told the younger members to investigate Sanger and me on account of our scholarship papers. With rare exceptions, all the members at any one time were close personal friends. It was a principle in discussion that there were to be no *taboos*, no

214

limitations, nothing considered shocking, no barriers to absolute freedom of speculation. We discussed all manner of things, no doubt with a certain immaturity, but with a detachment and interest scarcely possible in later life. The meetings would generally end about one o'clock at night, and after that I would pace up and down the cloisters of Nevile's Court for hours with one or two other members. We took ourselves perhaps rather seriously, for we considered that the virtue of intellectual honesty was in our keeping. Undoubtedly, we achieved more of this than is common in the world, and I am inclined to think that the best intelligence of Cambridge has been notable in this respect ...

But as Russell says, things changed as the Society became more and more dominated by what was later to be called the Bloomsbury Group:

Some things became considerably different in the Society shortly after my time.

The tone of the generation some ten years junior to my own was set mainly by Lytton Strachey and Keynes. It is surprising how great a change in mental climate those ten years had brought. We were still Victorian; they were Edwardian. We believed in ordered progress by means of politics and free discussion. The more self-confident among us may have hoped to be leaders of the multitude, but none of us wished to be divorced from it. The generation of Keynes and Lytton did not seek to preserve any kinship with the Philistine. They aimed rather at a life of retirement among fine shades and nice feelings, and conceived of the good as consisting in the passionate mutual admirations of a clique of the élite. This doctrine, quite unfairly, they fathered upon G. E. Moore, whose disciples they professed to be. Keynes, in his memoir 'Early Beliefs', has told of their admiration for Moore's doctrine. Moore gave due weight to morals and by his doctrine of organic unities avoided the view that the good consists of a series of isolated passionate moments, but those who considered themselves his disciples ignored this aspect of his teaching and degraded his ethics into advocacy of a stuffy girls-school sentimentalizing.

From this atmosphere Keynes escaped into the great world, but Strachey never escaped. Keynes's escape, however, was not complete. He went about the world carrying with him everywhere a feeling of the bishop *in partibus*. True salvation was elsewhere, among the faithful at Cambridge. When he concerned himself with politics and economics he left his soul at home. This is the reason for a certain hard, glittering, inhuman quality in most of his writing. There was one great exception, *The Economic Consequences of the Peace* ...

After my time The Society changed in one respect. There was a long drawn out battle between George [Macaulay] Trevelyan and Lytton Strachey, both members, in which Lytton Strachey was on the whole victorious. Since his time, homosexual relations among the members were for a time common, but in my day they were unknown.

BERTRAND RUSSELL, *Autobiography*, Vol. 1, 1967

❄

Keynes' escape 'into the great world' makes him a subject of compelling interest for one of the most distinguished of modern Chancellors of the Exchequer. An Oxford man – and Chancellor of that University – Roy Jenkins considers the Cambridge and Bloomsbury ethos with wry detachment. Keynes was the child of busy Cambridge academics:

[He] came from the Victorian core of the university and town of Cambridge ... He was taught at home and at a local preparatory school, and then at 14 went to Eton. He was a King's Scholar, eleventh out of 20 at his election, and Eton was in no way an inevitable school for him. His father had been at Amersham Hall, and his younger brother went to Rugby. ... In 1902 he went back to Cambridge, to King's with a closed Eton scholarship in the unusual combination of mathematics and classics.

If Eton was not an inevitable school for him, Cambridge was certainly an inevitable university. It thought of itself as very different from Oxford. When Keynes was a small child there was a rumour that his father might become Professor of Political Economy at that other university.

'Pray don't go,' Professor Foxwell wrote in half-serious horror. '... Think of the effect your move may have on your son. He may grow up flippantly epigrammatical and end by becoming the proprietor of a Gutter Gazette, or the hero of a popular party; instead of emulating his father's noble example, becoming an accurate, clear-headed Cambridge man, spending his life in the valuable and unpretentious service of his kind, dying beloved of his friends, venerated by the wise and unknown to the masses, as true merit and worth mostly are.'

The elder Keynes did not go, and his son was protected from the superficial worldliness of an Oxford education which Foxwell rather oddly thought would necessarily follow from such a translation. Maynard Keynes remained faithful to Cambridge, although not to any extreme version of its intellectual austerity. He eschewed neither epigram nor fame. And from the beginning of his time at King's, he appeared as a rather worldly figure. This impression was marred only by his enthusiasm. He did almost everything that an undergraduate could do. He joined all sorts of societies and delivered as well as listened to papers on subjects from Abelard to the nature of time. He pursued his mathematics but only to the extent of becoming twelfth wrangler. He diluted them by winning an English essay prize. He played golf at Royston. He bought rare books. He became President of the Union and a leading if cool Liberal. As a scholar he read the lesson in King's Chapel, and took great pleasure in doing so, until the Dean stopped him because, as a disbeliever, he would not promise regular attendance when he was not performing. For his first year he even continued to row.

Although he had 'never enjoyed himself so much before', as he wrote to an Eton friend, he was not swept away by King's to the extent of suppressing his critical spirit. The view that any institution which he surveyed was run in a fairly muddled way and that he could do it a great deal better was a constant ingredient of his life. 'I have had a good look round the place,' he said in his first term, 'and come to the conclusion that it's pretty inefficient.'

He had to wait 17 years before he could make King's more efficient, but in the meantime he was full of other occupations. In that same first term he began his tumultuous friendship with Lytton Strachey, which led on both to the main pattern of his early Cambridge relationships and to his Bloomsbury life. Towards the end of 1902 Strachey and Leonard Woolf, both at Trinity, visited him in his rooms in King's Lane. They had come to inspect him as a possible member of a self-consciously select university club known alternatively as 'the Society' or 'the Apostles'...

In spite of his sophistication, Keynes found the Apostles a heady experience ... The make-up perfectly suited his main intellectual interest which was then in the borderland between mathematics and philosophy, with the support of a wide range of reading, embracing much general literature, but centring upon the development of ideas. Whether its central outlook, with its elevation of abstract thought above action in the world, was ever fully acceptable to him is more doubtful. Certainly his later life did not meet this standard. Perhaps, in spite of Professor Foxwell's attempted inoculation, he was always something of an Oxford Trojan horse in Cambridge. He soon became too fond of the trains to London to be a strict Cambridge man.

ROY JENKINS, *Nine Men of Power*, 1974

RETROSPECT

---✹---

GONE DOWN

No longer will his name be found
Beside the College stair;
White-lettered on the old black ground
Another name is there.
In the calm court new footsteps sound,
In courts too calm to care.

FRANCES CORNFORD, *Travelling Home*, 1948

Getting a degree, going down, looking back. As the late vicar of Little St Mary's, James Owen, once memorably said, the academic glory of a Bachelor's degree is only the first step on the journey between Tripos and death. Christopher Smart's Ode on Taking the Degree of B.A., *of which we quote one stanza, plays with the euphoria, and confidence, of the new graduate still to discern that long road stretching ahead of him:*

'Tis done: – I tow'r to that degree
And catch such heav'nly fire,
That Horace ne'er could rant like me,
Nor is King's Chapel higher.

CHRISTOPHER SMART, 1743

Byron, predictably, had a suitably wry view of it all:

Behold him Freshman! forced no more to groan
O'er Virgil's devilish verses and his own;
Prayers are too tedious, lectures too abstruse;
He flies from Tavell's frown to Fordham's Mews.
(Unlucky Tavell doom'd to daily cares
By pugilistic pupils, and by bears).

Fines, tutors, tasks, conventions threat in vain,
Before hounds, hunters and Newmarket plain.
Rough with his elders, with his equals rash,
Civil to sharpers, prodigal of cash;
Fooled, pillaged, dunned, he wastes his term away,
And unexpelled, perhaps retires M.A.
Master of Arts! as *hells* and *clubs* proclaim,
Where scarce a blackleg bears a brighter name !
    GEORGE GORDON, LORD BYRON, *Hints from Horace*, 1810

❀

Roger Ascham's affection for the place he has left is palpable:

By this small mention of Cambridge, I am caryed into three imag-
inations: first, into a sweete remembrance of my tyme spent there:
than, into some carefull thoughts, for the grevous alteration that
folowed sone after: lastlie, into much joy to heare tell, of the good
recoverie and earnest forwardness in all good learning there agayne.
    ROGER ASCHAM, *The Scholemaster*, 1570

*Ascham writes to Edmund Raven, of St John's, on 18 May 1551, from
Speyer, where he was part of a diplomatic mission – Cambridge men, then
as now, might look for political as well as academic preferment:*

I trust Will Taylor, John Bee, and Thomas Wilson will not be
behind [in writing to me]. I pray God for these good fellows at
Cambridge, for there is the life that no man knows but he that
hath sometimes lacked it; and especially if one be able to live
plentifully there.

❀

*Samuel Pepys was an undergraduate of Magdalene College. By 1667,
when he makes one of his visits to the town on his way to his estate at
Brampton, he is doing rather well. He who had not been the best behaved
of youths (as the College records reveal) is now a man of property, the
Secretary of the Navy Board, a 'great person', the boy who made good: and
loving it, and loving being treated as such when in Cambridge:*

Away to Cambridge, it being foul, rainy weather; and there did take up at the Rose, for the sake of Mrs. Dorothy Drawwater, the vintener's daughter, which is mentioned in the play of *Sir Martin Mar-all*. Here we had a good chamber and bespoke a good supper; and then I took my wife and W. Hewer and Willett [*his wife's maid-servant*](it holding up a little) and showed them Trinity College and St. Johns Library, and went to King's College chapel to see the outside of it only, and so to our Inne; and with much pleasure did this, they walking in their pretty morning gowns, very handsome, and I proud to find myself in condition to do this; and so home to our lodging, and there by and by to supper with much good sport, talking with the drawers concerning matters of the town and persons whom I remember; and so after supper to cards and then to bed, lying, I in one bed and my wife and girl in another in the same room; and very merry talking together and mightily pleased both of us with the girl. Saunders, the only Viallin in my time, is I hear dead of the plague in the late plague there.

[*Next day*] Up and got ready and eat our breakfast and then took coach; and the poor, as they did yesterday, did stand at the coach to have something given them, as they do to all great persons, and I did give them something; and the town musique did also come and play; but Lord, what sad music they made – however, I was pleased with them, being all of us in very good humour, and so set forth and through the town, and observed at our College of Magdalen the posts new-painted, and understand that the Vice-Chancellor is there this year ...

... so we away and got well to Cambridge about 7 to the Rose, the waters not being now so high as before. And here lighting, I took my boy and two brothers and walked to Magdalen College; and there into the Butterys as a stranger and there drank my bellyfull of their beer, which pleased me as the best I ever drank; and hear by the butler's man, who was son to Goody Mulliner over against the College that we used to buy stewed prunes of, concerning the College and persons in it; and find very few, only Mr. Hollins and Peachell I think, that were of my time. But I was mightily pleased to come in this condition to see and ask ...

And he can be sniffy about the sort of behaviour of which only a few years earlier he had himself been guilty.

221

After dinner, away again and came to Cambridge, after much bad way, about 9 at night; and there at the Rose I met my [father's] horses, with a man staying for me; but it is so late, and the waters so deep, that I durst not go tonight; but after supper to bed and lay very ill by reason of some drunken scholars making a noise all night, and vexed for fear that the horses should not be taken up from grass time enough for the morning.

SAMUEL PEPYS, *Diary*, October 1667

✸

Benson, originally of King's, had been a master at Eton for some years. He describes his return to Cambridge:

August 4 [1907]: I experienced the most poignant and yet luxurious sensations. I have not been here for thirteen years, since I took my degree – partly huffiness at the policy of the college, partly affairs. As we drew near Cambridge all the familiar things began to come back: the inn at Whittlesford, where we used to have tea in the old bicycling days, the Gogs, the familiar fields, the conduit, etc. All the country was beautiful, the vegetation luxuriant. At Cambridge station a huge grain elevator and mill in buff brick – hideous, but impressive. Drove down to King's ... Everyone, porters, dons, bedmakers, were extraordinarily welcoming – chid me for my absence, overwhelmed me with kindness. I felt like coming home ...

On Saturday did little businesses; breakfasted in Combination Room pleasantly, with fine Victorian plate. In the afternoon walked about Zion. Saw Queen's, a fine new chapel – Peterhouse, a beautiful place, but a stronghold of the Philistines. I *like* the [Peterhouse] chapel transparencies now; if only people would have faith, and keep work as long as it is careful, expensive, thought out and put up with love. Then in Pembroke garden, a beautiful, embowered, bird-haunted place ...

To Emmanuel, and saw an elegant African black undergraduate, slim and nimble, playing lawn-tennis with Englishmen. All these gardens are trim and rich with flowers, much smarter than they used to be. I suppose that married fellows system tends to harmonise; they seem to give up the gardens much more to undergraduates, while the little tutors hurry off to small, new, redbrick houses on the Trumpington road. The men, too, seem gentler and more decorous than of old, but I suppose only the mildest are up just now …

The Diary of Arthur C. Benson

Cambridge nowadays draws back its graduates time after time, to Alumnus weekends, to the graduation of children, to College reunions. Now men and women of substance in the world, they once again feel young (or some do). It could hardly not be an emotional experience, particularly after a long passage of time. But this feeling is not new: Coleridge came to Cambridge, after a long absence, for a scientific meeting in 1833.

My emotions at revisiting the university were at first overwhelming. I could not speak for an hour; yet my feelings were on the whole very pleasurable, and I have not passed, of late years at least, three days of such great enjoyment and healthful excitement of body and mind. The bed on which I slept – and slept soundly too – was, as near as I can describe it, a couple of sacks full of potatoes tied together. Truly I lay down at night a man, and arose in the morning a bruise.

SAMUEL TAYLOR COLERIDGE, Table Talk, 1836

Soberly and sourly, Benson muses in his diary about ageing, and meeting Old Members of the College returning for a reunion dinner:

July 14, 1904: At 8.00 to the dinner – about twenty guests, most of them, it turned out, about my age … Afterwards talked to various men, civil, sentimental, pleased. It gave me rather a horrible sensation. Many of them were obviously drunk, and the awful stupidity of the talk … I really felt myself to be cleverer than some of the guests. Several people asked to be introduced to me, said they wished to make my acquaintance, and then talked *continuously*. One man asked me for a photograph, for his wife – said he didn't himself care about such things. But it seemed to me

223

a vile thing to see the kind of mess people make of their lives – the inevitable mess – and then becoming pursy and short-winded and red-nosed and stupid beyond words. None of them (except an interesting man, a doctor) could *talk*; they could only go on with endless repetitions. And then they could do little but tell tales of their desperate deeds, when one *knows* them to have been harmless creatures, and the only people they admired were 'blues'. It all seemed to me such an ugly business, and man to be an animal very little removed from the pig, unpleasant to see and hear and smell – and with no idea of what he was doing or where he was going – no emotion about it all. Surely an education must be very bad to break down so horribly in middle-age as this – so many failures, and complacent failures ...

The Diary of Arthur C. Benson

In 1963, the Cambridge University Press invited F. R. Leavis to compile a selection from Scrutiny, *the critical periodical he had started with his wife and their friends in the early 1930s. The selection was anticipated in a short pamphlet,* Scrutiny: A Retrospect, *in which Leavis reflects on those years when he and his circle attempted to revitalise 'the Idea of a University' and lay down sound values for the English Tripos. Established reputations were questioned, complacent academicism challenged and, inevitably, enemies made. Yet when Leavis explicitly identifies* Scrutiny *with Cambridge at its most vital, bracing and pure, few will find it easy to dissent.*

Only at Cambridge could the idea of *Scrutiny* have taken shape, become a formidable life, and maintained the continuous living force that made it hated and effective. It was (to deepen the emphasis) a product, the triumphant justifying achievement, of the English Tripos. I express, and intend to encourage, no simple parochial enthusiasm or loyalty in dwelling on these truths. I had better, in fact, add at once the further testimony that *Scrutiny* started, established itself and survived in spite of Cambridge. And it will be my duty to insist on this ungracious note. If you are intent on vindicating the Idea of a University (an inseparable undertaking, we felt – we who founded *Scrutiny* – from that of vindicating the Idea of Criticism), and on the peculiar need, at this

224

moment of history, to have the Idea realized in a potent living actuality, you will have no difficulty in understanding how the word 'academic' acquired its pejorative force, and you will know that, even at the cost of indecorum, you must do all that can be done to discourage illusions. You will know that the academic spirit may smile upon and offer to take up the causes of your advocacy, but that it will none the less remain what it is and be, in the academic world, always a present enemy.

We who founded *Scrutiny* could have no illusions. It was an outlaws' enterprise, and we were kept very much aware of that from the outset to the close. The research students and undergraduates who used, in the early 'thirties, to meet at my house, which was very much a centre, did not suppose that they were meeting at an official centre of 'Cambridge English', or one that was favoured by the official powers. They gravitated there because it had become known as a place where the essential nature, the importance and the possibilities of the English Tripos were peculiarly matters of preoccupation – where in such preoccupation the 'Cambridge' ethos that had made Cambridge the university to come to had an intensified conscious life.

... This was the heyday of the Marxising literary intellectual. We were anti-Marxist – necessarily so (we thought); an intelligent, that is a real, interest in literature implied a conception of it very different from any that a Marxist could expound and explain. Literature – what we knew as literature and had studied for the English Tripos – mattered; it mattered crucially to civilization – of that we were sure. It mattered because it represented a human reality, an autonomy of the human spirit, for which economic determinism and reductive interpretation in terms of the Class War left no room ...

Cambridge, then, figured for us civilization's anti-Marxist recognition of its own nature and needs – recognition of that, the essential, which Marxian wisdom discredited, and the external and material drive of civilization threatened, undoctrinally, to eliminate. It was our strength to be, in our consciousness of our effort, and actually, in the paradoxical and ironical way I have to record, representatives of that Cambridge. We *were*, in fact, that Cambridge; we felt it, and had more and more reason to feel it, and our confidence and courage came from that. In the strength of the essential Cambridge which it consciously and explicitly represented, *Scrutiny* not only survived the hostility of the institutional academic powers; it became – who now questions it? – the clear triumphant justification to the world of Cambridge as a humane centre. In Cambridge it was the vitalizing force that gave the English School its reputation and influence, and its readers in the world at large, small as the subscribing public was, formed an incomparably influential community. A large proportion of them were concerned with education in schools and universities. The achievement of our quixotic anti-academic design, the demonstration of the power of essential Cambridge to defeat the academic ethos from within in the most positive and creative way, could not have been more complete and significant.

F. R. LEAVIS, *Scrutiny: a Retrospect*, 1963

Anne Stevenson, the American author of this poem, was born in Cambridge in 1933:

COMING BACK TO CAMBRIDGE
(England, 1971)

Casual, almost noticeable,
it happens every time you return.
Somewhere along the flat road in
you lose to voluptuous levels
between signposts to unnecessary dozing villages
every ghost of yourself but Cambridge.
Somewhere – by Fen Drayton or Dry Drayton,
by the finger pointing aimlessly to Over –
you slip into a skin that lives
perpetually in Cambridge.

It knows where you are.

As you drive you watch a workman
wheel a bicycle around a stile,
hump onto the saddle and

ride off past a field of cows.
A few stop chewing to stare.
And you know where you are even before
the landmarks (beautiful to the excluded)
begin to accumulate.
The stump of the Library.
The lupin spire of the Catholic church.
Four spikey blossoms on King's.
The Round Church, a mushroom in this
forest of Gothic and traffic and
roses too perfect to look alive.

The river is the same – conceited,
historic, full of the young.
The streets are the same. And around them
the same figures, the same cast with a
change of actors, move as if concentric
to a radiance without location.
The pupils of their eyes glide sideways,
apprehensive of martyrdom to which
they might not be central.
They can never be sure.
Great elations could be happening without them.

And just as the hurrying, preoccupied dons
tread the elevations of their detachment and yet
preserve an air of needing to be protected,
so, also, these wives choosing vegetables in the market,
these schoolchildren in squadrons,
these continental girl-friends and black men,
these beards, these bicycles, these
skinny boys fishing, these lovers of the pubs,
these lovers of the choirboys, these intense shrill
ladies and gaunt, fanatical burnt out old women
are all more than this. Arrogant.
Within the compass of wistfulness.

Nothing that really matters really exists.

But the statues are alive.
You can walk in and out of the picture.
Though the mild façades harden before and
behind you like stereographs, within them
there is much to be taken for granted.
Meals and quarrels, passions and inequalities.
A city like any other, were it not for the
order at the centre and the high
invisible bridge it is built upon,
with its immense views of an intelligible human landscape
into which you never look without longing to enter;
into which you never fall without the curious struggle back.
    ANNE STEVENSON, *The Collected Poems, 1955-1995*, 1996

Tennyson's In Memoriam *is an elegy for his friend and fellow Apostle, Arthur Hallam, who died quite suddenly aged twenty-two. In the eighty-seventh lyric of that great work he revisits Cambridge and relives – with some pain – the time of their companionship:*

> I past beside the reverend walls
>   In which of old I wore the gown;
>   I roved at random thro' the town,
> And saw the tumult of the halls;
>
> And heard once more in college fanes
>   The storm their high-built organs make,
>   And thunder-music, rolling, shake
> The prophet blazon'd on the panes;
>
> And caught once more the distant shout,
>   The measured pulse of racing oars
>   Among the willows; paced the shores
> And many a bridge, and all about
>
> The same gray flats again, and felt
>   The same, but not the same; and last
>   Up that long walk of limes I past
> To see the rooms in which he dwelt.

Another name as on the door:
    I linger'd; all within was noise
    Of songs, and clapping hands, and boys
That crash'd the glass and beat the floor;

Where once we held debate, a band
    Of youthful friends, on mind and art,
    And labour, and the changing mart,
And all the framework of the land;

When one would aim an arrow fair,
    But send it slackly from the string;
    And one would pierce an outer ring,
And one an inner, here and there;

And last the master-bowman, he,
    Would cleave the mark. A willing ear
    We lent him. Who, but hung to hear
The rapt oration flowing free

From point to point, with power and grace
    And music in the bounds of law,
    To those conclusions when we saw
The God within him light his face,

And seem to lift the form, and glow
    In azure orbits heavenly-wise;
    And over those ethereal eyes
The bar of Michael Angelo.
    ALFRED, LORD TENNYSON, *In Memoriam*, 1850

❋

The criticism a younger Tennyson had voiced in 1830 (see page 133) is perennial – as rife now as it has ever been, indeed. Carlyle quotes the view that the studies of the two Universities are 'nearly useless, and even ill done of their kind' (Life of John Sterling, 1851); H. G. Wells makes one of his characters discuss them thus:

I have revisited Cambridge and Oxford time after time since I came down, and so far as the Empire goes, I want to get clear of those two places ...

Always I renew my old feelings, a physical oppression, a sense of lowness and dampness almost exactly like the feeling of an underground room where paper moulders and leaves the wall, a feeling of ineradicable contagion in the Gothic buildings, in the narrow ditch-like rivers, in those roads and roads of stuffy little villas. Those little villas have destroyed all the good of the old monastic system and none of its evil ...

Some of the most charming people in the world live in them but their collective effect is below the quality of any individual among them. Cambridge is a world of subdued tones, of excessively subtle humours, of prim conduct and free-thinking; it fears the Parent, but it has no fear of God; it offers amidst surroundings that vary between dinginess and antiquarian charm the inflammation of literature's purple draught; one hears there a peculiar thin scandal like no other scandal in the world – a covetous scandal – so that I am always reminded of Ibsen in Cambridge. In Cambridge and the plays of Ibsen alone does it seem appropriate for the heroine before the great crises of life to 'enter, take off her overshoes, and put her wet umbrella upon the writing desk.'

H. G. WELLS, The New Machiavelli, 1910

The Undergrad
With his little Dad
Who in his time
(Forgive my rhyme)
Was an undergrad
With a little dad.

A drawing by H. M. Bateman from the May Week
Number of the *Granta*, 1912.

Bertrand Russell, too, had severe criticisms to make of Cambridge. For him, however, the faults were far outweighed by the one outstanding virtue he had learnt there:

Cambridge was important in my life through the fact that it gave me friends, and experience of intellectual discussion, but it was not important through the actual academic instruction. Of the mathematical teaching I have already spoken. Most of what I learned in philosophy has come to seem to me erroneous, and I spent many subsequent years in gradually unlearning the habits of thought which I had there acquired. The one habit of thought of real value that I acquired there was intellectual honesty. This virtue certainly existed not only among my friends, but among my teachers. I cannot remember any instance of a teacher resenting it when one of his pupils showed him to be in error, though I can remember quite a number of occasions on which pupils succeeded in performing this feat. Once during a lecture on hydrostatics, one of the young men interrupted to say: 'Have you not forgotten the centrifugal forces on the lid?' The lecturer gasped, and then said: 'I have been doing this example that way for twenty years, but you are right.' It was a blow to me during the War to find that, even at Cambridge, intellectual honesty had its limitations. Until then, wherever I lived, I felt that Cambridge was the only place on earth that I could regard as home.

BERTRAND RUSSELL, *Autobiography*, Vol. 1, 1967

Russell was not alone in his affection and respect. But it is not always easy, on returning to the city, to recover the old emotions.

When, after an absence of almost seventeen years I revisited England, I made the dreadful mistake of going to see Cambridge again not at the glorious end of the Easter term but on a raw February day that reminded me only of my own confused old nostalgia. In every way the visit was not a success. I had lunch with Nesbit (now a gentle professor) at a little place which ought to have been full of memories but which, owing to various changes, was not. He had given up smoking. Time had softened his features, and he bore now no resemblance to Gorki, or indeed to any other Russian writer. An accidental worry (the maiden sister who kept house for him had just been removed to the hospital) seemed to prevent him from concentrating on the very personal and urgent matter I wanted to speak to him about. Bound volumes of *Punch* were heaped on a table in a kind of small vestibule where a bowl of goldfish had formerly stood – and it all looked so different. Different too were the garish uniforms worn by the waitresses, of whom none was as pretty as the particular one I remembered so clearly. Rather desperately, as if struggling against boredom, Nesbit launched into politics ...

He looked at his watch, and I looked at mine, and we parted, and I wandered around the town in the rain, and then visited the Backs, and for some time peered at the rooks in the black network of the bare elms and at the first crocuses in the mist-beaded turf. As I strolled under those sung trees, I tried to put myself into the same ecstatically reminiscent mood in regard to my student years as during those years I had experienced in regard to my boyhood, but all I could evoke were fragmentary little pictures: M. K., a Russian, dyspeptically cursing the after-effects of a College Hall dinner; N. R., another Russian, playing with tin soldiers on the floor, like a child; P. M. storming into my room with a copy of *Ulysses* freshly smuggled from Paris; J. C., quietly dropping in to say that he, too, had just lost his father; R. C., charmingly inviting me to join him on a trip to the Swiss Alps; Christopher something or other, wriggling out of a proposed tennis double upon learning that his partner was to be a Hindu; T., a very old and fragile waiter, spilling the soup in Hall on Professor A. E. Housman, who then abruptly stood up as one shooting out of a trance; S. S., who was in no way connected with Cambridge, but who, having dozed off in his chair at a literary party (in Berlin) and being nudged by a neighbour, also stood up suddenly – in the middle of a story someone was reading; Lewis Carroll's Dormouse, unexpectedly starting to tell a tale; E. Harrison, unexpectedly making me a present of *The Shropshire Lad*, a little volume of verse about young males and death.

The dull day had dwindled to a pale yellow streak in the grey west, when, acting upon an impulse, I decided to visit my old tutor. Like a sleepwalker, I mounted the familiar steps and automatically knocked on the half-open door bearing his name. In a voice that was a jot less abrupt, and a trifle more hollow, he bade me come in. 'I wonder if you remember me ...' I started to say, as I crossed the dim room to where he sat near a comfortable fire. 'Let me see,' he said, slowly turning around in his low chair, 'I do not quite seem to ...' There was a dismal crunch, a fatal clatter: I had stepped into some tea things that stood at the foot of his wicker chair. 'Oh, yes, of course,' he said, 'I know who you are.'

VLADIMIR NABOKOV, *Speak, Memory: A Memoir*, 1951

One Mile to Great St Mary's

ENVOY

———— ✳ ————

'I DON'T know how it is,' said Ted, 'but whenever people write books about Cambridge they make the bad undergraduates go to gambling-hells on the Chesterton Road and the good ones be filled with ennobling thoughts when they contemplate their stately chapel. Did you ever go to a gambling-hell on the Chesterton Road, Tom ?'

'No. Do you ever have ennobling thoughts when you look at the stately chapel? Of course you don't. You think it's deuced pretty, and so do I, and we both play whist with threepenny points. And as a matter of fact we don't fall in love with each other's cousins at the May races, nor do we sport deans into their rooms, nor do deans marry bedmakers. Oh, we are very ordinary!'

'I feel a temptation to walk across the grass,' said Ted.

'Yes, you're the wicked B.A. who leads the fresh, bright under-graduates, that's me, into all sorts of snares. What fools people are.'

E. F. BENSON, *Limitations*, 1896

And the last word goes to Thomas Gray …

20 March, 1738: I don't know how it is, I have a sort of reluctance to leave this place, unamiable as it may seem; 'tis true Cambridge is very ugly, she is very dirty, & very dull; but I'm like a Cabbage, where I'm stuck, I love to grow.

THOMAS GRAY, *Letters of Thomas Gray*

ACKNOWLEDGEMENTS

———— ❀ ————

The publishers would like to thank the following for their permission to use extracts in this anthology:

John Murray (Publishers) Ltd for letters by Byron from *In My Hot Youth – Byron's Letter and Journals* by Leslie A. Marchand; The Master and Fellows, Magdalene College, Cambridge for extracts from *The Diary of A. C. Benson*; A. S. Byatt for *Possession*, Chatto & Windus, publishers; Cambridge Evening News for 'Cambridge Pays Tribute to Trevor Hughes'; Diana and Peter Boston for *Perverse and Foolish* (now *Memories*) by Lucy M. Boston; Carcanet Press Ltd for *These The Companions: Recollections* (1982) by Donald Davie; Carcanet Press for 'Two Cambridge Images' and 'On The Demolition of The Kite District' from *Selected Poems* by Clive Wilmer; Chatto & Windus for 'Sleeping Out in a College Cloister' from *Poems* (1935) by William Empson; A. P. Watt Ltd on behalf of Trinity College, Cambridge for the extract from the Foreword to *Pausanias's Description of Greece* by J. G. Frazer; Hamish Hamilton for *Margot Fonteyn, Autobiography*; Queens' College and Revd. Dr Jonathan Holmes for the extract by Sir James Beament from *Queens' College Record*; Faber & Faber for 'His Rooms in College' from *The Passages of Joy* by Thom Gunn; Queens' College and F. Hanania for 'Gaining Admission in 1932'; Faber & Faber and P. D. James for the extracts from *An Unsuitable Job for a Woman*; A. P. Watt Ltd on behalf of The National Trust for the letter by Rudyard Kipling to his daughter; Laurence Pollinger Limited and the Estate of Frieda Lawrence Ravagli for the extract from *Letters* by D. H. Lawrence; Executors of the F. R. Leavis Estate for *The Critic as Anti-Philosopher* published by Chatto & Windus and for *Scrutiny: a Retrospect*; The extract from *Nine Power of Men* by Roy Jenkins © 1974 is reprinted by permission of the Peters Fraser & Dunlop Group Ltd; The Society of Authors and the Estate of Rosamond Lehmann for the extracts from *Dusty Answer*; *Pepys Diary* re-transcripted by Latham & Matthews by permission of Peters Fraser & Dunlop Group Ltd; *Memories* © Frances Partridge 1981 is published by Phoenix Paperbacks, an imprint of Orion Books Ltd, reproduced by permission of the author c/o Rogers, Coleridge & White Ltd, 20 Powis Mews, London, W11 1JN; Faber & Faber for *Letters Home* by Sylvia Plath and 'Watercolour of Grantchester Meadows' from *The Colossus* by Sylvia Plath; Faber & Faber for *Period Piece* by Gwen Raverat; The Provost and Scholars of King's College, Cambridge and The Society of Authors as the literary representatives of the E. M. Forster Estate for *The Longest Journey* and *Selected Letters*; Professor John Holloway for the verses from his poem *Civitatula*; Methuen for *Lions and Shadows: An Education in the Twenties* by Christopher Isherwood; The Bertrand Russell Peace Foundation for

Autobiography and *Selected Letters* by Bertrand Russell, 1967; A. P. Watt on behalf of The Literary Executors of the Estate of H. G. Wells for the extract from *The New Machiavelli*; Thames & Hudson Ltd for the extracts from *The Diary of Baron Waldstein* translated by G. W. Groos; The Society of Authors, as Literary Representatives of the Estate of Virginia Woolf for extracts from *Jacob's Room* and *A Room of One's Own*; *Varsity*, for the extracts from Varsity Handbook; The literary executors of the Estate of Frances Cornford, c/o Barr Ellison, 39 Parkside, Cambridge CB1 1PN for the poems 'Autumn Morning at Cambridge' from *Poems* 1910 and 'Gone Down' from *Travelling Home*, 1948; 'Coming Back to Cambridge' is reprinted from *The Collected Poems of Anne Stevenson* 1955-1995 (1996) by permission of Oxford University Press; The extract from *Small Talk at Wreyland* by Cecil Torr, 1979, by permission of Oxford University Press; extracts from *Letters of Alfred, Lord Tennyson* ed. Lang & Shannon, Clarendon Press 1982, by permission of Oxford University Press; Philippa Scott for the extract from *The Eye of the Wind* by Sir Peter Scott; Weidenfeld & Nicholson as publisher of *Speak Memory: A Memoir* by Vladimir Nabokov; Robert Rhodes James for the extract from *Albert, Prince Consort*; *Correspondence of Thomas Gray*, including letters quoted by Charles Victor de Bonstetten, edited by Toynbee & Whibley, revised Starr, published by Clarendon Press in 1935 and re-issued in 1971, by permission of Oxford University Press; *The Journeys of Celia Fiennes* was edited by C. Morris, published 1947; The extracts by Zacharias Conrad von Uffenbach are quoted from *Cambridge in the Reign of Queen Anne*, ed. by J. E. B. Mayor, 1911; *Collected Letters of Samuel Taylor Coleridge*, ed. Earl Leslie Griggs, Vol 1 (1785–1800) Oxford: Clarendon Press, 1956, by permission of Oxford University Press; Clive Wilmer for 'Epitaph for a Derelict' from *Devotions*; Arthur Sale for 'The Bridge in Motion' from *The Bridge*; extract by William Soone is quoted in *Annals of Cambridge* by C. H. Cooper, from Gentleman's Magazine, 1843.

For illustrations: The Syndics of Cambridge University Library for the portrait of John Nicholson, the West View of the Gate of Cambridge Castle and the Map of Cambridgeshire from Relham Vol. 1, Emmanuel College Garden, Collegium Emanuelis, Trinity Hall 1808 from Views X, 6, One Mile to Gt. St. Mary's and Prospect of Cambridge from the West, from Views X, 5; Fitzwilliam Museum Cambridge for Smuggling In; the City of Cambridge for The Arms of the City of Cambridge; Yale Center for British Art, Paul Mellon Collection for Rowlandson, Thomas, R.A. (1756–1827) The Undergraduate's Room and Bucks of the First Head c.1785; A. P. Watt Ltd on behalf of the Royal Literature Fund for the drawing by G. K. Chesterton; the drawing by H. M. Bateman copyright © Estate of H. M. Bateman 1998; Michael Barratt FSA for Jemmy Gordon's Frolic by Thomas Rowlandson; Mr and Mrs J. G. Pollard for The Public Library by Thomas Rowlandson.

Every effort has been made to contact authors and copyright holders of material. It has not been possible in every case to do so.

INDEX OF AUTHORS

———— ❀ ————

Prospectus CAN

She released the girl's breast and at the same time snapped her fingers loudly. She closed her eyes and cocked her head to the side as if she were asleep. She then looked up to see if the man understood. He grinned and nodded.

"Nipple knockout drops," he shook his head. "A Mickey Finn from mother's milk," he laughed.

The woman didn't understand him but laughed even louder. She handed the flask to him.

"You take. You take. Five girls. Take. Take." She pressed the flask to his chest.

"Okay. I take. How much for you?" he asked.

The woman looked confused.

"Now how much for you? You. You," he said, smiling at her.

The woman's eyes were locked on the rows of rotten teeth in his mouth. She forced a smile.

"You got no humor, lady."

"You funny fellow."

"Yeah, me funny fellow. I better be a "lucky" funny fella, you old Chiney whore. If these girls ain't on the up-an'-up, I'll buy your bony ass from Wu Ta and take you down to Bodie. Those miners 'ill wear you out in a week, old woman."

The woman acted as if she didn't understand him. Her eyes darted from his teeth to the long billfold he removed from his coat. Then back to the rotten teeth and then to the billfold.

"I'll be back for them tomorrow night."

"Yes, yes."

He paid her off and took the flask. He followed the two men back to the door at the alley. They opened it and the little phantom was there waiting for him. He started into the foggy night. He called to the little man to halt. He unbuttoned his pants to relieve himself. The alley filled with the odor of his urine. He could smell the rum in it that he had been drinking most of the day.

CHAPTER SIX

The herd was on the move with Tom moving up and down one side and Print flanking on the other. Billy brought up the rear with the packhorses. The plan was to head in the direction of Jordan Valley. Print had decided to bypass the Crowleys' place by heading a little more south and pushing to get to the river's edge of the Owyhee to let them graze. Print rode through the moving herd and over to Tom.

"W're makin' great time, but we're gonna have ta ease up in the next day or so. We got no idea what the forage will be like out there. The Moncrieffes won't pay for hide an' hoof."

"I ain't pushin' them. They seem plenty up for it," replied Tom. "They're mor'n up for it. Thing is, they don't care what price they bring."

Print looked up at the sun's position. "Let's keep movin'. No stoppin' at noon. Let's wait until two an' then they can have a good, long graze. Billy okay?"

Tom shrugged. "He seems content to eat dust. I figger he'll let us know when he's had enough."

Print moved back through the herd to take up his position on the other side.

Not long after two in the afternoon, Print brought the herd to a halt. He raised up in the saddle, looking around to get his bearings. He sat back down and trotted off to the south. A couple hundred yards away, he waved for Tom and Billy to move the horses to him.

As the horses milled about, Tom rode over to his uncle while Billy hung back. The trailing dust washed over them.

"Plenty of grass here. We'll call it a day. Let's set up over there," he said, pointing to a deep cut in the ground.

"What's that?"

"A cave. Camped here many a night. Nice an' cozy."

"Not too cozy, I hope," said Tom as he looked over his shoulder in the direction of Billy.

"I'd only sleep in it if the weather turns. No, it's just a good spot to camp. I'm gonna ride out a bit while you two set up."

"Sure ya don't need company?"

Print smiled. "No. Just pay attention to the prevailing wind."

Print squeezed Bob Tate and headed off to the east. He liked prowling around while the others set up camp. It was one of the few rights he felt he earned with his age.

The grass was good here, and the herd needed all they could get. He had no idea what was ahead for them. The spring sun felt good on his back. High overhead raptors were riding the thermals. The range was really budding up, he thought. Purple clumps of Russian thistle mixed in with yellow rabbitbrush stretched out as far as one could see. Desert primrose was in abundance. Way off the forms of several pronghorns undulated in the heat waves rising off the basin's floor.

It is so big out here, he thought, you didn't even have to think. Its vastness just sops the thoughts right out of your head. To him it was bigger than anything he had ever seen. Bigger than the prairies east of the Rockies. Bigger than the ocean. He had been to Seattle once, but never to sea. That was another thing his curiosity had wanted him to do. He had often thought that he was a sailor. He knew why seamen thought and talked of their ships in the first person. He had talked to all the cow ponies whose ears he had looked between and steered all over the endless West. Of course, it wasn't endless, but then neither were the oceans. But somehow the desert range of the Great Basin seemed that way. It left a nice, quiet ache in you. The older a man got, the more he seemed to go for plainer and simpler. He let Bob Tate pick his own way. The sun worked its way through his coat. His mind just bled out.

"'Bout time the cook got back," said Tom as Print dismounted.

He untied a bunch of wild onion he had picked. With one hand he undid the cinch strap and hauled the saddle off the big horse's back. He walked to the fire, dropping the saddle and handing the onions to Tom. He went back to his horse and removed the blanket and slipped off the bridle. The chestnut stood for a moment and then took off to go give himself a good roll in the dirt.

"One day he might take off for good."

Print turned to his nephew. "Not as long as I keep givin' him my fritters soaked in bug juice. Let's see what we can whip up tonight."

The day had turned to evening, but the ground still held the sun's warmth. Print had fed them boiled pork with chopped-up onions, prunes, beans, biscuits, and gravy. Tom poured a cup of coffee as his uncle tamped tobacco into his pipe.

"Did ya take a look in the cave?"

"Not much."

"If ya go way back in there, they say there's a lake with blind fish in it."

"Ever eat one?"

"Na. Don't think I could work up much of an appetite for blind fish."

"Saw some figgers on the walls. A few bones. Lotta soot from fires."

"Been all sorts of folks through here. Know how this range got its name?"

"Not really."

Print poured a little whiskey into his tin cup from a bottle under his saddle blanket. He offered it to Tom, who declined.

"Takes the ache outta an old man's hands. It was Frenchys, French trappers that come into this region long time ago. Seems they'd bought a string of native fellas from the islands off a sea captain down the coast. Captain had swapped 'em out for some truck he was freightin' back from the Orient."

"How much of this am I supposed to swallow?" asked Tom as he tossed a few sticks on the fire.

"All 'r none. It's up ta you. But it is the truth, historical truth."

Tom stretched out, laying his head in the seat of his saddle. He tilted his hat over his face. "Go on. I'm listening."

"Well, the old salt puts in somwheres down near San Francisco. This was a long time ago, near a hundr'd years ago. So the Frenchys swaps a hefty load of beaver pelts for this gang of native boys."

"Why would they do that?"

"I'm gettin' there. They was plannin' on bringing them up north ta skin out and tan the hides an' pelts they took. Give the dusky boys the dirty work."

"What would they know about beaver pelts?"

"Well, there ya go. 'Course they didn't. They had no knowledge or need for beaver pelts, or any other fur, for that matter. They come from a nation of nearly hairless people, 'cept for their heads. There's more hair on a hen's egg than was on those folks. 'Sides, it's so damn hot back in their lands, they hardly have need for any clothes."

"Sound like poor folks for the fur trade."

"Tell that ta the Frenchys. Had they been after fish, or

seashells, or coconuts, they might have been on the right track."

Print belched slightly. Tom tipped up the brim of his hat to look over at his uncle. Print shrugged and puffed his pipe.

"Ain't much callin' for coconut peelers up here."

"Somewheres in all this, you're gonna reveal how the range got named?"

"Well, the frogs brought those poor lads up here. Guess they started them in on jackrabbits an' coy'ot, 'cuz things was pretty thin in the beaver department 'round here."

Both men chuckled.

"It ain't really funny when ya think about it. Imagine what was goin' through the minds of those poor souls. Never seen a snowflake back home and they get hauled up here just in time for winter."

"So what happened to them?"

"They lasted 'bout as long as spit in that fire. They never made it to Thanksgiving in their new country, I'm sure. But leave it to the frogs to put a shine on their endeavors, even their screwups. An' they are an arrogant people when it comes to other folks' language. They named this the Great Owyhee Range after them pitiful, brokenhearted lads from Hawai'i."

Print sipped the last dram from his cup.

"You gonna have a story every night, Uncle?"

"I might. You might wind up a fairly educated fella 'time we get to Sheridan."

Tom pushed his hat back and sat up. "Think I'll have a touch of that," he said, holding out his cup.

Print poured whiskey into the cup, looked over at Billy, who was sitting off a ways. "He's a respectful lad, I'll say that."

"He don't seem to have much choice. Have ya got a whiff of him yet?" asked Tom, looking at the cowboy finishing the last of his supper.

"Nope. Maybe it ain't that bad."

Print struck a match and sucked deeply on the pipe, puffing a thick cloud of smoke around his face. He flicked the spent match into the fire. "Hey, Billy, how 'bout some more chuck?"

The young cowboy, sitting cross-legged, looked up. "Thanks, Mr. Ritter. Think I've had my fill."

"Well, come on over and get yerself some coffee. I hate wastin' coffee."

Billy rose and came over to their fire and squatted to get the coffeepot. Instinctively his hand went to his side. He poured himself a cup and stood. Tom was the first one to get a whiff and then Print. It wasn't as bad as he had thought it would be, but it wasn't that good either. Both men tried to pretend that they couldn't smell him. But Billy was keenly sensitive to how his presence affected others. He took a sip, then said, "I'll stay up with the horses. You fellas get some sleep."

As he walked away, he turned. "Thanks, Mr. Ritter, Tom."

"You bet, son. Check the hobbles on those lead mares."

"Yes, sir."

Print took out the figurine he had been whittling on from a vest pocket and then his pocketknife. Tom rolled a smoke.

"Don't be too free with those invites, Uncle. That's enough to make yer eyes water."

Print took a puff and scraped the little wooden horse with his blade. "I smelled worse, lots worse."

"Like what?"

Print quit whittling and looked into the dark at the departing young man. "Oh, like a dozen men cut ta pieces by a round a grapeshot. They done more than just leak shit. Yes, sir."

Tom lit his smoke and Print looked up into the

evening sky.

"Somethin' about a starry night that just jerks yer head up, ya can't help it."

Tom exhaled and looked up too. "He seems like a pretty good hand."

"Yes, he does."

Print took a sip from his cup and Tom poked at the fire.

CHAPTER SEVEN

They were making good distance, considering the bleak land they were traveling through. They had crossed Duck Creek, the Owyhee, and Cow Creek. They had put Jordan Valley behind them and crossed into Idaho. They had done all that without losing a horse, although several were gimpy. Billy was more than pulling his own, and most of the time, uncle and nephew hardly knew he was there. The weather had held. They did get snowed on just south of the Mahogany Mountains. It was just a dusting and kept the herd fresh.

They made camp on the bank of Reynolds Creek and could see the lights of Silver City off to the east. Print dropped a load of broken sagebrush on the fire, then stepped back as it popped and flared.

"Time to reprovision. Thought we might go inta town in the morning. Hey, Billy, think you can handle things if we go into town for supplies in the mornin'?"

Out in the darkness, Billy called back. "Yes, sir. No problem."

"Anything you want while we're in there?"

Silence.

"You already got wages due ya, son, whatta ya need?"

"I could use some cotton cloth or towels if they got any, sir. Some makings maybe."

"That's it?"

"Yes, sir."

"How 'bout a pretty little hurdy-gurdy gal?"

"No, sir. Not unless she's got a busted sniffer."

"What about one of them squaws that's had their nose cut off? Would that do?" asked Tom.

"I don't believe so, Tom. I think you'd just have two people that was fairly unattracted to one another."

"That doctor didn't take off mor'n your appendix, did he?"

Silence.

"We're just givin' ya a little raze, son. No slight intended."

"Yes, sir. I know."

"Well, when we're in town, we'll do an inventory of the felines, an' if we find one with a malfunctioning snout, we'll set you up. How does that sound?"

"I'd be most grateful, sir, but I won't hold my breath waiting." Billy laughed at his own joke and the men joined in.

The next day Print saddled up the red roan he had ridden back at the round barn and Tom rode a mousy gray. Billy was picking up firewood as they rode off. It was a raw day that kept threatening bad weather. The herd was bunched up with their asses into the wind. The two rode in silence most of the way to town.

Silver City was a mining town that sort of ran uphill in several directions. It was past its glory days but still an active camp.

They walked their horses up to the front of the Idaho Hotel where a clerk was sweeping its front boardwalk. They watched as the man swept dirt and kicked dried chunks of mud into the street. One good-sized clod landed between the feet of the mousy gray. The gray snorted and the sweeper looked up.

"Gentlemen."

Both men nodded.

"If it's rooms you want, we're all booked up. Mine engineers out from Minnesota, here all month. Might try the War Eagle down the street."

"No rooms, thanks. We're here for supplies and a quiet drink."

"Whiskey and quietness we got. Constable an' the deputy board with us, so we never have trouble."

"What about supplies?" asked Tom.

"Mister, this is Silver City. We got four mercantiles, two hotels, three churches, a brewery, an' a carbolic acid factory—let alone the parlor houses and emporiums."

"Real up to date."

"If it's supplies you're lookin' for, Cosgrove's should have what ya want. He don't gouge too much. ... About that drink. We got good rye whiskey right through them doors." He pointed with the broom handle to the entrance of the hotel. Both men dismounted and loosened their cinch straps.

"Nephew, it has occurred to me that I have overlooked an important item for this trip, and that's a decent shotgun. There's too much game on the wing for us to be passin' up. We can't be stoppin' in every town along the way ta feed ourselves."

Print took a coin purse from his vest and handed Tom a gold double eagle. "See what ya can find and I'll meet you over at this Mr. Cosgrove's, the man that don't gouge too much," he said, looking at the hotel clerk. "An' get plenty of shells too."

"Might try the constable's office. He complements his town salary sellin' confiscated weaponry. He don't gouge too much either," interjected the sweeper.

Print looked up at the clerk. "You'll speak up if ya see us doin' business with any fellas that *does* gouge too much, won't ya?"

"Surely."

Tom walked up the street, leading his horse in the direction of the constable's office. Print went in the other direction with the red roan.

Shortly, Tom emerged with a long-barreled side-by-side that had been well taken care of by its previous owner, a gentleman from Indianapolis who thought that because he was out West, it was acceptable to urinate in the street, even on Sunday morning when folks were going off to church. Short on cash, the reasonable constable of Silver City accepted the thoughtless pisser's shotgun to cover his fine.

The cold weather had given way to a warming sun. Tom flipped open a saddlebag and took out a soiled rag and stuffed two boxes of shells inside. He broke open the shotgun, wrapped the cloth around it, and tied it behind his saddle. First the stock and then the barrels. From down a side street, he could hear someone plinking on a badly tuned piano. The sound reminded him he was thirsty. Leading the mousy gray, he decided to investigate.

The magistrates of Silver City had obviously done a lot of thinking when laying out the town. The churches commanded the high ground, and the objects of their Sunday sermons were more or less confined to down below, symbolism not lost on their parishioners.

The keyboard music emanated from a building that wore a sign, "The Lemon Drop." Under that, in slightly smaller lettering, "Fresh and Tart." Tom set his course for the hitching post in front.

Parked at a slant in front of the Lemon Drop was a wagon. It was a cross between a prairie schooner and a city freight wagon, four iron hoops topped with canvas with its sides rolled up. Inside sat four Chinese girls. They looked road weary with more than a sprinkling of dust. Tom barely gave them a look as he tied his horse directly in front of the window. He made sure that he could keep an eye on him from inside.

He entered a long, deep room seemingly lit by the light from the windows and doorway. Business was slow at that hour, with only a card game in the back and one other cowboy at the bar. Several women in the back, dressed as if they were expecting a hot spell, watched the card game that seemed to have come to a halt as a rat-faced fellow with a stewpot hat was showing off a small Chinese girl to the card players. Tom could not hear what was being said, but his sense of it was that the men were more interested in getting on with the game but listened patiently. Tom turned to the bartender, a balding chap with a clean apron tied fast.

"Whiskey, please."

"Glass or bottle?"

"Glass."

The bartender placed a thick glass between them and poured. Tom emptied the tumbler. Neither fast, nor slow, but completely. He placed it on the countertop. The bartender slightly dipped his head in the direction of the empty glass. Tom savored the full effect of that first jolt and then nodded yes. The barkeep lifted the glass and wiped the bar with a rag. He set the glass back down and filled it to the brim. Tom placed a silver dollar on the bar and drank the second whiskey at an even slower rate.

He looked out the window. The mousy gray was still tied and sleeping. He ordered a third round as one of the girls who had been watching the game sidled up to him.

"Buy a girl a drink?"

Tom looked down at her, trying to calculate how much longer his uncle would be shopping. "Why not?"

She raised her hand to the bartender. "Otto?"

She was pretty enough. More than pretty. It was hard to put an age on her. Her yellow curls were gathered up on top of her head and she wore a kind of clothing that Tom was not sure was outer- or underwear. She had a black ribbon tied around her throat and wore dark purple stockings that were striped. She had an uncomplicated face, and when she smiled, she seemed to be in possession of all her teeth. She had big, billowy breasts whose primary job seemed to be that of holding up her dress. She smelled of lavender. Otto the bartender interrupted Tom's assessment.

"Here."

"Lemonade?"

She lifted the drink as if to salute. "Fresh and tart."

"One more whiskey."

Tom put another dollar down and they clinked glasses. As they each sipped their drinks, the lavender lemon drop reached down and ran her hand up the inside of Tom's thigh. It came to rest on his crotch and she left it there. Tom felt the heat rise in several different regions of his body.

"How 'bout some bareback ridin', cowboy?"

"Can't, I got people waitin' for me."

"Oh, come on. What's yer name?"

"Tom. Tom Harte."

The hydromechanics of Mother Nature were starting to work on Tom. She squeezed the growing bulge in her hand as she looked straight into his eyes. "Well, Tom Harte, I can have that sanded down in no time."

Tom was turning red from the neck up. It had suddenly gotten very warm in the darkened saloon, and it wasn't all from Otto's liquor.

"Damn it's been a while since a fella blushed over me. Come on, Tommy, let me take the tension outta your britches."

Her hand and the whiskey were making it hard for Tom to calculate the time he needed to rendezvous with Print. She kept a hard grip on his crotch and started making a circular motion with her wrist. "Come on, cowboy, that critter needs exercise."

Tom's problem with the math was giving way to her sense of logic. He finished his drink and, holding his hat in front of him, followed the yellow-haired lady who was so full of common sense. They walked toward the gymnasium out back, past the stalled card game and the rodent-faced man with the little girl.

◎ ◎ ◎

Print was surveying the contents of Cosgrove's Mercantile, waiting for the proprietor to finish up with two round women wearing bonnets that were several years behind the current fashion. He looked at a basket of turnips on the floor. He pulled out a stub of a pencil and a piece of paper and made a note.

The ladies, with laden baskets, passed Print.

"Can I help ya, mister?"

"Yes, sir. I need flour, bacon, salt pork … "

"Whoa, hold on there. How much and what kind?"

"How 'bout ten pounds of flour, the kind that don't have weevils. Whatever configuration yer bacon an' salt pork comes in, I'll take ten pounds of that, each. Then six bags of Arbuckle's, two dozen sticks of Mexican vanilla, a sack of chili beans, six cans of evaporated milk, couple of jars of whatever jam ya got handy … "

The clerk was writing as fast as he could.

"Three tins of cut tobacco. Three plugs too, an' four boxes of therapeutic papers. Oh, yeah, I'd like a bag of yer turnips."

"Will that do it for you?"

"Whatta ya got in the way of cotton? Like toweling?"

"Right now, all I got is a bolt of cotton muslin. Got some bunting, but that's gonna cost a lot more."

"Got somethin' I can put all that in?"

"Will flour sacks do?"

"They'll do just fine."

"Three cents apiece."

Print gave him a hard look but said nothing. "Do you

sell whiskey?"

"No, sir. Bug juice you can get 'round the corner at the Lemon Drop."

"How are their prices?"

"I wouldn't know. I'm of the Baptist faith. I do know a man's got the right to make a profit on his labor."

"Town seems ta be adhering to your way of thinkin'."

Print paid up. Weighted down with twelve cents' worth of flour sacks and goods, he carried his load out to the red roan. He tightened the cinch on the saddle and then tied the provisions to either side of the pony's shoulders by way of the horn. The young horse came to life and snorted.

"Easy there. Now ain't the time to get scar't of a couple of sacks of beans an' jam."

He stroked the pony's neck, waiting for him to relax, and when he heard the pony exhale in a way he wanted, he untied him and went in search of the Lemon Drop whiskey emporium. He saw Tom's horse tied up outside. He secured the roan and noticed the girls in the wagon next to him.

As he entered, he brought in a wisp of light and a smell of the old manure that had been ground into the dusty street baking in the sun. He saw Tom talking to a short woman with yellow hair. At his approach, Tom straightened up as if he had been waiting for Print for quite a while.

"Uncle, this is Miss Lucy Highsmith. Miss Highsmith, this is my uncle, Prentice Ritter."

Print tipped his hat. "My pleasure, Miss Highsmith. This coltish lad ain't leading you astray, I hope?"

"He was just givin' me a lecture on horsemanship."

"You be careful 'round him, ma'am. He tends to get overmounted at times."

"He was very enthusiastic in his demonstration, but

he was quick about it."

Print shook his head. "As they say, 'Youth is wasted on the young.'"

"If you have something you'd like to add to the subject, we run a pretty fine equestrian school out back."

"Thank you for the offer, Miss Highsmith, but I better get my nephew back ta camp 'fore he signs up for yer next equitation class."

"In that case, I'll leave you two as I got new students waitin' for lessons. Giddyup."

The two men watched her disappear toward the back of the room.

Print turned to Otto. "A whiskey, please. What about you, mister bronc rider?"

"Sure."

Print sniffed. "Interestin' shade a lavender yer wearin'. Or is that lilac?" He sniffed again. "No, definitely lavender."

"How long am I goin' to have to be hearing about this?"

"I figger at least 'til Lander."

They downed their drinks, ordered three bottles to go, and paid up.

Outside, Print shifted two of the sacks to Tom's horse. They mounted up and headed down the street that led to the edge of town.

"Tell me, nephew, did ya have ta wear yer spurs? Looked like a lot of spirit there."

"She was a nice lady, Uncle."

Print laughed out loud. "If she was a lady, she'd be tampin' a tambourine 'stead of a mattress."

With the lights of town behind them, they turned back to camp. They never even noticed the wagon filled with Chinese girls that bumped along to the east.

CHAPTER EIGHT

Print was ladling beans and rectified prunes onto plates with thick strips of bacon and biscuits. "Come on, boys. Get it while it's hot."

Tom took a plate and Billy, standing off a bit, came forward to take a plate and pour a cup of coffee. He walked away to sit on an old log by a clump of hackberry. The men ate in silence.

"Interestin' town there," said Print as he wiped his plate with a half a biscuit. "They sure seem preoccupied with who's gouging who." He took the biscuit for one last round on the plate. "It's been my experience that when ya come across people that are so concerned with other folks' transgressions, ya better watch out, 'cuz mor'n likely, that's what they got in store for you."

"Maybe it has to do with being a mining town. Men underground gouging rock outta the earth and the rest of the residents aboveground gouging the refined and minted ore outta the topsiders."

"Now that's a damn good theory, Tom. Gougers versus miners. I like it. I can see yer gettin' more educated by the mile."

"I think I came out all right on that shotgun."

"Ya did indeed. That's a fine piece of avian artillery ya picked up from the constable."

Tom placed his plate and fork into the big skillet that doubled as a washbasin and rummaged through the flour sacks until he found a box of therapeutic papers and headed off for his own clump of hackberry bushes.

Print added his plate to the skillet, stood up, and poured himself some coffee. "You fellas trying ta triangulate me?"

"How's that, Uncle?"

"Well, I got Billy leakin' off ta my right and you on my left, layin' cable just a little too close ta camp. I know we're on the trail, but ya might try an' make your privy farther from where we sleep."

"I think you'll survive."

"Survivin' ain't the point. By the way, the man guaranteed me those papers got no splinters in 'em."

"Beats buffalo grass or corncobs."

Print took a handful of grass and dirt and went to work on the skillet and plates. He then took the water bag and rinsed everything.

"Billy, get that little roan I rode yesterday up for me. Think I'll give Bob Tate another day off."

"Yes, sir, Mr. Ritter."

They had the herd moving, and by afternoon, they were coming off the Owyhee front. They skirted north of the Nickel Creek Mesa and were about to cross the confluence of Corral Creek and Currant Creek when Print heard a mustang stallion calling out from up in the rocks. Looking up he saw a little bay stallion with a band of about a half a dozen mares set back from him in a stand of junipers. He gigged the red roan into a lope in Tom's direction. He pulled up short beside his nephew.

"Look at that," he said, pointing up to the pile of big rocks that lay strewn below the mesa.

"Where'd he come from?" asked Tom.

"Wild mustang. See his mares off in the trees?"

The stallion called out again.

"He's bold as brass out here in the daylight."

"He figgers he's safe enough up in the rocks. Probably

wants ta add to his harem."

"Not unless he's got cash money, he ain't."

"If he makes a run at the herd, yer gonna have ta drive him off. Either that or shoot him."

"Why wait?"

Tom pulled out his cut-down Remington Rider from the saddle scabbard. He thumbed back the hammer to full cock, rolled the breechblock back to expose the chamber. He slid the big cartridge in and eased the breechblock back in place. He swung down out of the saddle and handed his reins to Print.

"Not sure that's necessary, Tom."

"I'm not gonna shoot him, just scare him off. I don't want to have to be looking back all day."

He raised the rifle, sighted down on the rock facing, above the bay mustang. The Remington roared and Tom was enveloped in smoke. The slug ricocheted off the stone wall, sending shards of granite flying. The stallion bolted toward the mares that were already flushed from the trees. The red roan was backing up with Print, who was trying to hold on to Tom's horse.

"Whoa, whoa. Easy there, easy."

Print looked toward the back of the herd for Billy. Billy was standing up in the stirrups. Print yelled to him. "It's all right, Billy. Don't let 'em run back on ya!"

Tom and Print watched the mustang and his mares disappear into the boulders.

"That oughta take the edge off any amorous ideas he might have."

"I'd rather scare him than have to shoot him."

Tom slid the Remington back into the scabbard, took the reins from Print, and mounted. The shot had sent several of the horses running off from the herd and they turned to gather them in.

That night they camped by a slow-moving little creek

that had a small draw next to it that made it easy to keep the horses penned up. There was enough wild ryegrass for a night's grazing. With the packhorses and Bob Tate picketed behind them and a good fire going, they settled down for supper. Tom noticed that Billy was making his camp closer to them every night but still kept a respectful distance.

It was a moonless night, and downwind from the campfire, the little bay stallion breathed in an array of scents and odors. His girth was streaked from serum and puss that oozed from a wound on his withers. A strong colt had challenged him and kicked him high. A well-placed hoof had caught him at the base of his neck. He finally drove the determined suitor off, but two nights later, he came back. By then the swelling had turned into a corruption beneath the skin and it was so painful the stallion couldn't lower his head to graze. The challenger was content to leave with one mare.

The infection had eventually broken open, pouring down his sides. With it went most of the pain. The greenhead flies were vicious and eventually drove him to roll in the deep sand of the creek bottoms. The wound was crusting over and the sharp pain had given way to a dull ache. Tonight he sniffed the air. He pawed the ground and called out to the herd in the draw.

All three men looked up at the sound of the little stallion. Billy walked over for some more coffee. Print filled the bowl of his pipe.

"Think I'll set up a while with ya, Billy. That ol' stud has got ever'thing on edge tonight."

"Whatever you like, Mr. Ritter. Mind if I change out my towel for some of that muslin you bought?"

"Help yourself."

Tom was field dressing the Remington. Print lit his pipe.

"Ever thought of upgrading ta somethin' a little more modern, like a repeater?"

"I'd rather spend my money on a new saddle."

"Well, how about somethin' that at least burned smokeless powder?"

"It serves my needs."

Print blew a puff of smoke and took out his knife and wood. Billy ripped off a length of the rough cotton and headed off for the darkness.

"Here that?"

Tom looked up from his gun cleaning.

"Sounds like a curlew."

A two-note whistle followed by a rattle came from the direction of the creek.

"There he goes. Down in the cattails. Know the difference between a curlew and the snipe?"

Tom had gone back to cleaning his rifle. "No. Not something I think much about."

"Maybe ya should. Some knowledge of ornithology might come in handy."

Tom ran the oily rag down the length of the barrel. He looked over at his uncle. "Ornithology?"

"Sure, ornithology. The study of birds."

"The study of birds."

"Why, sure. Think 'bout it. Next time ya pay a visit ta Miss Lucy Highsmith, ya can tell her all about the spoonbill an' the titmouse an' the red-headed woodpecker—not to be confused with the red-cock woodpecker. Might even throw in a dissertation on the double-breasted bed thrasher."

Tom was forced to chuckle.

"Why, ya got that sexy species, the sparrow. Ya got the seedeater, the dickcissel, an' the soft-tailed. Probably no need ta bring up the thrush an' the western peewee."

Tom stared at him as he kept wiping the gun.

"Where do you come up with all this?"

"I read, son, I read. *Audubon's Guide to Land and Water Birds*. I always got somethin' close at hand ta read."

Tom shook his head.

"Bet she's tired of hearin' all the theories of bareback ridin'. She might welcome a conversation about birds. Ornithology. Think about it."

The curlew called out again from the creek bank. Tom changed the subject. "Did you get a good look at the stallion today?"

Print stopped whittling and relit his pipe. "It's the Spanish in 'em. Mosta the wild horses ya come across out here is stock that was turned loose 'r wandered off. But he's the genuine article."

Print gestured with his pocketknife. "Bit of a Roman nose, big, high-set eyes, an' a great front end."

"Wouldn't mind coming back here an' catching some of his children."

"They been on the loose for a long time. When the Indians first laid eyes on 'em, they called them God Dogs."

"Maybe we could spend next summer up here gatherin' up some."

"Sure. But let's get yer herd delivered first."

"It's a damn sight more your herd than mine."

Print put away his pocketknife and figurine. He knocked his pipe against the heel of his boot. "I don't feel that way an' I don't think your ma would've either."

Tom pulled out the letter that Print had given him back on the first day. He opened it and leaned closer to the light of the dimming fire. He read aloud. "Tom, as you seem to have little interest in the homestead, I see no reason to burden you with its ownership. You are free to seek your own opportunities. Your mother."

Print let out a long, slow sigh, tugged on his earlobe, and looked off into the darkness. "Not very generous."

Tom folded the paper, slipped it into the envelope, and then into his shirt pocket. Print watched him. Tom looked up.

"She was plenty generous with the cane."

"Never knew the warmin' of a lad's backsides ta be the ruin of him."

"She enjoyed it a little too much. She never forgave me for runnin' off to buckaroo."

"Losin' yer pa made her a hard woman."

"She was hard before that."

Print said nothing.

"I always sent money home after every season."

"We get these horses ta Sheridan an' we'll come on up here next spring."

Billy had finished changing and walked off toward the herd. Print slipped off his boots and britches and untied his kerchief and stretched out. The fire had turned to coals. The night sky glowed with green bands of light that danced and waved overhead. Ribbons of red and soft yellow lit up between the green waves. The aurora borealis was putting on quite a show as the two men watched from their bedrolls.

"Whenever I see them lights up there, I think the old man up there ain't happy."

Print smiled to himself. "Funny. I always got the feelin' it meant he was sorta pleased."

Print pulled the bedroll up to his chin. "This is a great life—when it ain't rainin' or snowin'."

CHAPTER NINE

Print was riding at the head of the herd with Tom flanking off to the right and Billy not quite in the drag position, as the horses were tending to stay more or less bunched up. They were following an old wagon road that would eventually tie in to the north branch of the Oregon Trail.

They had crossed the Bruneau uneventfully, except one colt got to scrambling on the far bank and had pulled something and was pretty lame. He would either sort it out or not. Print never expected to get to Sheridan with all the horses.

They slowly hazed the herd up a long incline. As Print crested the brow of the low-slung rolling hill, he looked down, and in the distance, he could see what looked like a light freight wagon moving east. Off to the left, a hawk was skimming across the flat land. There was a puff as he hit a dove or a pigeon. He banked and slowly headed off with his meal.

Even at a slow pace, the herd was gaining on the wagon. In a half an hour, the herd was coming abreast of the wagon on its left. Inside, Print and Tom could see five young Chinese girls and a man at the reins wearing a stewpot hat. He brought the two mules pulling the wagon to a halt and looked over at the herd. Print waved to Tom to join him as he loped over to the wagon.

The girls sat silently in the back of the wagon, watching the two riders approach.

"Afternoon," said the driver with a mouthful of yellow teeth.

Print nodded and then looked over at the girls. "You off ta church?"

The driver grinned even wider, revealing gaps where several teeth had rotted down to the gums. "No, sir. No indeed. Name's Billy Fender. Capt'n Billy Fender."

Print continued to watch the girls.

"How 'bout you boys?"

Print turned to look at Fender. "Print Ritter. This is my nephew, Tom Harte."

"Quite a herd ya got there. You goin' ta Fort Hall?"

"No. You?"

"Well, gentlemen, I purchased, at great expense, five virgin exotics in San Francisco, direct and intact from the Celestial Empire. I got another two in Sacramento. I'm headin' ta the mining camps, where hard men will pay good money for the opportunity to deflower these little Mongolian blossoms."

Bob Tate stomped at flies on his leg. Print shifted in the saddle.

"The boys linin' up for seconds, thirds, an' fourths 'ill pay well too. I'll let you boys punch the sirloin. I aim ta make a tidy sum workin' the tenderloin."

Tom kept looking at Fender's mouth and thinking that he would probably stand a better chance being bitten by a rattler than having this fellow sink his incisors into him.

"We seem ta be headin' in the same direction. Mind if I share the trail with ya? Conversation's been a bit thin," he said, jerking his head in the direction of the girls.

Print looked at Tom. Tom shrugged. He looked back at Fender. "We're workin' a faster pace than you. You'll be in our dust most of the time."

"Dirt never bothered me."

"Suit yerself."

He struck Tom as the type who had a deep-seated aversion to soap and water.

Print and Tom turned their horses back toward the herd. Tom pulled aside Print. "Why let him tag along?"

"What's my choice? I can't rule him off the range. I'd rather know where a fella like that is 'stead of worryin' where he might pop up. He'll tire of our dust soon enough."

Print kept the herd moving for the rest of the day, rather than stopping early to let them graze. The distance between the herd and the wagon grew, and as the sun cast long shadows out in front of them, the wagon was out of sight.

They had made camp and were cooking two good-sized rabbits that Billy had picked off when they heard the wagon approach in the dark. Fender called out, "I'll set up my own camp over here."

Print gestured with the wooden spoon he was using to stir the pot of beans. "Just don't spook the horses. Might want ta tell those girls ta steer clear of the herd."

Fender laughed. "I'd have better luck talkin' ta them mules. Don't worry 'bout the Celestials, they'll nest right under the wagon."

"We got a couple a rabbits if ya want ta join us," said Print.

"A kind offer, Mr. Ritter. You fellas pull a cork?"

"I'll have a sip at night. Good for the arthritis."

Fender had the girls pulling wood from the cooney, slung under the wagon, and soon had his own fire going. The girls seemed to know the drill and went about preparing their own supper. Fender joined Print and Tom. He offered a bottle of whiskey, pouring some into the men's tin cups. He drank from the bottle.

Print took a sip and then ladled out beans on a plate. He added biscuits and a leg of cooked rabbit. Fender took the rabbit and tore into it with his rotten teeth. Warm grease dripped down his chin. "Oh, that's good."

He sputtered as bits of food flew in the direction of the fire. He held the plate to his mouth and shoveled in beans and stuffed a whole biscuit in behind the beans. Mashed food seeped out of the corner of his mouth, which he wiped away with the back of his hand. He licked the residue with his tongue. He took a long pull on the bottle, looked into the fire, and gave a loud belch. "Ya'll set a fine table."

"What about the girls?" asked Print.

"Pickier eaters y'all never find. Rice eaters, but that's okay, I didn't buy 'em for their eatin' habits."

Print took another sip and Tom placed his unfinished plate of food by the fire's edge.

"There's a lotta expense attendant ta these gals. They're dumb as dirt at understandin' English an' want ta wash themselves ever' day. Ha! I'd like ta see them out on the prairie soapin' up their little powder puffs come the new year. They'll learn. But that won't be my concern as I'll be cashed outta this deal by then."

Print took out his pipe and tobacco. Tom sipped from his cup but didn't return to his plate. "Thought you said you bought seven girls."

"Did. Had ta sell one ta help with the travelin' expenses and one just up an' died on me. As a businessman, ya have to expect som' percentage of spoilage of yer inventory."

Fender rose and recharged the men's cups. He took a swig and raised the bottle. "Travel with equals or travel alone, I always say."

Print saw that the girls were watching them closely. He took out the little wooden horse he was whittling and went to work on it with his knife.

"How'd you come to be a capt'n?" Tom asked.

"Well, it's more an honorary title given me for services rendered with the home guard back 'n Arkansas."

Both men took him for the liar he was. They all

looked up at the sound of Billy approaching in the darkness. Tom noticed the girls draw together. "Billy, grab a plate. Want a short snort?"

"No, thank you, sir. It tends to irritate my problem."

"Billy, this here's Capt'n Fender. Fender, Billy Via."

"Captain Fender," said Billy as he piled on the biscuits. "I'm gonna go back to the horses. They're acting a bit edgy tonight."

"It's the mules," said Tom.

As he carefully walked away with coffee in one hand and his plate piled high in the other, he glanced over at the girls, who were watching him. Coyotes yapped out in the night.

"Nice young man," said Print. "Got a leakage problem. That's what that smell comes from."

Fender looked up from his plate. "I don't smell nothin'. Stench don't bother me a'tall. 'Cept rancid butter. A whiff a rancid butter'll turn my insides every time."

He tossed his empty plate on the ground and picked up his bottle. "I don't mind tellin' you boys I got a problem. These girls was all virgins when I bought 'em, but since leavin' San Francisco, I've deflowered two of 'em, cuttin' down on their enhanced value considerably."

"Enhanced value?" asked Tom with a look on his face as if he smelled something a lot worse than Billy.

"Sure. Uncharted territory. A one-time prize. Must be an acquired taste. I like a gal that already knows what she's doin', but some men will pay well to take the first slice of the cake. So, ya see, now close ta forty percent of my existin' inventory is slightly used."

Print took out his pipe and tobacco. Tom had never been to San Francisco and wondered if it was populated with more rodents like this Fender.

Fender took another swig and offered the bottle to the two men. Both declined. Fender rolled on, oblivious to the fact that the two men in front of him were drawing some hard and irrefutable impressions of him.

"Now that littlest Chink, with the itty-bitty feet, cost as much as two of the others. Those Mongolian bastards break their toes an' fold 'em under an' then bind 'em up tighter than Dick's hat band. Now is that heathen savagery fer ya?"

"Guess they're lucky to have you come along an' save 'em," said Print without looking up from his carving.

"Well, I guess they are. They claim it gives 'em stronger sex'al urges. I have been assured that the men in the camps'll pay premium for her. Ain't much on independent locomotion. I wind up carryin' her ever'where."

Fender finally realized that he had been doing all the talking and that the other men seemed inordinately quiet. He gave them both a long look. "If you boys are interest'd, I let ya have a stab at the 'almost' virgins for a dollar apiece."

Neither Print nor Tom said anything.

"Married men?"

They shook their heads.

"Bachelors? Well, I'm all fer bachelors. I always say that bachelors know more about women than married men, else they'd be married too."

Fender roared at his own joke and finished off the last of the bottle. He tossed the empty bottle back in the direction of his wagon. It hit the ground but didn't break. The girls flinched at the sound of the bottle. "'Nother dead Indian."

With considerable effort, Fender rose and headed back to his wagon. The girls cringed at his approach. He attempted to dance a jig and nearly fell.

> "Oh, whiskey is the life of man.
> Always was since the world began.
> I'll drink it from an old tin can. ... "

He slurred the words. He jumped to click his heels and almost fell again. The girls pulled themselves under the wagon. Tom turned to Print. "Hope you ain't planning on sharing the trail with him much longer. You think he really bought those girls?"

Print shrugged, looking over at Fender as he rummaged in the back of his wagon. "We'll put the distance on them tomorrow."

Fender threw back a canvas tarp and extracted another bottle of whiskey. He clenched the cork between his rotten teeth and pulled. With his back to the other camp, he removed from inside his coat the flask given him in Chinatown. He poured from it into the bottle. He slipped the flask deep in a pocket and turned and headed back to Print and Tom, pushing the cork into the bottle.

"Gentlemen, another bottle." He paused to dance a step. "I do love to dance."

He poured into Print's cup.

"Last one fer me."

"Me too," said Tom, tossing the butt of his smoke into the fire.

"Of course, gentlemen. Let he who sins while drunk be punished when he's sober, I always say."

His little ferret eyes gleamed in the firelight. Print pressed the pocketknife against his thigh to close it and slipped the little wooden horse back in his vest pocket. I gotta stop being so friendly out here, he thought. Shit-bird like this one is nothing but trouble. Too bad about those girls.

He raised the cup to his lips and swallowed its contents.

CHAPTER TEN

Print dreamed he was sleeping in a hearth. It was cold and there was a terrible pain in his head. His mouth was full of cinders. It was the fireplace in the cabin of his youth. The cold would not let him sleep. He was looking up the chimney. It was long and dark with sunlight at the top. His bladder was full. He squinted and the chimney gave way to gray light. He rolled over and pain ran through his head. He thought he was going to be sick. He forced himself up on an elbow and looked around.

The herd was grazing, unconcerned about the change in weather. He saw Fender's wagon and the girls still huddled there, looking over at him. He rolled over onto all fours and rose. I'm gettin' too old for this shit, he thought. He looked down and saw Tom out to the world. He staggered away from the camp and unbuttoned his pants to relieve himself. The weather surely had changed. A cutting wind from the north had chilled the land. He buttoned up and felt for his money belt. It was gone. He felt again and turned back to his bedroll. His feet were swollen and hurt from sleeping with his boots on. He reached down and lifted the bedroll and shook it out.

"Tom! Tom! Wake up! That shit-bird stole my money belt."

Tom looked up at his uncle from his own dream. He heard him yelling, but he couldn't understand him. His uncle left, and he stared up at the sky. A moment later he returned and was pouring his canteen on him. He sat up.

"Tom, boy! Get up. That shit-bird Fender doctored the bug juice and swapped stock on us."

Print was filling the palm of his hand and slapping water in his own face. Tom stood, looked around, and then trotted gingerly in his stocking feet over to the girls.

"Where the hell's our money and our horses?" he screamed at the terrified girls.

"Easy, boy. They sure as shit didn't take 'em." Print slowly turned a complete circle, scanning the land. "Go get Billy."

Tom returned to his bedroll. "That spivvy li'l' shit took my boots!"

He whipped back his bedroll to reveal his carbine and their sidearms. "At least we're still heeled."

"Go get Billy," Print repeated.

Print tossed sticks and wood on the embers of the fire and tossed the dregs of old coffee out of the pot. He rinsed it out and reached for the sack of Arbuckle's. He looked over at the girls. They seemed not to have moved since last night's supper. What am I gonna do with you little daughters of joy? he thought.

The fire started to come to life. He heard Tom yelling from the other side of the herd. He rose and looked across the horses, who swung their tails back and forth. He trotted on his bandy legs around the herd. As he came up on Tom, he stopped. Tom stood looking at him and he knew it was all wrong. Billy lay on top of his bedroll. He slowed to a walk and saw that Billy's head was covered in dark, crusted blood.

"He killed him. He stove his head in. He killed Billy."

The wind had blown his kerchief up and it had stuck to his cheek. His hat rested beside him. His sandy hair matted in the blackened blood. His pockets were turned out. His boots were gone.

Print's mouth pursed. His upper lip twitched. He

sucked air through his teeth. "Looks like he took a couple of horses. … He took Bob Tate."

Print looked out at nothing. "I am such a fool. A damn fool."

He looked down at Billy and then back out at the skyline. "I get older, but I don't get smarter. Check the rest of the horses an' get some coffee."

Tom walked away and Print looked down again at the dead cowboy.

Print had the fire roaring when Tom walked back. He poured a cup of coffee and handed it to his nephew.

"Looks like he took three, maybe four horses. Guess they're not gonna tell us what happened," he said, looking over at the girls.

"We know what happened. Notice anything 'bout them?"

Tom walked a few steps toward their camp and looked. "There's only four."

"Yep. Must a took one for company."

"Or he stove her head in too and stuck her some-place."

Print took his kerchief from his vest pocket and lifted a pot of bubbling beans from the fire. He walked over to the girls and pointed to the pot. "I know you ladies can't understan' a word I'm sayin', but you must know what food's about."

They stared up at him, afraid to move. He squatted in front of them and placed the pot on the ground. "I'll let you figger it out."

He walked back to his fire as Tom was buckling his gun rig.

"What're you doin'?"

"I'll need some of that food yer givin' away."

"What for?"

"I'm going after our money an' horses."

"What makes ya think you should go?"

"'Cause that's the only way I'll ever get my hands on what shoulda been mine."

He took off his kerchief and placed a handful of dried prunes in it. Then some jerky and three biscuits from last night's supper. He rolled it up and placed it in his saddle-bag. He put a box of cartridges in the bag on the other side. He slid the carbine in the scabbard.

Print sat down on the ground and pulled off his boots, tossing them at Tom. "They'll do you more good th'n me."

Tom stood on one leg and then the other, pulling on the boots. He wiggled his toes. He had never realized how big his uncle's feet were. He tightened the cinch strap, slipped the canteen over the horn, and mounted. He shoved his hat down tighter and pulled his coat collar up against the wind.

"I'll get it back. Bob Tate too."

"I c'n get another horse. It's nephews I'm shy on. You just make sure you get back."

Tom looked down at him and then over at the girls. The pot sat where Print had left it. They hadn't touched it. He put his pony into a walk, skirted the herd, and headed north into the rising wind.

Print watched him go. He was a tough enough of a kid. He never knew him to do stupid things. He seemed to be well thought out in all things he did. He had been that way even as a boy. Print turned and hobbled back to his fire. He poured a cup, sipped, and saw the pot of beans where he had left it.

He walked toward them. Their faces were grimy with trail dust, and they looked like they hadn't slept all night. "Ladies, I guess it's time we was introduced."

He squatted, the pot between them. He lifted the cover and took out the wooden spoon and ate a mouthful.

He offered a spoonful to the girls. They neither moved nor spoke. He tipped the brim of his hat back. "This just ain't gonna do."

He put the spoon in his mouth and then extracted it and pointed to the little girl on the left. "Yer gonna be Number One. One. Number One. Say 'One.'"

The girls pulled closer together. Their baggy pajamas looked like one garment and they like a four-headed person. The biggest girl snapped at Print and the spoon that he was pointing at them.

Print leaned back. "Oh, no. Take 'er easy. I ain't gonna harm you. We might just be stuck with one another for a while, so we gottta figger out some way of talkin'."

He noticed the big girl, who hadn't taken her eyes off the spoon. He quit pointing it at them. He held up his other hand, palm toward them. He modulated his voice. "This must be a pretty scary deal for y'all. I don't know what yer story is, but if you was in the company of a sack a shit, I'm sure it wasn't good."

He shifted his position and the girls cringed. He kneeled on his right leg, crossing his forearms and resting them on his raised left knee, the wooden spoon pointed toward the ground. He paused, hoping that if he went slowly, they might start trying to listen to him rather than act as if he were going to harm them. He relaxed his face and smiled slightly, even though the kneeling position was already starting to bother him. He took a breath and sighed. "I know ya can't understan' a word I'm sayin', so let's start again. Yer Number One."

He pointed to the littlest girl on his left. He held up his index finger and repeated himself. He said the word "One" slowly. "Yer Number One. One … One … One … "

The girls looked at one another and then back at him.

"Com' on now. You can do it. One … One. Yer a smart little girl. One. Just gimme a 'One' one time."

The little girl moved her head a little closer to him. "Ong."

"There ya go. One. Yer Number One," he said, nodding his head. He smiled at her and she almost smiled.

He turned his face to the second girl. "Now yer Number Two. How 'bout it? Gimme a Two. … Two … Two," holding up two fingers each time he repeated himself.

The little girl on his left managed a tentative "Twu."

"No, no. Yer Number One, she's Number Two," he said, changing fingers each time.

The big girl started talking excitedly to the others. She nodded her head vigorously. She was explaining to the others what it was that Print was trying to do. She spoke rapidly, mostly out of fear, Print thought.

"There ya go. You listen ta her. Yer One an' yer Two."

He pointed to the big girl. "Now yer gonna be Number Three. One … Two … an' Three."

She repeated the words out loud. "Ong … Twu … Tree."

"That'll do 'er. An you, little cherry blossom, are gonna be Number Four. That's right. Four. One, Two, Three, an' Four."

The last girl reacted violently to Print when he held up four fingers.

"He is giving us numbers for names, that is all. It means nothing," the big girl, Number Three, said to the last girl.

"No. No. Four is the number of death. No."

"It is only a word. It mean nothing to us here. Be brave."

"No. It is death."

Print had no idea what was going on but let them talk it out. Number Three turned to him and held up her hand with her thumb and fingers spread wide.

"Oh. She don't wanna be Four? No problem. We'll make her Number Five. Five … Five." He held up his hand with all fingers spread. Number Five nodded excitedly.

"Fii ... Fii."

"Sure. She can be Number Five, and when Tom brings her li'l sister back, we'll make her Number Four. So, let's get this right. One ... Two ... Three ... an' Five. Now get it right or I'm gonna paint numbers on yer backs."

Print tried to rise, pushing off his left knee. It was a struggle, as his other leg had gone to sleep. He grunted and staggered slightly. The girls reacted in fear. He righted himself and turned and walked back to the fire. Using the spoon as a baton, he called out to himself, "One, Two, Three, Four, an' Five."

He tossed the last of the wood on the fire and kicked a piece that missed with his bootless foot. "Now that we all know one another, there's work ta be done."

CHAPTER ELEVEN

The temperature continued to drop and Tom felt the sting of snow flurries on his face as he rode into the wind. He had cut for sign early on and had picked up the trail not far from camp.

Fender didn't care much about being followed, or he didn't know how to cover his tracks.

They had set a good pace in the beginning but had slacked off. Tom assumed that Fender had tired of the sobering aspects of hard riding or thought that no one would come after him. Rats can be cunning, but they aren't always smart, he thought. There was no way he was going to lose that money, and then there was Billy. He had held his thoughts when Print took him on. It was too early on the trail to start crossing swords with his uncle. But Billy had turned out to be okay. He was a good hand, just like he said he was, and he hadn't been any trouble. Actually Tom was getting used to getting more sleep at night. He was like a working dog, always out on the edge, doing his job. You didn't have to talk to him much, but when you did, it was short and usually pleasant, depending on how the wind was blowing. He remembered what the cowboy had said to them about Billy: "There's some things that just wasn't intended to live." That may be, thought Tom, but it ain't up to no cowboy nor no shit-bird Fender to make that call.

◎ ◎ ◎

Print had put the girls to work gathering rocks to help cover the dead boy. He was going to wrap him up in his bedroll but decided that it would be better used for the girls, as it seemed that Fender had provided nothing in the way of bedding for them.

He had gone through Billy's belongings to see if there was any clue to a family that might want to know what happened to him. He found nothing other than a small leather-bound Book of Common Prayer. It was frayed and wrapped with a string to keep it together. Inside was a handwritten inscription:

> To William V. McKay
> From his grandparents
> Marshall Johnson
> Ellen DeButts Johnson
> Malvern, Arkansas 1887

On the facing page, written in a different handwriting, was scrawled,

> There abides in us faith, hope, love, these three; but the greatest of these is love.

He was a sweet boy, Print thought. There had been many kind and thoughtful lads back in Virginia. Like Billy, they had been maimed and blown apart and wrecked. Like Billy, they had learned to live a different way. To sign their name with their other hand. Or turn the plow at the end of the furrow with only one arm. To put on pants that only half of you filled. And to go on as best a ruined and damaged lad could.

At least they had given him a chance. He would make inquiries when they got to Sheridan. He fashioned a cross out of two sticks and placed pebbles at the foot of the grave that spelled out Billy Via. He knew it wouldn't last, but then, what did? Maybe an Egyptian pyramid. Maybe not even that.

The front was really bearing down, and he turned his attention to getting more wood, as he had no idea how long Tom might be gone. In this matter the girls were as tractable and willing as they had been in gathering rocks. He threw up a picket line for the mules and piled green juniper along the windward side of the wagon for protection. He had the girls snug it up with small limbs of long-needle pine. He slipped on an extra pair of heavy woolen socks, as his toes were starting to feel numb. It seemed to him that although the girls were not gleeful, they did appear more relaxed. Keeping them busy seemed to help.

The flurries had turned into a full blow. The change in weather was not surprising for this country, but it was a damn nuisance when tracking, especially wearing someone else's boots that didn't fit. Tom tightened the stampede string on his hat to keep it in place. Fender's trail edged around a butte that was in its last millionth-year disintegration. Scattered ponderosa ringed its base. Tom was staring at a fresh pile of horse manure that still gave off a little steam. Tom dismounted, took out his carbine, and proceeded on foot. He was careful, even though the wind muffled his approach. He walked around the lee side of the hill to where the wind kicked up again. In a small stand of evergreens he saw horses tied, their butts to the wind. Beside them was a sheer rock outcropping, about twenty feet tall. The snow was blowing left to right and cut way down on visibility. Tom tied his horse to a fat juniper bush and walked on. As he got closer, he could make out figures lying on the ground. One lay on top of the other. He was ten yards from them before he could hear the girl's sobbing over the wind.

The grunting Fender dug tracks in the snow with Tom's boots as he tried to get a better position on top of the struggling Chinese girl. She cried out in pain, and that excited him even more. His feet slipped in the snow. He tried to gain more traction. His lip curled upward and his eyes rolled back in his head at the very moment that he felt the cold barrel of the Remington pressed against the base of his skull.

◎ ◎ ◎

Print, with the help of the girls, had gotten the camp pretty well buttoned down. There was a good pile of wood and a vigorous fire going. He had made a stew of beans, flour, and cut-up jerky. He had tried to interest the girls in it, but they seemed to prefer the rice that Number Three had made. He had found a piece of tarp in Fender's wagon and had placed it around the girls to try keep the wind off them. Always wary, they took the canvas and pulled it close about themselves.

"Wonder if y'all get snow in yer part of China? This ain't unusual a'tall. Sweatin' one day, freezin' the next. It won't last. T'morrow it'll be gone an' sunny again. ... One ... Two ... Three ... Five," he said, pointing to each girl.

The girls repeated their new names.

Print stoked the fire and added pine boughs to the side of the wagon to protect against the wind. The girls watched and talked quietly.

Number One asked the oldest, Sun Foy, where she thought the other man went. Sun Foy thought he had gone to get Ye Fung back and that they should do nothing to make these men mad. *"This old man has fed us and kept us warm, but none of them are to be trusted."*

When Tom reached down and grabbed Fender by his collar and yanked him halfway to his feet, the girl rolled away and scrambled into the gathering darkness. He let Fender hang, suspended, thrashing about and gagging for air. He looked to see where the girl had gone, so he didn't see the knife Fender had pulled and then tried to plunge into Tom's thigh. Because he didn't have any footing, his aim was off and the blade cut across Tom's front leg. It was a wicked weapon and sliced through the leather chaps and cut deep into the meat of his leg. He dropped Fender, who took another swipe at Tom, missing, and nearly stabbing himself. Tom brought the butt of the Remington down on Fender's face, between his upper lip and nose. It knocked Fender senseless. He coughed up blood and a badly rotted tooth. Tom kicked the dropped knife away and placed his boot heel on the side of Fender's jaw. He put his weight into it and turned his heel until he heard Fender's mandible snap.

⊚ ⊚ ⊚

Print ladled water out of the wooden keg strapped to the side of the wagon to thin out his stew into something more like soup and arbitrarily spooned it over the girls' rice. They watched in silence.

"Go on. Eat up. Eat. I got no idea a what ta do with little Mongolian girls from the Celestial Empire an' sure won't know what ta do if ya get sick on me. Don't care if it don't appeal ta ya. Go on, eat."

He looked at them staring at him. He pantomimed eating. Snowflakes landed in their black hair and then melted. A drop of water ran down Number Five's brow. Whether Tom got their money back or not, this was a hell of a deal that he had gotten them in and it was going to take more than jerky stew to get them out if it.

◎ ◎ ◎

As Fender curled up in a ball on the ground, gargling and whimpering at the same time, Tom bound his long bandanna around his thigh, which was oozing a good flow of blood. Fender turned his head to look up at Tom. Blood bubbled from both corners of his mouth. His lower jaw was offset and gave him the appearance of a man who had suffered a stroke. He made nonsensical noises. The burning feeling from Tom's leg wound was already turning into a sickening ache. Fender reached out to grab the bottom of Tom's chaps. He whined gibberish. Tom pulled his leg away and brought the heel of his boot down on Fender's wrist. Fender screamed and choked.

Tom limped off in the direction of the girl. He found her crouching at the far end of the rock. She was shaking violently from fear and the biting wind. He removed his coat and stepped toward her. She pulled back, and he knew she was going to bolt on him. He heard Fender groveling where he had left him. The captain was searching the ground for his knife, or maybe a sidearm, Tom thought. He dropped his coat on the ground and limped back to Fender.

"You so much as twitch and I'll stake you to the ground."

Fender whimpered and cursed at the same time. Tom returned to the girl. He picked up the coat and carefully extended it to her. She made no move. He let it fall at her feet. He stepped over to Fender.

"Get your coat off."

Fender blubbered.

"Get it off and my boots too."

Fender managed to squirm out of the coat but could

not pull off the boots, as the hand that Tom had stomped on was no longer working. Tom bent down, grasped a boot heel, and tugged. Off came one and then the other. He reached down and removed Fender's leather belt. He secured it over the bandanna, which was soaked.

"The money belt."

Fender pointed to his chest. Tom ripped open the front of Fender's shirt, unbuckled the belt, pulled it out, and slung it over his shoulder. He looked back at the girl. She had put the coat around her. It was now almost dark as Tom rolled Fender over onto his stomach, facedown. He walked back to where he had tied his horse. The belt had slipped and he tightened it more. He led his horse back to Fender and the girl. He removed his rope and played out a small loop from the hondo. He slipped it over Fender's head and tightened it around his neck. Fender squealed and frantically turned to face Tom. Tom pushed his face back into the dirt. He flung the rest of the rope over the rock face. He led his horse away. Fender tried to see what was going on without moving his head. Tom walked around to the other side of the rock and picked up the rope. In the darkness he saw a stout aspen sapling. He walked the rope around the tree and back to his horse. He dallied the rope around the horn of the saddle and snugged it tight.

He led the horse away from the rock, and Fender felt the line tighten and then start to pull him. First toward the rock, and then up. He flailed about, clawing at his neck. The rope tightened against his own weight. His eyes bulged. He couldn't even gag. Snot and blood came out of his nose. A thick blue-black tongue stuck out of his mouth. Tom moved the horse slowly. He didn't want to snap Fender's neck. The taunt rope jumped at Fender's movements. He patted the horse's neck, making sure he would stand, and then limped to the edge of the rock and looked down. Fender was quickly starting to fade. He kicked and the soles of his feet slapped the ground. Tom went back to his horse and had him take two steps forward, leaving Fender completely airborne. Tom stroked the horse's neck with one hand and held the other on the taunt rope, feeling the vibrations lessen to naught. He slackened the rope around the saddle horn and finally tossed it to the ground. He led the horse back around. Fender sat like a child's doll, legs splayed out in front, head cocked to the left and slightly down. His face was the color of raw liver. One eye bulged almost out of its socket.

Tom picked up Fender's coat and walked over to the girl. He tried to trade his coat for Fender's, as the dead man's was much too small for him to wear, but the girl was having none of it. In the end, he took the blanket from under the saddle on Billy's horse, which Fender had stolen, and got her to wrap herself in it and give Tom his coat back. He resaddled the horse and got her up on it. He knew that without the blanket, the saddle would probably gall the horse on its withers and back, but he figured it would have time to heal before they got to Sheridan. He mounted, grabbed the lead rope on the girl's horse. He looked back at her. She was cold and shaking, but at least she was alive, he thought. He walked past Fender the rag doll at the base of the sheer rock.

"Dance now, you son of a bitch."

◎ ◎ ◎

Like many of these spring snowstorms, it put on a good show but never really amounted to much. As Tom led the horse and girl back to his uncle's camp, the wind was still howling, but the snow was easing up.

He dismounted and limped over to the wagon. The fire was all but gone. He helped the girl off the horse. On the lee side of the wagon was a snow-covered canvas tarp that covered a large pile. He kicked the pile. He kicked it again.

Print pulled down an edge of the tarp. "Tom? You all right, boy?"

"What ya doin', Uncle Print?"

"Hell, I'm tryin' ta stay warm, son. What're you doin'?"

Tom tossed a pair of boots on the tarp. Print pulled the cover down farther, revealing the heads of several of the girls.

"Returnin' the loan of yer boots."

Their voices woke the other girls, who peered out and saw the shivering girl beside Tom. They started talking, and Number Three slid out from under the tarp and went to the freezing girl. She talked excitedly to her and led her back under the canvas covering.

Print saw the blood-soaked chaps. "Want me ta take a look at that?"

"I packed it in snow. I want to sleep."

"Well, crawl in here. The herd ain't goin' anywhere tonight."

CHAPTER TWELVE

A trickle of water ran down a crease in the canvas. Snow was melting in the morning sunlight. Summer had returned, and you could hear driblets of melting snow everywhere. Tom pulled back the canvas and closed his eyes to the bright sun. He smelled the wood smoke and the bacon. He raised up and immediately felt the dull ache in his leg turn to a stabbing pain. Print was squatting by the fire and looked over at him.

"You're lookin' a little peak'd, Nephew."

Print rose and walked over to Tom, who sank back in his bedroll, covering his eyes with his forearm. He felt clammy and hoped that he wasn't getting a fever.

"Made a poultice fer your leg. First let's skin them chaps off ya."

The belt Tom had put on had slipped loose in the night. He untied the bloody kerchief. Print grabbed the bottom of each leg as Tom undid the buckle. Tom winced as Print jerked the chaps off and kneeled down for a closer look. He poked his finger into the sliced pants and long underwear. He ripped both for a better look. He poured water from a canteen over the wound, which started to bleed a little. From his tin cup he swiped a big glob of gray grease and swabbed it on liberally with two fingers.

"Made a poultice outta Slippery Elm, some fire ash, an' bacon grease. Wish I had som' bayberry or comfrey, but this'll do. Wound's not deep enough to stitch up. 'Sides, you'd probably rip 'em out anyway, ridin'."

"This ain't gonna lay me up."

It was a question as much as an answer.

"No, but it's lucky the captain left us a wagon. You can drive that for the next couple a days."

"What about the herd?"

"I'll work the herd. You bring up the rear. We'll go slow. It shouldn't be a problem. Thing is, I don't want this to turn sour on you. Give it a couple a days' rest. Let's get ya on your feet."

Print extended a hand to Tom and pulled him up. He helped him over to the fire. He eased Tom down to a sitting position. The girls were busy gathering more wood. Except for the girl Tom had brought back in the night. The girl that would soon be called Number Four. She sat across the fire from Tom. She made no eye contact. Tom sipped coffee.

"Did she eat this morning?"

"Not much. None of 'em much, 'cept for rice, an' it looks like we're gonna give out on that soon. Naw. She didn't eat hardly anythin'."

Print handed a plate of food to Tom. "Was he sober?"

"What?"

"Capt'n Fender, was he sober? 'Member, he said, 'If ya sin when yer drunk, y'll pay when yer sober.'"

Tom blew on the cup of coffee. He was looking over at the girl. "Sober enough."

The girls returned with wood and dumped it on the pile beside Tom. He looked at them, and they looked at him. Mostly his blood-soaked pant leg.

"Ya ain't been introduced."

Again pointing with the wooden spoon, this time at Tom, "This here's Tom … Tom … Tom. Come on, now. Say, 'Tom.' Tom."

Little Number Five, the girl with the bound feet said, "Tahm."

"Ther' ya go. Tom."

The other girls mouthed the word. Number Four was silent and seemed unconcerned with what was going on.

"This here's Number One, Number Two, Three, an' Number Five.

"The little one you brought back is gonna be Number Four, but I think we'll wait a day or so ta work on that. Think the big on', Three, is the one that's in charge."

"What do they call you?"

Print turned to the girls and thumped his chest with the spoon. More or less in unison, they said, "Honkle Pren."

"So, whatta ya think?"

Tom looked up from his plate. He laid it beside him on the ground. He reached and got the coffeepot and poured a cup. "I go and get our money and horses back, and had to stretch a man to do it, an' you've gone and set up a school for Chinese girls."

Tom reached inside his shirt and pulled out Print's money belt and tossed it to him. Print picked it up and looked down at his nephew. The smile on his face was gone.

"You all right, kid?"

"Yeah. Sure, I'm all right. Had to leave my rope back there."

"Man like that ain't worth the food he eats, much less the price of a decent rope."

Tom nodded and sipped his coffee.

CHAPTER THIRTEEN

A chipmunk scooted up a ponderosa at the sound of the approaching horses. From a limb, he gnawed on a small grasshopper as the herd passed by. They had struck camp, with Tom driving the wagon. The girls rode in the back, and Print led the herd slowly. Sometimes he would drift over to the left flank and press the horses in on themselves. Then he'd ease back to the front and later repeat the process on the right flank. Because of the snow the night before, the wagon wasn't subject to drifting dust.

Print was back on Bob Tate. He was more than a little relieved that Tom had made it back. The lad was lucky. The wound was the kind that could go septic easily if not tended to. He was glad his nephew had retrieved the best horse he'd had in the last twenty years.

He had had a dream that night, with the girls all huddled up under the canvas. He had dreamed of her. Ann Blackwell. Ann Cetia Blackwell. Actually he had dreamed of the little girl, and Ann came and went in the dream. It was mostly about the little girl, and like all dreams, it was vague. Not all dreams, he thought. Some were so real and profound that they hung about him for days. But this one was vague. He hardly ever even remembered his dreams anymore. The little girl stood on a porch of a house. But the house was his papa's house back in Virginia, and that couldn't be. She wore little black button-up shoes, and he had brought her a zebra pony for her birthday, and that couldn't be right either. Ann came out of the house and took the girl inside. He could tell she didn't want to go. He could tell that Ann was not happy with him. He didn't think she had ever really been happy with him, but maybe she had never been happy, period. Happiness was too elusive a thing to spend your life trying to chase, he thought. But he did think of the little girl with curly auburn hair. In the dream, she went to the window to see him and the zebra pony. Her mother came up behind her and led her away from the window.

A zebra pony. He shook his head. No wonder he hardly remembered his dreams anymore.

At the noon rest, they ate biscuits from the morning and jerky. Tom got down from the wagon to limp off and relieve himself. When he returned, Number Three was sitting up in the front of the wagon.

"Thought ya might give 'er her a lesson on drivin' the wagon. Hopefully you'll be back on yer horse in a day or so. Som'body's gotta drive."

Tom struggled to get on board with his stiff leg. He held a biscuit between his teeth and took the reins in his hands.

"Remember, she's Number Three, the jigger boss of this sorority. I think she'll do pretty much whatever ya show her."

The mules started up and rocked the girl backward. Tom put his arm behind her and nodded for her to repeat what he had done. She did, and again the mules moved forward; this time they kept moving. He removed his arm from her back and let her go. He could hear the girls behind him, talking. Number Three said, *"Be quiet and pay attention. Pay attention to everything."* The mules drifted off to the left, and Tom took her right hand and showed her just how much she needed to correct them. He looked over his shoulder and saw that the girls in the back were watching him, except for the girl he brought back from Fender. She was curled up, as if asleep.

The afternoon was hot, and that kept the herd at a

slow pace. All traces of the snow were gone and the footing was good. The girl drove the mules with a look of concentration on her face. If she saw a good-sized piece of wood, she would bark to the girls and either Number One or Number Two would jump out of the back of the wagon and retrieve it. Running beside the wagon, she would toss it into the cooney that was slung beneath the wagon. With the help of the other girl, she would climb back on board. Number Five, the little one with the bound feet, couldn't participate, and Number Four spent the day sleeping.

They camped late in the afternoon, so the herd could graze on good, hard grass that they came upon. Tom forced himself to walk around on his stiff leg. The girls helped with the firewood and even hauled water from a nearby creek. Print took the shotgun and put a handful of shells in his vest pocket. He slipped out of his chaps.

"Think I'll scare up somethin' for the pot tonight. How's the leg doin'?"

"It's sore as hell but mostly stiff."

"Well, don't walk on it too much. Ya gotta give it time ta granulate."

With his leg straight out in front of him, Tom lowered himself down and finally plopped on the ground. Print, carrying the shotgun in the crook of his arm, walked off away from the herd and the camp.

He walked along the side of the creek, feeling stiff himself. They had pitched camp on the west bank of Sailor Creek, and he was trying to calculate how far they had ridden since that first camp on the north shore of Malheur Lake when a pair of wood ducks beat it out of a line of gooseberry bushes beside the creek. It startled him and he broke open the shotgun and slipped two shells into the barrels.

He had figured that they must have covered close to two hundred miles so far, and things were going all right. Well, except for that fella Fender and now these five little girls on their hands. And there was Tom's sliced-up leg. Still, he felt confident that they were making good time and that luck was on their side.

A pair of doves flew up and then landed in a persimmon tree. He raised the gun and walked toward the tree. The doves took flight, and Print led them with the gun. He fired. One, then two. He retrieved the birds and stuck them in his left vest pocket.

Print continued along the bank, flushing another pair of doves and bagging one of them. He found the birds in some willows. He took his knife and pared green bark from the willow until he had two handfuls. He picked another handful of buds from the slender tips and he stuffed it into an empty sack of tobacco makings.

He walked out of the cover and turned to make a wide loop back to camp. Walking through knee-high grass, Print flushed a grouse and took it on his second shot. He found the bird easily, as it wasn't dead and flopped about in the grass. He gave it a quick twist of the neck. Print broke down the shotgun and extracted the two empty shells and put them in a pocket. He cradled the gun in one arm and carried the grouse by the feet in the other. He backtracked to the willows and cut three long pieces as big around as his thumb, and then headed back to camp.

He returned to find the camp set up and a good bed of coals for cooking. "How's some bird meat for supper sound?"

Tom had been washing the wound and bloody pants with a pan of warm water and his cleaned kerchief. He straightened up at Print's approach. "Sounds good. There's not much in the way of food that I won't eat."

"Would that include deep-fried grasshoppers?"

"That I might pass on, thank you."

"Considered a delicacy when cooked in buffalo marrow."

"No, thanks. What did ya get?"

"Couple a birds an' a grouse. Got some stuff ta help

with that leg," he said, pointing to the stained pant leg.

"I got it pretty well cleaned up."

"Now don't be doin' too much cleanin'. The body's got its own medicine for such things. I did get some willow ta make you a tea, though."

Print kneeled and took the empty coffeepot and ladled water into it from the water bucket beside the fire. He set the pot on the coals to heat and took the little sack out of his pocket. He unknotted his kerchief and spread it out on the ground. He sprinkled the contents of the tobacco sack on it and pushed the bark shavings and buds about with his finger. He tossed a handful into a tin cup and waited for the water to boil.

"What's been goin' on here?"

"Not much. Can't figure out how I can sit on a horse all day with no problem but sit on the ground for an hour and my ass aches."

"One of the unanswered mysteries of life."

"Nothing in your book reading to shed some light on it?"

"Nope. How're the girls doin'?"

"They're keeping themselves busy. 'Cept for the one I brought back. She's in pretty rough shape, if ya ask me. He was forkin' the hell outta her when I came up on them. He must have knocked her around too."

"Maybe I'll give her some tea too," he said, reaching for the pot.

"She'll need more than roots and hot water."

"She come from the country of tea drinkers. Give 'er time. She'll sort it out."

He poured the water into the cup and swirled it around. He set the cup down and prepared another cup and did the same. "Here, drink this down, but don't toss out the dregs."

"This tastes awful," said Tom, taking a sip.

"So's blood poisonin' an' gangrene. Just drink 'er down."

Print rose and took a cup of the brew over to the wagon to where Number Four lay. He gently shook her foot and she jumped. He extended the cup to her. She looked at him. He nodded yes and reached closer. She took the cup and he backed off and walked over to Tom.

"That's good medicine yer drinkin' there, son. Cleans the blood, mends the flesh, an' eases the pain."

"When did you find time to fit in being a doctor al'ng with punchin' cows and book reading?"

"I learned it from your grandma. She knew all about the roots an' barks. Berries, nuts, an' thistles too. There was a time when that's all ya had. Not like today, with all the modern medicine ya got now. No, sir. She made teas an' salves, poultices an' syrups, balms an' pomades. Made 'em outta ever'thin' from bear grease ta beeswax."

Tom took another sip and grimaced. "Was that my ma's ma?"

"Yep. A fine ol' Huguenot gal. Her kin came over by way of Alsace, France."

"Ma told me they came from Pennsylvania."

"They did, once they got ta America. They was a long line of carpenters. Found there was calling for well-built barns. They built barns all over Pennsylvania. Then they drifted south, comin' down the Shenandoah. Couple of generations an' they'd worked their way down the valley."

Print gutted and dressed the birds as he talked. Feathers and down swirled in the light breeze. "Your grandad was working at a sawmill over by Piper's Gap. They sent him with a wagonload a timber ta where the Bouchees was puttin' up a barn. That's where he first saw Miss Juliett Bouchee. Well, that was all it took. Just the sight a her sunk the hook in Reuben Ritter, an' 'fore you know it, she had him buildin' a fine log house. His future brothers-in-law helped him. It was as right an' tight as any barn they ever built. Right in the shadow of Beamer's Nob, they started makin' a family. They was good at it too. They had ten children."

Print skewered the doves on the green willow sticks and ran two sticks through the grouse.

"Four of 'em died at birth or as infants. But four boys an' two girls made it. There was Nimrod, Levi, Mason, and me. On the girl's side, there was your ma, Julie Bouchee Ritter, and Haney Louise Ritter. Your ma was the baby of the family."

Print got up and planted the sticks into the ground, leaning over the fire. He added another stick and waved to the girls to come over. Number Three came to him and he handed her the bucket and motioned to the creek. She nodded and took the bucket.

Soon they were eating, although the girls still were shy about the food. They were careful when eating the doves. Print and Tom had no problem putting an end to the grouse, along with beans and biscuits.

"How did they meet?"

Print put his plate aside and brought out the whiskey bottle. "Medicine for you," he said, and then, lifting the bottle, "Medicine fer me."

"I'm not exactly sure how they met. Yer daddy was from over to Floyd County. But I believe his people were from somewheres on the New River. He may have been workin' for the brothers-in-law, buildin' barns. Same thing happened ta him as old Reuben. He saw your ma, and that was pretty much it. Those Bouchee women all made their fiancés build 'em a nest 'fore they walked down the aisle. It helped ta have relatives that was carpenters if you were plannin' to seriously court a Bouchee gal. Even one that was half Ritter. They was practical in all things."

Print drained his cup and rose. "Think ya can orchestrate gettin' the dishes done? I'm gonna check on the horses."

He walked among the horses until he found the flea-bitten gray. The one that Tom had already said he wanted to keep for himself. He checked her hobbles and that of the two other mares that were always near her. He walked slowly through the herd to the other side. The pace they had been going at was working out well. The horses were good and tired at the end of the day but were in good flesh, and other than a couple of gimpy ones, all were sound.

Print breathed in the night air, unbuttoned his pants, and relieved himself. He walked on around the perimeter of the grazing herd. The moon hadn't come up yet and the night sky was brilliant with stars. The same sky he had been looking at for over sixty years, and still he never tired of watching it.

He saw a log that had once been a ponderosa that some west wind had long since pushed over. He sat down and took out his pipe and tobacco. He paused and softly whistled a few bars of "The Maid of Fife" to make sure the horses were aware it was him and then struck the match. He cupped it quickly and sucked on the pipe.

Print mused about his earlier conversation with Tom. He sometimes forgot how much family history he knew. There had been little call from anyone to repeat it. He had gone for what seemed like years without thinking about the family and his youth. It was sure a different world he came into than the one he would be leaving. Even now, this was so far away from the steps of the courthouse in Galax, where he and other country lads had volunteered when called. There were plenty of hot speeches, but not all were so ready to leave families behind and farms that would have to be tended to by women and younger children. Even in his family, there had been arguments for and against.

The pipe had gone out and he relit it. He listened to a bobwhite and the peepers down by the creek. The same kind of sounds as back home, but this surely wasn't Carroll

County, Virginia. He smoked the last of the pipe, then tamped it on the log. He ran his little finger around the bowl and tamped it again.

CHAPTER FOURTEEN

Print woke up the next morning to find that little Number Five sometime in the night had dragged her bedroll over and curled up next to him. He carefully slipped out of his bedroll. The morning light was just coming up as Tom limped over to the fire.

"Horses sure are falling into the routine."

"Sure they are, an' that's good now that we're back to two men. Probably should have taken on another hand back at the Malheur. Wasn't countin' on the extra company."

"Glad you brought it up. What are we going to do with them?" Tom said, nodding in the direction of the sleeping girls.

"I been thinkin' about it. We need to get them ta some proper authorities that are set up ta handle such things, 'cuz we sure ain't."

"Any idea where and when that might be?"

"We'll need to reprovision soon enough. Probably then, why?"

"Well, they sure are a drag on our goal to get this herd to Sheridan."

"Son, if they was five ladies from Canyon City, you an' me'd be about ready ta slit our own throats just ta get away from the gagglin' an' prattle that would be goin' on. No, sir, these little ones are pretty easy on the nerves."

"I'll feel better when we find a place to leave 'em and get back to the job at hand."

"Well, of course ya do. So do I. Until that time, it's no

use in takin' it out on them."

"Sure," said Tom, tossing the dregs of his coffee.

"Here, put this on yer leg couple times a day, but don't mess wit' the wound too much. Just let nature an' yer grandma's medicine do their work."

Print handed Tom a tin cup. Tom sniffed the contents.

"Mostly bacon drippin's an' mashed-up willow buds."

They were on the move and the weather held. Good now, thought Print, but it could go dry on us and there was a lot of distance between the herd and Sheridan. Number Three took to the driving, and in little more than a week, Tom was back in the saddle, although he did spend the first few afternoons back in the wagon. Again the land was changing as they bumped along the country of southern Idaho, past the Sawtooth, and south of the Twin Falls.

The crossings were mostly creeks, which were easy enough, and the one river, the Clover, had been down, so it was easy too. All the time they kept edging slightly north, getting closer to the Oregon Trail, which Print had traveled west on so long ago. They forded Goose Creek and pushed on for the Raft. They arrived late in the afternoon and found their side of the crossing occupied by a large flock of sheep. There was a round sheepherders' wagon with a piece of stovepipe sticking out of the top. Several men walked along the edges of the flock.

Print gigged the red roan into a lope, heading him toward the sheep. He was giving Bob Tate more time off; as he felt the grind of the trip, he knew that the horse was too. He was the only horse that Print was really interested in riding anymore, and he tended to forget that the big chestnut could get just as bone weary as himself.

As he neared the flock, he brought the roan down to a trot and then to a walk. Hearing his approach, one of the shepherds turned and started walking toward Print. He walked with a staff and wore a sheepskin vest, woolly side out. A shapeless felt hat covered a face the color of a cured ham. A week's growth of silver stubble stood out against the darkened face.

"Afternoon," said Print as he brought the roan to a stop and made him stand still.

"And to you, too," replied the herder.

He grinned and showed a mouthful of very white teeth. Now that's what I like in a fella, thought Print. This here's a man that what's on his face, ya know is in his heart.

"You local boys or just passin' through?"

"Heading north," replied the shepherd, pointing with his staff.

"Comin' up from Old Mexico?"

The old man laughed and shook his head. "No, from Navarra."

Print cocked his head as if to think about the man's reply.

"Navarra. Navarra, Spain. We are Basque. Sheepmen."

He extended his hand up to Print, who leaned forward to grasp it.

"Valinten Ugalde."

"Print Ritter. Pleased ta meet ya, Mr. Valentine. How's the trail east ta here?" he said as he sat back in the saddle.

"We are heading north. We were told in Almo that there is trouble with some Utes and Paiutes that have left the reservation. I cannot afford to lose my sheep. ... I would not go farther east, especially with such fine-looking horses."

"Hard ta believe that there's still any around that want to start trouble."

The old man shrugged. "It is very dry to the south. Worse than dry. From Elko to Wells and almost all the way to here."

"Thanks for the advice. Say, Mr. Valentine, ya think ya

might sell me one of them sheep? We're kinda played out on rabbit these days."

The old man smiled and pointed back to the flock. "Perhaps you would like lamb rather than mutton."

"Even better."

The old man pointed his finger at Print. "You buy the lamb and I will cook it for you. We are going to camp here for the night. And you?"

Print looked up, beyond the sheep, and then back at the old man.

"I was thinkin' the same thing. We'll move up a ways. The horses have been a breeze so far, but ya never know."

The old man nodded in agreement, and Print turned the roan and trotted back to Tom, who had stopped the herd and was waiting on Print.

"Basque. Come up from the south. Say there's problems with some Utes and Paiutes. Recommends we change course. Says it's parched an' pretty well blowed out all the way down ta Elko."

A big greenhead fly landed on the rump of Tom's horse. It swished its tail, but the fly didn't move.

"Tomorrow let's point 'em more ta the north and we'll tie in ta the south fork of the Oregon."

Tom nodded at the same time his horse put in a half-hearted buck to dislodge the fly. Tom kept his seat, ignored the buck, and reached behind him to swipe the fly away.

"I told the old man we'd put 'em up ta the left. Don't know about you, but I'm lookin' forward to some lamb."

They made their camp between the horses and the flock of sheep. Tom got the girls to haul water to replenish the water keg on the wagon while he tended to the horses and Print made a pot of beans. He noticed how covered with dust and tired the girls looked. Number Four seemed to be coming around a bit.

"Tom, tell those girls that this is a good place to bathe

an' wash up. There's good water in the shallows."

"Uncle, how am I suppose to convey that thought to them?"

"Well, son, I had 'em named an' numbered in a snap. I am sure you can figger out how ta get yer point across."

Tom shook his head and picked up the wooden bucket. He felt self-conscious and just plain stupid calling them by their numbered names. But it didn't seem to bother his uncle or the girls.

"Hey, you. You, Number Three. Yeah, you. All of you," he said, gesturing with both of his arms. "Come and follow me. I'm gonna show you where to take a bath."

Number Two and Three looked at him. Little Number Five and Number One stood up. The littlest girl shuffled toward him with her tiny feet.

"Take a bar of that brown soap and som' of that muslin that I bought for Billy."

Tom retrieved the items from the wagon, which they were now using to stow their gear.

He turned to the girls, who were now standing. "Well, come on." He gestured and started to lead them to the water. He shortened his steps to allow them to keep up with him.

He walked upstream, out of sight of the camp. Twice he had to tell them to keep going, as they grew apprehensive and hung back. He found a spot that had a small sandbar and was set back from the faster moving water. Willows hung over the bank and made a natural screen. He walked out onto the sandbar.

He turned to the girls. "Come on. This is a good enough spot ta wash up."

Again he gestured to them. They stood all in a row, watching him. He pantomimed washing and scooping water up and drying off. He placed the bucket in the sand along with the soap and muslin.

He stepped over the two feet of water that separated the bank from the bar. He reached for Number Five, who pulled back.

"Now don't be like that. I ain't gonna hurt ya. Come here."

He picked her up, her eyes wide open, more from surprise than fear, and with one foot on the bank and the other on the sandbar, he turned and placed her down. He turned and offered a helping hand to Number Three. She waited a moment and then took it and stepped over. One, Two, and Four followed.

He stepped back on the bank and turned to face them. He talked and gestured at the same time. "You go on an' wash up. I'm gonna go back to the wagon. I'll come back an' fetch you."

He remembered Fender saying that they was "dumb as dirt at understanding English." Maybe they didn't understand English, but they wasn't dumb, and he felt that they did understand what he was trying to tell them. He started back for the camp. He turned back, and looking directly at the oldest one, said, "Now you have any problems or get scare't, you just holler."

He held his hands to his mouth. He turned and stepped through the willows and walked back to camp.

"Mai Ling, help me with her bandages," said Sun Foy to Number Two as she knelt to help Ghing Wa. She removed the special slippers from the little girl's feet.

The shepherd and Print were busy preparing dinner. Valinten had the lamb on a spit and was basting it. Print was working on a second round of biscuits to cover the additional guests and had a pot brimming with beans and a generous application of dried sliced apples. He had found a currant shrub not far from the water and had added several handfuls of golden currants.

"Nephew, we're goin' ta dine tonight. I have fallen in

with a fellow disciple of gastronomy. Like me, he's one of the wanderin' kind."

The smiling Basque looked up from his basting of the lamb. "Do you share your uncle's taste for lamb?" asked the shepherd.

"Oh, I'll eat pert near anything," replied Tom.

"Now see there, Valentine, that's the work I got cut out for myself, to educate this lad's mind an' his palate 'fore we get to Sheridan."

Tom leaned in close on the lamb that the shepherd turned slowly. "You'd think all I ate was pinecone an' buffalo chips ta listen to him. I know what good food tastes like when I get it in my mouth."

"Well, yer gonna get yer chance tonight. Though ya might have stayed with the girls."

"They wasn't gonna do no bathing with me even in earshot of them."

"How 'bout a short snort, Mr. Valentine? An' the other sheep fellas too?" asked Print as he produced his bottle.

"Only if you let me return the money you paid for the lamb. I cannot accept such generosity and money," he said as he took the tin cup from Print.

"We'll talk about that after supper."

Print poured into all the men's cups. He lifted his to toast them. "Confusion to our enemies."

The men drank from their cups, the sheepherders not sure what to make of Print's toast.

Print recharged their cups as they settled down around the fire. "How's that lamb comin' along, Mr. Valentine?"

"Not yet, but soon."

"What ya slatherin' on it?"

"I use olive oil, garlic, paprika. What I have leftover I add: onions, dried peppers, and wild mushrooms, and maybe I slice up some chorizo."

"There ya go, Nephew. This might be the best meal

we'll get the entire trip. ... Think you oughta check on the girls. I told Mr. Valentine the circumstances of their bein' with us."

"I'm not going back there to pester them. I told them to holler if they needed help."

"Oh, you did, did you?"

"Yes, I did."

Tom stretched out his game leg and started to roll a smoke.

"That shit-bird Fender did say they was attached to the idea of cleanliness."

Tom struck a match and puffed. He offered the bag of makings to the sheepmen. One nodded and he tossed it over to him.

"Hygiene. Now there's a subject we haven't touched on yet."

"Is there that much to talk about?" asked Tom, flicking the match into the fire.

The sheepman tossed Tom's makings back to him.

"God, yes. Why I got a whole theory on hygiene."

Tom shook his head. "Maybe these sheep fellas won't be as interested in your theories as me and the Chinese gals have had to be, Uncle."

"What are you talking about? First time I saw Mr. Valentine here, I knew right off he was an inquisitive man. Curious 'bout the world around him."

Valinten carefully painted the roasting lamb. He held a tin plate under it to catch the drippings. He looked over at Print but said nothing.

"The history of cleanliness goes way back, farther than the Greeks. They had a god for cleanliness. Hygeia. Mighta been a goddess. Sounds more like a goddess name."

"It takes my uncle a while to get 'round to the point on some of these stories, Mr. Ugalde," interrupted Tom.

Print offered the bottle to the other men, who

declined. He poured a short dram for himself.

"See, Mr. Valentine, I am trying to instill in my nephew if not a hunger, at least a passin' interest in that world beyond his horse's nose. On this subject of hygiene, I can tell ya that you can measure the success of a civilization based on the weight it puts on matters of hygiene."

Print stopped and looked up at the approach of the girls coming back to the camp. "Could I ask for a better example?"

The girls walked slowly over to the wagon, their hair damp and slicked back. Number Three hung the bucket by the water keg, and Number One took the strips of muslin and placed them over the scrub bushes behind the wagon. They sat down almost under the wagon and looked at the men, who were looking back at them.

"Like I was sayin', mosta the great civilizations had an enlightened way a thinkin' when it came to hygiene. Settin' here tonight reminded me when I first come west with the wagon trains. You could almost always tell when ya had a river crossin' comin' up, 'cuz you could smell it from three miles away."

"Ya mean like Billy?" asked Tom.

"Same ingredient. See, folks usually gathered up the night before they crossed, made camp, an' then attacked the crossin' the next day. Well, didn't take long for the area to start getting' ripe as it was used by thousands of people, an' mosta them all went cros't at the same place. ... Mr. Valentine, you got any rice?"

"I am sorry, sir, but I do not. It is expensive and not always easy to get."

"That's all right. If ya did, I was gonna stock up on it for the girls. ... Where was I? Oh yeah. Folks was only goin' ta be there a night, so they didn't care a fig 'bout the others comin' along after them. They was all travelers, so ya can't point the finger at 'em too much. But if ya let that kinda attitude prevail in a metropolis, pretty soon ya got cracks showin' in the foundation of society."

Print got to his knees and, using his kerchief, he pulled the Dutch oven away from the coals. He looked up at Valinten.

"Almost," said the shepherd.

Print sat back and took a sip. "Show me a critter in the wild that lives in his own shit."

"What about pigs?" asked Tom.

"Pigs? Pigs're fine animals. Smarter than most. Study a pig sometime. A pig 'ill never sleep where he shits. If possible. If he does, it's 'cuz people have forced him to. No, left on his own, a pig is a tidy fella."

"You got that out of a book?"

"Like I said, study a pig. The worst mistake you can make is to think you can get all yer knowledge from a book. You'd be better off never seein' a book than fall fer that trap of believin' that it all comes from books. No, sir."

"Guess I'll add pig studying to the list, along with birds."

"'Course, some things ya need the books for. The Romans was the best in the world at sewage an' civiliza-tion. Fer that ya need books. They brought water from the mountains right inta their town. Had sewers for bathin' and swampin' out the latrines. Even had a sponge on a string ta clean yer backsides when yer done doin' yer busi-ness. Course ya had ta rinse it out when yer through. Now that's the heart of civilization. People respectin' one another. Actin' civilized. Take that an' apply it ta anything. Racin' wagons and horses down Main Street. Stealin' other folks' money outta banks. Pickin' up dead dogs lyin' in ditches."

Print picked up a smooth stone beside him and opened his pocketknife. He spit on the stone and stroked it with the blade's edge. He enjoyed playing the wag sometimes.

"Let things slide, though, let folks start tossin' chamber pots out the widows on their neighbors passin' by, an' ya know what ya got?"

Tom sighed and Valinten shook his head.

"Ya got the Dark Ages, Mr. Valentine. Let a few folks get away with it, an' pretty soon ever'one's slingin' piss pots out the window. Then ya got a whole continent wadin' around in shit. Next comes plague an' pestilence. They say almost half the people in the world died a disease. But that ain't the worst."

Tom struggled to his feet with his sore leg. He got himself a plate and a fork. "It ain't?"

"No, it ain't. The worst is the loss of knowledge. Ya lose that an' ya lost ever'thing. And mankind almost did. That's why they called it the Dark Ages."

"I guess we're safe from that on this trip," said Tom. "We got a walkin', talkin' encyclopedia to keep us topped off with knowledge."

"Ya bet ya do," replied Print, folding up his knife and struggling to his feet.

"Mr. Valentine, if you don't start dishin' up some a that delicious-smellin' lamb, I'm gonna start actin' uncivilized."

He turned to the wagon. "Ladies, time ta eat. One, Two, Three, Four, an', come on, Five. Let's go."

He waved to them, and they stood up and came over to the fire. He handed out plates and forks. The shepherd sliced long strips of meat from the lamb's shank and placed them on everyone's plates. He cut off ribs.

"Better give the ribs ta the girls. We're kinda shy on knives. They can gnaw, though."

Print ladled beans and apples laced with currants onto the plates. The girls started back to the wagon.

"Hold on there. Hey, Three, come on back here."

The girl turned as Print motioned for them to come back and sit down. She spoke to the others and they all found a spot around the fire. Silence overtook the camp as the men devoured the food on their plates.

Print wiped his chin with the back of his hand and saw that the girls were picking at the food. He studied them as he finished his supper. He put his plate down and rose to his feet. He stretched and walked over to the wagon and rifled through the three-cent flour sacks. He dug out a jar of jam and walked back to the fire.

He tried to open the jar, but the lid wouldn't budge. He squatted and held it close to the fire. He tried it again and it opened. Next he took out his knife and cut a biscuit in half and spread a generous dollop of jam on one of the halves. He handed it over to Number Three. He did the same with the other half and handed it to Number Two. She took it, and he made another one and gave it to Number One.

"Go on, eat up."

He gestured to them, and they took a bite and then another. Print started cutting up more biscuits and slathering jam on them. He passed them to all the girls, who started eating.

"Look at that, Nephew, we was just fishin' with the wrong bait."

Print got them to use the biscuits to push beans on their forks. A forkful of beans and a bite of biscuit. A bite of meat and a mouthful of biscuit and jam.

"Just a matter of primin' the pump."

The girls looked at him as he spoke. Red jam smudged the corners of their mouths.

After supper the camp settled down. Print was fast asleep, snoring. Valinten and two of the shepherds could be seen inside their wagon, playing cards. The light from inside played their silhouettes on the canvas cover of the wagon. Tom was out among the horses on the north side of the camp, and another shepherd was tending to the flock on the south side.

The girls had taken to sleeping under the wagon, and this evening they lay on the blankets and bedroll looking out from under it. Out into the darkness. A big moon was rising. Like a slightly squashed pumpkin, a golden orange color. Except for the great North Star, Polaris, which shone in the constellation of the Little Bear, there was nothing else in the sky. The night was purple-black and devoid of all other stars. Even the Milky Way. The moon hung like a paper lantern. Slowly it floated up. It wasn't part of heaven and it wasn't part of Earth.

"Look, there she is," said Number Five.

The others looked into the darkness and then at her.

"What?" asked Number One. *"Nobody is out there."*

"Look, there she is. There," said the little girl, pointing into the night sky.

"What? The moon?" scoffed Number One.

"Yes. She comes over the fields of my family's village," replied the little girl.

"Don't be stupid. The moon is everywhere."

"Stop it, Ghee Moon," interrupted Number Three.

"It means we are close to my village. She is leading us home," said the little girl.

"Stupid."

"Be quiet, Ghee Moon. She is young, but Ghing Wa is right," snapped Number Three. *"Maybe the moon will show us the way home. But we must not fight with one another. We must help each other and be brave."*

"She is not always there. Many nights she is gone," replied Ghee Moon.

"She is like us. Sometimes she cannot reveal herself. We have to do the same. We must be as silent as the moon. Show little of ourselves to anyone but one another. She will guide us. We must believe this," said Number Three.

"Did the moon guide us to the man who defiled Ye Fung?

Where was the moon when we nearly died on that boat? Was it she who led us to these men? These men who will defile us too and then kill us?"

"*Do not talk that way! Your fear and bitterness will be our ruin. We must protect each other. We must,*" whispered Number Three.

"*You may be the oldest, Sun Foy, but I do not have to take orders from you. I will make my own decisions.*"

Sun Foy reached across Number Two, Mai Ling, and little Ghing Wa and grabbed Ghee Moon and pulled her toward her. "*I am not going to die because of your stupidity. You are so arrogant!*" Sun Foy hissed at her. "*These men saved Ye Fung. They feed us. They want us to eat. To bathe. I do not know what is in their hearts, but I know that they have not touched us or harmed us.*"

"*Sun Foy is right,*" said Mai Ling. "*If we displease these men, it could be the end for all of us.*"

"*You should listen to what Mai Ling says,*" said Sun Foy. "*The old man talks much, but he is not stupid. If you act this way, he may tire of your arrogance and sell you to someone who will want to do more to you than give you food. We will be done with you and you will be on your own.*"

Sun Foy released her grip on the girl, who rolled away from her. They were all silent. Mai Ling and Ghing Wa looked first at Sun Foy and then to Ghee Moon. Ye Fung said nothing. She lay on her stomach with her chin resting on her folded arms, looking at the rising moon. It was turning from orange to yellow the more it rose in the sky.

Before dawn Print woke and found that Number Five and Number Two were sleeping next to him.

CHAPTER FIFTEEN

They parted company with Valinten and the sheep. They crossed the Raft River and directed more to the north. A week of cold rain all but mired them down. Print kept the herd grazing more. One particularly bad morning he decided not to even break camp. Instead he and Tom went over the wagon, greasing axles, checking wheel pins, and mending a long tear in the canvas cover. The girls stayed in the wagon and Tom rigged a fly sheet for himself and Print, which managed to keep the wagon just cold and wet enough to be somewhere between uncomfortable and miserable. As Print repeated numerous times, "There ain't no such thing as a warm rain in this part of the country."

As much as Print disliked the damp and cold, he knew that the forage would continue to be good for a while. A front finally came through and warmed things up and put quite a shine on things. The pink prairie primrose was everywhere. Purple spikes of larkspur shot up, and Print's favorite, Indian paintbrush, made its appearance. He took the point on the herd simply so he could see all this before the herd obliterated it. He watched the meadowlarks and grasshoppers take flight as he flushed their cover. Tom was still lame, and Number Three had taken control of running the wagon. It had not gone unnoticed to the men how the girls seemed to be trying hard to lend a hand. He figured that they were over halfway across Cassia County, heading northeast to hook up with the old Oregon Trail.

The trail took more turns now as they had to zigzag

around the last of the hills and mountains of several ranges that started up north, beyond the forty-ninth parallel, and petered out at the south end of the state. There was plenty of game and they ate well, as long as there was a town or camp to reprovision. So far they had only lost three horses, a fact that surprised and worried Print. He had calculated for much greater losses, and the fact that they were so low gave him pause. Not an overly superstitious man, a moderately long life had given him a grasp of basic statistics.

Late morning on a bright day with already four hours on the trail had the herd rounding the base of another small range. Up ahead they saw smoke from the chimneys of a small village. They walked the herd toward the town until they came up on a shallow pond fed by several rivulets that trickled down from the surrounding hills.

The horses waded into the water to drink. Tom rode over to Print, and the wagon drew up along the trail, which was taking on all the looks of a road the closer they got to the village.

"Looks like a good place to stock up. I'm gonna go in. Anything ya want?" asked Print.

Tom rose up in the saddle. He pulled back his shoulders and then settled back down. "If you can find a piece of rawhide, I wouldn't mind patching these chaps."

"Good idea, we oughta have some on hand anyway. That's it?"

Tom thought for a moment. "Ya might replenish your arthritis medicine."

"I intend to."

"Oh, how 'bout a big sack of peanuts?"

"I ain't goin' inta downtown Omaha. Peanuts? We'll see."

Print looked back at the wagon, then turned and trotted off toward the smoking chimneys. Tom dismounted and led his horse over to the pond for a drink.

The trail did become a road, a muddy track that split a dozen or so buildings. At the edge of town, he noticed an old wagon rotting away, its wheels buried past its axles. He slowed to a walk and parked Bob Tate in front of a store declaring itself to be Burstram's Dry Goods and Mercantile. A man in an apron was leaning a box of potatoes against the front of the store. Several other crates of vegetables were arranged the same way.

"Mornin'," said Print.

The grocer straightened up and turned to face him. "Good morning to you, sir," said the man, brushing his hands on his apron.

"Nice little town ya got here."

"More than nice. I've seen lots of them. You couldn't ask for anything better, if it suits your style."

"That makes all the difference in the world. Ya open for business?"

"I am a merchant, sir. I am always open for business," smiled the grocer.

Print eased Bob Tate sideways and stepped off so as to miss the mud and set foot on the planking. The grocer noticed his maneuver.

"Guess you saw it, just out of town."

Print looked at him, not knowing where he was going with the conversation.

"The wagon. The one that's permanently sunk in the ground. That's my wagon. Been there since the first day I arrived at this little dale."

Print looped his reins around the hitching post. He made a cursory inspection of the vegetables on display. "I did notice it. An interesting artifact."

"Oh, more than an artifact, mister. More like a monument. A testament."

Print turned from the crates to face the grocer. "Is that a fact? Seen lots a monuments but never a mired wagon before. Name's Print Ritter." He extended his hand.

The grocer reciprocated. "Andrew Burstram. I doubt if you ever will."

"What's it a testament to?" asked Print.

The grocer knew he had a new audience, and Print could tell that he was about to hear a story that Burstram set a lot of stock in and had told many times before.

"Step inside, Mr. Print Ritter. You look like you could use a cup of coffee," the grocer gestured with his arm.

Print looked back up the muddy track and then stepped inside the store. He was impressed at the depth of inventory that Burstram had to offer, considering that the size of the town didn't seem to warrant enough commerce for such supplies.

Burstram disappeared behind a curtain in the back and then appeared with a china cup of coffee. Print took a sip and took a seat on a nail keg. He could tell that the grocer was getting puffed up in preparation to unload more of a tale than Print had time for this morning. Burstram seated himself on a keg facing Print and placed his hands on his knees.

"Welcome to Albion."

Print tipped his cup in the grocer's direction.

"We were with a party that had started out from Indiana. All of us had our possessions freighted by rail. The intention was to go to Salt Lake City and from there use wagons to come to Idaho. Well, the man who was holding the money we'd paid out cut us short and the whole party of pilgrims were off-loaded with every stick of our goods, courtesy of the Central Pacific, at a watering stop just east of Rawlins."

Print shifted on the keg, which was already getting uncomfortable. He sipped the coffee and listened.

"We managed to pool enough money together to purchase wagons and oxen with the money that we hadn't given to the thief who had stranded us. Two families bought tickets to Davenport, and one unmarried man said he was going to find the agent who had left us in such a dire predicament. We all chipped in some money to help him in his endeavors. Never heard from him or the whereabouts of the thieving agent. How's the coffee? Another cup?"

"I'm fine, thank you. I do need to get some supplies, though."

"Of course you do. So we headed out. Wettest summer on record. Mud was our middle name. We came into this little valley late one evening in a driving rain. All of us had been soaked for a week. We were all too tired and cold to make much of a camp. Well, that night a Mrs. Thomas Hackett kind of went 'round the bend and commenced to stabbing her husband in his sleep. She stabbed the hell out of him with a good-sized kitchen knife, and he succumbed to her efforts. It rained all that night and kept on raining, even as we buried the victimized husband the next day. Buried him on the high ground just outside of town. Time we got through putting Mr. Thomas Hackett to rest, our wagon was sunk up to its axles, just like you saw it. I told Mrs. Burstram 'It must be a sign 'cuz I am not digging that wagon out of the mud ever again.' Told those pilgrims we had seen the elephant and we weren't goin' any farther."

Print stood on the mistaken belief that the grocer's story was over.

"Here now, don't take off before you hear the rest of this little history."

Print rubbed his buttocks and sat back down.

"They pulled out of here with Mrs. Hackett tied fast for her own safety, and theirs too, I suspect. Headed for Glen's Ferry to give her over to the authorities. So there we were. Alone and sunk in the mud. Now my wife, Mrs. Burstram, is a well-read woman, and she said we should name this place Albion after a French king who was murdered by his wife, the queen. In honor of Mr. Thomas Hackett, our first permanent resident. We operated right out of that wagon until I got a cabin built, and then we put the store on the front of it."

The grocer patted his knees and smiled at Print, who didn't say a word, afraid that it might elicit another round of history.

"So, you in need of resupply?"

Print rose, rubbed his numbed backsides again, and proceeded to tick off his requirements. "Got any jam?" Print asked.

"No, sir. However, I do have clover honey."

"I'll take all ya got. We crossed the trail with some sheepherders that said it ain't safe to travel east."

"Hostiles off the reservation. Shoshone, I heard. Mostly stealing livestock. You got livestock?"

"Five hundred–plus horses."

"I'd say that qualifies as livestock. Family?"

"Five Chinese girls."

The grocer looked at Print in a whole new way.

"It's our plan ta hook up with the Bozeman and move north ta Sheridan," said Print, placing the empty cup on the counter. The grocer slid his hands into his pants pockets, under the apron.

"I'd say that's a big plan, considering you got maybe seven hundred miles to travel with a herd of horses and a wagon full of women."

"Five girls," Print corrected him.

"Your best bet is to head north toward the American Falls. There's plenty of soldiers at Fort Hall, so I suspect the Shoshones will stay clear of that country. If you loop well north until you cross into Wyoming, you can drop south and pick up the Overland."

"Sounds outta our way," replied Print.

Burstram shrugged. "You're the one with the herd of

horses and girls," said the grocer, stuffing supplies into the flour sacks.

"You charge for those sacks?"

The grocer looked at him. "I am a merchant, not a robber," replied Burstram.

"Nice town ya got here."

"Thank you."

Bob Tate picked his way through the muddy ruts back to Tom and the girls. They off-loaded the supplies into the wagon, bunched up the herd, and headed north. On a knoll outside of the village, they passed the grave of Thomas Hackett, the first permanent resident of Albion.

CHAPTER SIXTEEN

They pushed north and east toward American Falls and Fort Hall that lay beyond. The weather turned again, and more cold rain pelted them for three days. Finally Print called a halt, and they camped on the south bank of the western Snake River.

They had passed an Irish tinsmith leading a big dog that was pulling a goat cart with his tools and gear. He said that Fort Hall was only eight miles to the north, but that it wasn't a place where an honest tradesman could earn his keep. He said if he owned such a herd of fine horses, he wouldn't go near the fort, as the army was known to requisition livestock, cattle, and horses for its needs. Such transactions were done with papers or chits that were supposed to be backed by the U.S. Treasury. Finding an alchemist in the government bureaucracy who could actually convert those papers into gold, or anything close to it, was not always easy.

They shared their supper with the tinker, and then, declining an offer to stay the night, he led his dog and cart into the drizzling twilight.

"I have been thinking that the fort might be the place to find some folks that can take proper care of these girls," said Print as the girls were cleaning the plates.

Tom was using an awl and a heavy leather palm pad to repair his chaps. "Maybe I should go up there. Leave the herd with you and the girls," replied Tom as he turned the chaps and punched a hole through the rawhide patch and into the stained chaps. "Don't like the idea of losing the herd to some major that will probably pocket half the money for himself."

"I was thinkin' right along those lines too. 'Cept I think I'll go. Don't want ya getting sidetracked by one a Miss Lucy Highsmith's cousins."

"Suit yerself. We could use some Prince Albert."

The rain came back and continued all night. Print was awake long before daylight but lay in his bedroll, putting off getting up and facing another wet morning. When he finally did get up, he saw that there were now three girls sleeping around him.

After a breakfast spent trying to stay out of the rain, he and Bob Tate headed north to Fort Hall. The ponderosas were taller and the land definitely had a big northwoods feel to it. He saw three mule deer in a thicket of spruce, hunkered down out of the weather. His approach was not enough to roust them into the cold rain.

He was trying to count how many days the girls had been with them. He knew they had been in his care long enough that he was not looking forward to parting company with them. The prospect of spending the rest of the journey with a stoic buckaroo nephew was as depressing as the rain that was seeping through his slicker. The girls were a big liability, though, and he had to be practical. Fort Hall was probably the place that could take care of them.

Halfway to the fort, the rain slackened and then ended. The sun didn't come out, but he could tell that the temperature was going up. He eased Bob Tate into a trot when he saw the stockade in the distance.

Fort Hall was like many of the forts the army had strung across the West. Originally it had been a trading post. It still was, with a Sutter's store and a garrison of soldiers. There were always a number of Indians in and around the fort. Mostly people who no longer had a band or tribe to be with. Many had fallen victim to the whisky traders. All were on a low-grade trail to oblivion. Outside the stockade was a collection of tents and shacks awash in deep mud. It was here that most of the frontier capitalists dwelled. The whisky traders, whores, and gamblers plied their trade. Then there were the teamsters, mule skinners, tinkers, and low-class travelers who were the recipients of that trade.

Little streams of mud and manure trickled away from the shantytown as Print pulled up the big chestnut. The break in the weather had most of the residents and visitors out of the tents. An approaching rider always managed to get a welcoming committee of the saddest women of the oldest trade. Two women clutching shawls around their shoulders waded out in the muck to meet Print. Other less-motivated gals called out to him from plank stoops in front of the shacks.

Print smiled and tipped his hat to the waders who were slip-sliding through the mire. They hung on to each other for balance and were still trying to keep a grip on their shawls. He pressed his right leg hard against the horse's side, and the chestnut made a lateral walk away from the women.

"Hey there, cowboy. Want ta ride the tiger?" one of the whores called out to him from her secure perch on the decking.

Again Print tipped his hat and turned his head at the same time, hoping that would suffice for all the remaining doxy women. "Ladies."

This cesspool was built on ground that sloped away from the entrance to the stockade. It added to the feel that it was all about to slide down on itself. The sucking sound of Bob Tate's hooves filled Print's ears as he carefully navigated the slippery footing.

"Come on, you old billy goat, gimme a ride. Ya kin'

do me all night if ya got the strength."

Print looked straight ahead, not wanting to make eye contact before he cleared the fort's gates. From the side of a shack, a young man stepped toward the horse and rider. He moved quickly and almost slipped.

"Mister. Hey, mister."

He placed himself almost directly in front of Bob Tate. Print pulled up, irritated and ready for trouble. The man placed the palm of his hand on the horse's shoulder. Print saw that he had a purple mouse under one eye and a swollen lower lip that was split and scabbed.

"Mister, I'm sorry to stop you here, but I need help and I could tell watching you coming in that you might consider lending aid to someone in trouble."

He stroked the horse as he talked, and Print took in everything without moving his eyes.

"Take yer hand off my horse, son."

The young man jerked his hand away as if it had been bitten. "Sorry, mister. Please listen. I'm not part of this riffraff. They're the reason I'm in this predicament. I don't want money. I just need help."

Print eased a little. He wiped the bottom of his moustache with the back of his forefinger. He was casual in his movement. He did it to make sure his arm was free and clear to draw the big Colt if needed. He could tell that this lad was in trouble. He was in trouble and scared.

"Mister, if you could just help me get clear of this place, I'll do whatever is required to make it up to you."

I got no need ta add this fella's troubles to mine, Print thought. He sighed and moved his head as if to look up at the entrance to the stockade. But he kept his eyes wide to any and all movement around him.

"Young man, I've got business inside the fort. I doubt if I can be of any help ta you."

Bob Tate took a step forward, and the man placed his

hand on the horse again.

"Son, I asked ya not ta put your hand on my horse."

This time he did not remove it. "I have been taking care of myself for a long time, sir. I am not the sort that goes around asking for help. But they have me treed here, sir."

"As I said, I've got business in there," said Print, nodding to the entrance. "When I leave, if yer still here, we'll talk."

The young man removed his hand from the horse. "My name's Henry Gilpin. You can call me Heck. Be careful in there, sir. There can be less law inside those walls than there is out here."

That stopped Print. He looked at the lad. "Son, I got over five hundr'd head a horses down the track. Is there somethin' I need ta know about 'fore I go in there?"

"I wouldn't go in there with five horse collars and a one-eyed dog, sir."

Print said nothing. He looked down at Henry "Heck" Gilpin.

Heck spoke. "There's a Major Bolen that's in charge of the garrison. He'll take your stock, your cock, and the gold from your teeth. I'd put as much distance between you and this place as possible, sir. I'm not saying this because I need help. It is the truth, mister."

Off behind Print, he could hear one of the whores yelling, "Hey there, old-timer, you don't look like the sort that favors boys. Com' on back here an' I'll show you what the Lord really intended that piece of lumber for."

Print looked from Heck to the stockade, then back to the desperate lad in the mud, and then turned in the saddle to see several working girls gathering and watching him and Heck. He looked down at Heck. "Get yer horse an' come on."

"Sir, I don't have boots, much less a horse and saddle," said Heck, lifting one leg to show a mud-caked foot.

"Shit. ... Shit. Climb onboard."

Print offered the toe that protruded through the stir-rup as a step and his hand to help Heck swing up behind him. Print pulled and sucked him out of the mud. Bob Tate took a step under the added weight. Print turned the horse slowly away from the fort.

He didn't look at them, but he saw them. The whores and several layabouts who had been watching the men.

"Aw, come on, mister. That's a sacrilege. Let me show you the true way. Hell, I'll speak in tongues to that little tent pole of yours."

The crowd laughed and a chicken flew from atop one of the shacks and landed in front of Bob Tate, who was carefully making his way through the slippery footing. The chicken struggled to free itself from the mud and briefly took flight, only to land in more mud. It was all Print could do not to gig Bob Tate into a lope and put heels to this pustule smear of shacks.

CHAPTER SEVENTEEN

On the ride back to the herd, Heck told Print how he had come to be in such a sorry state. He had gotten in a protracted card game with several soldiers and luck was with him all the way until the "blue boys" decided to amend the rules and took him out back and reversed his financial situation. They then beat the tar out of him. Took his horse and anything else they thought had value. They picked him clean and left him to the mud and the whores and whisky peddlers. He was from back East. He had been on the move for almost five years. He claimed he could turn his hand at almost anything. He said he was game and not afraid of hard work. He was from Pennsylvania. A damn Yankee, Print thought.

They drifted into the camp as Tom was trying to get supper ready. He and the girls watched silently as Heck swung down and cringed as one of his bare feet landed on a stone. Then Print dismounted. Bob Tate gave himself a good shake. Tom was looking at the unshod young man his uncle had brought in.

"Whatta we got here?" asked Tom.

Print followed his gaze to Heck's muddy feet. "Work of another boot stealer."

"Footwear must be at a premium in this part of the country."

"Heck Gilpin, meet Tom Harte, my nephew. He's the *segundo* of this outfit."

The men nodded to one another.

"Mr. Gilpin has asked if he could sign on to help us.

Claims he's a hand. We'll see."

Tom kept staring at his feet. He turned and walked to the back of the wagon and leaned in. He pulled back and held a pair of worn-to-hell boots.

"If your feet ain't too big, you might fit into Capt'n Fender's boots," he said, handing them to Heck. Heck pulled a pair of gray woolen socks from his coat pocket.

"Thank you, Mr. Harte."

"Tom. There's only room for one mister in this outfit," Tom replied, looking over at Print, who was already making a plate for himself.

"I'll go wash up," said Heck, jerking his head in the direction of the riverbank. He gingerly walked away carrying the dead man's boots.

Tom turned to his uncle. "No horse, no gear, no boots?"

His back to Tom, Print didn't look up. "I know. I got a feeling 'bout him. He mighta saved this herd for us."

"He don't leak, does he?"

"No, not this one."

Heck returned in Fender's boots. He was looking at Print eating.

"Grab a plate," said Tom.

◎ ◎ ◎

Heck hadn't lied. He could sit a horse. Uncle and nephew put him to work. He switched off riding flank on either side and drag. Print put him on the red roan and he showed that he could ride without showing off. Both men watched him and he passed muster.

Print liked that he took to the night work, and in the three days he had been with them, he never once asked about the girls. He must of come from a good Yankee family, thought Print.

Tom liked the idea that he was getting more sleep and that maybe Heck could take over as the recipient of his uncle's theories on the universe, cooking, and birds.

Print decided to end the idea of heading north. It was a land he was not that familiar with, and the prospects of possibly running into a few braves on a jaunt off the reservation was starting to bother him less than the chance that the authorities—and any other people of lighter pigmentation—might just be more of a threat to them. The problem was that the change in their trail required them to divert somewhat south to avoid the higher ranges that had little or no passes to get through. He was beginning to feel the clock starting to run against him.

His plan now was to aim for the Wyoming line near the Star Valley and then skirt the Salt River range and move directly on to Lander. Somewhere along the way, they could hope to find someone to take the girls.

The morning of the third day since picking up Heck, they started to move out, Print on point with the gray mare and her lieutenants on her tail. Heck and Tom rode flank, and the wagon with Number Three at the helm brought up the rear. They had barely cleared camp when Tom, turning in the saddle to look back at the wagon, saw a horse standing by itself. He wheeled and loped back to the lone horse. It had made no attempt to follow the herd and it wasn't grazing.

He dismounted, dropped his reins, and walked over to the gelding. It didn't seem to be favoring a leg and there was no blood to be seen. He carefully ran his hand down the legs. First the front and then the hind. As his hand stroked the left hind, the horse pulled the leg up and tried to step away. On the inside of the leg just below the spavin was a deep cut and there was dried blood. The hock was swollen and hot to the touch. Tom went back to his horse and removed his revolver, which was wrapped in an oily rag, an old La Mat .44 caliber from his saddlebag. Over his horse's rump, he saw that Number Three had stopped the wagon and the girls were watching him. He stuck the revolver in his belt and removed his rope and walked back to the injured horse.

He played out a small loop and slipped the rope over the horse's head. He made another loop for the nose, making a temporary halter. He stepped back and with his forefinger drew an "X" between the ears and the eyes, the center being in the middle of the animal's forehead. He pulled the La Mat from his belt. He placed the barrel on the imaginary spot of the intersecting lines. He fired, and the horse sat back on its haunches like a dog. Tom held the rope tight. It then keeled over on its side, legs stretched out. It shivered once and then went stiff. The girls had turned away at the sound of the shot, except for Number Four. She didn't flinch. She continued to look at the dead horse, even as Number Three started the wagon moving.

Tom rewrapped the revolver, first removing the spent cartridge and replacing it with a new load. He placed it back in his saddlebag and then retrieved his rope, coiling it up. He mounted up, secured his rope, and rode back to the herd, which had stopped at the sound of the gunshot. He rode up to Print. Heck watched him from the other side of the herd and turned to look back at the dead horse on the ground.

"Busted hock," said Tom.

Print listened, nodded, and then moved on.

◎ ◎ ◎

Late that afternoon they stopped to let the horses graze on some good forage. There was no creek or watering hole, but the grass was too good to pass up. Besides, they had had nothing but water almost everywhere on the trail. Print was sure they would hit water in the morning.

The men were still mounted when Heck called out, "Mr. Ritter, we got company."

Walking toward Heck on the other side of the herd were three mounted braves. Print caught Tom's attention and motioned for him to ride around the herd. Print did the same from the other direction. He came up behind Heck, who had the red roan pointed toward the visitors. Print stopped a few paces behind Heck.

Tom took up a position farther away, off to the left. As he rode around the horses, he had removed the Remington from its scabbard. It now rested across the pommel of his saddle.

The visitors rode thin ponies rigged in war bridles. They were representative of their people. Coppery, oiled skin. Little of their clothing was native. Ill-fitting white men's pants and boots. A woolen coat. A broadcloth shirt. One wore a deerskin shirt, greasy and devoid of any decorations and embellishments. All wore their hair long. One had a red ribbon braided into his. Even with the blended clothing, you could tell they were different. You could see it at a hundred yards. They had a look. A way they carried themselves. So at ease, bareback on their ponies, with braided rawhide for their bridles. Their faces revealed nothing that they didn't want you to know.

"They look like Crow, Mr. Ritter," said Heck over his shoulder, not taking his eyes off them.

"Crow? You know Crow when ya see them?"

"I spent time at the agency in Laramie. Are you conversant in Crow, Mr. Ritter?"

"Hell no. Are you?" asked Print, carefully removing his gloves.

"I can sign and muddle my way through a little."

"Well then, muddle on, and let's find out what these sunburned children of misfortune want."

Heck eased his horse forward. He started to sign and

talk at the same time to the three mounted men. The one with the yellow neckerchief talked. He barked at Heck. Short bursts. Very declarative.

Heck turned his head to the left and spoke over his shoulder. "He says we are crossing their land and that you must pay to do so."

"Are we in Crow country?" asked Print.

"No. Not really."

Print carefully folded his gloves and tucked them into the fork of his saddle, beneath the pommel. "You figger they got any legitimate claim?"

"No, not really."

"An' that would include the ground we're standin' on right now, I suppose."

"You can be sure of that, Mr. Ritter."

"So, what's the tariff?"

Heck talked and signed some more. "He says it is going to cost you two horses to cross their ancient hunting ground."

"This feels like a shakedown ta me," said Print. "Tell 'em they can have one horse. Their pick."

Again Heck talked. Tom looked back at the wagon and noticed that the girls were nowhere to be seen.

"They say two, Mr. Ritter."

"Bullshit," snapped Tom as he lifted his rifle from where it rested on the pommel and held it in both hands.

Once more Heck addressed Print over his left shoulder, never taking his eyes off the three braves. "It's your call, Mr. Ritter, but from where I sit, they do have the look and smell of wildness about them."

Print said nothing for a long moment.

"Mr. Ritter?" asked Heck.

"You tell 'em I said I'm an old man. Tell 'em I'm sick. Tell 'em sick an' dyin'. Tell 'em I don't give a shit if I die today or tomorrow. One horse."

Heck talked and then there was silence. After several long moments, Print squeezed Bob Tate and eased him up past Heck and right up alongside the fellow who was doing all the talking. His left boot touched the shoulder of the Indian pony. The pony took a step backward. Print had a thin smile on his face and never took his eyes off the brave.

He could see the grime on the faded yellow scarf. The brave's face revealed nothing. He was completely self-contained and yet serenely confident at the same time. He looks like he don't give a shit if he dies or not, either, thought Print.

Keeping locked in on this warrior's eyes, Print ever so slowly reached into his vest pocket and removed the little wooden figurine of a horse he had been whittling. He raised up in the saddle and reached over to offer it to the brave, who broke eye contact for a moment to look at what was in Print's hand and then looked right back to Print's eyes.

Print never stopped looking at him, even as he nodded a silent yes at the shiny face that was the color of brick. He felt the wooden horse leave his grasp, and he sat back slowly. He raised his hand, holding up two fingers. Then he picked up the reins and backed Bob Tate until he was abreast of Heck.

"Tell him to go pick out the other one."

Heck said nothing, but from the corner of his eye, Print could see him gesture with his hands. They all just stared at one another. One of the Indian ponies stomped at a fly. Print slowly turned to look over at Tom, who had his cut-down Remington resting in the crook of his left arm. He brought his gaze back to the brave.

As if on cue, all three ponies backed up and kept going backward for a good twenty feet. Then their leader barked like a dog, and they turned right and leapt forward to skirt the herd. Print, Tom, and Heck turned their mounts to keep facing the departing braves, who went about cutting out a dandy blood bay. From nowhere, one of them slipped a braided rawhide line over the horse's neck. The bay, frightened, started to back up and toss its head in resistance. Instantly another rider swatted it across its rump with the carbine he was carrying and the blood bay jumped forward. They barked and whooped and turned heels to the herd and were gone.

Print and company watched in silence. Tom spat.

"He knows horses," said Tom, wiping spittle from his chin as he saw the last of one of their better horses disappear.

"Yer right, Hank, there is a look an' smell of wildness about 'em. Even young bucks off the reservation."

Print turned for the wagon and saw Number Three leading the other girls from a thicket of hackberry bushes. "We gotta find a place for these gals 'fore we lose the herd, our scalps, an' them," muttered Print to no one in particular.

Late that night Sun Foy got up and went off to the bushes to pee. As she was squatting, she looked off to her left and was sure she saw a brave looking at her in the dark. She rose and hiked up her pants and ran back to the wagon. She snatched her blanket and joined Ghing Wa and Mai Ling next to Print.

CHAPTER EIGHTEEN

On top of a rock outcropping up in the timberline, a Cooper's hawk held a chickaree in its talons. With its yellow beak, it ripped meat and entrails from the dead squirrel. Far below, the herd of horses moved in a long line followed by the wagon.

Print had explained to Heck the story of the girls and why it was now so important to find a place for them. Heck told him that the next town of any consequence was Cariboo, a mining camp down the track. After that there was Soda Springs. Then nothing that he knew of until long after the Wyoming line.

"I'm not sure it is what you are looking for, Mr. Ritter. Like most of these camps, it's as rough as a cob. But then you don't have a lot of choices out here."

"Ya got that right, Hank."

"Actually it's 'Heck,' Mr. Ritter."

"'Course it is, Hank."

It was a Rocky Mountain summer day. Hotter than it felt and brighter than a young man's possibilities. The land was thicker with spruce and ponderosa, but the meadows were carpeted in buttercups and wild violets. You could smell the pine sap in the air. From way above them, the Cooper's hawk uttered a deep-throated cackle followed by a long, high-pitched whistle. "Swee-hee." Print breathed in the smell of the evergreens, the horse sweat of the herd, and the crushed plants they trampled underfoot. He was going to miss these little girls.

By afternoon they could see smoke rising from a small vale in the distance. Heck said it was probably Cariboo and Print called a halt to the day. He said they'd give the horses more grazing. They made camp and Print announced that he was off to look for supper. With the side-by-side resting against his shoulder and a pocketful of shells, he trekked into the timber. It was easy pickings as he shot a dozen quail and two partridge. Print dropped them into a flour sack he had brought along. He came to a stream and knelt and then lay on his stomach and drank. He splashed his face and cupped cold water over his hair. He sat beneath a big hemlock, his back to the rough bark, laid the shotgun beside him, and closed his eyes.

Print had dreamed last night about the little girl with the button-up shoes. Her crinoline dress. Her brown eyes. He could not remember where the dream was. There was no zebra pony this time, but the girl's mother, Ann, was there. She led the child away, but the little girl returned. The dream woke him and he propped himself up and looked around the darkened camp. The Chinese girls were sleeping around him. He lay back and drifted back to sleep.

The more he thought about his dream, the sleepier he got. He felt the warm sun and heard a meadowlark in the field behind him. Soon he dozed off. He dreamed of the Chinese girls dressed in white dresses and riding horses on a merry-go-round. But the horses were real and leapt from the spinning wheel with the girls on them. He stood on the turning platform, hanging on to a pole. He watched the girls on the horses disappear. From deep in the sleep of the dream, he heard a sound near him and snapped his head up. He grabbed for the gun and saw the girls approaching him.

They stopped when they saw him reach for the shotgun. He was still half asleep and unfocused. When he realized that he was awake, he took his hand from the gun on the ground. The girls stood in their tracks.

"Come on over here," he called. "Ya caught me nappin'. I was dreamin' all about you gals."

Sun Foy, the eldest, stepped forward. Print got to his feet. Picked up the shotgun and the flour sack. He handed the sack to Number Two to carry.

"Did Tom send ya to fetch me?"

"Tham," Number Five repeated to no one.

They walked back toward camp. Insects hovered over the wildflowers and grass. Swallows dove and turned and banked and dove again at the insects flitting in the afternoon sun.

"Remind me to tell y'all about swallows and how far they come just ta eat our bugs up here. Fascinatin' story."

They flushed a grouse and Print swung the gun up and dropped it with one shot. The girls stood wide-eyed at the sound of gun. Number One ran ahead to where the bird had fallen. She held it up for the others to see.

Print took the bird from her and examined it. "Thought it was a grouse," he said. "But this ain't no grouse. Least not one I ever seen."

He held the bird at arm's length and turned it over. "Maybe a ptarmigan. Well, we'll see if it tastes like a grouse," handing it back to Ghee Moon.

They got back to the wagon and he showed them how to pluck and dress the birds. He then went and saddled up Bob Tate and walked him over to the girls. He tapped Number Five on the shoulder and motioned for her to come with him. Ghing Wa looked to Sun Foy to tell her what to do. She nodded and told her to go on.

Standing next to the horse, Print reached down and lifted the little girl up on the saddle. He set her sideways and hooked her right leg over the horn as if it were a sidesaddle. He placed her hands on the saddle horn and patted her knee. Ghing Wa looked to the other girls and Sun Foy nodded her reassurance.

Print removed his lariat and slipped a loop over Bob Tate's head and stepped back. The little girl reached for him. He grabbed her hand and replaced it on the horn and stepped back again. Print winked at her and told her not to be afraid. He flipped the lariat, and Bob Tate started to walk. He walked slowly in a circle around Print, walking in time to the clucking sound Print made.

Ghing Wa was terrified, but she held on. Print smiled at her and said she was doing just fine. The girl and the horse made three trips around Print and then he clucked louder and flipped the rope again and the big chestnut broke into a slow trot. Ghing Wa squealed. The girls called out to her and in their own tongue told her she was doing just fine.

"Easy. Easy does it. Relax. Yer doin' fine."

When it came to her that she was not going to fall off and die, she almost smiled and breathed. Print lightly tugged the rope and the horse transitioned back to a walk. Then the girl really did smile.

Beyond the girls stood Heck and Tom, watching. Print tugged again and Bob Tate planted himself. Print walked toward the horse and rider, coiling the line. He laid his hand on her tiny, slippered foot and gave it a pat. He told her she was brave and that she was a natural at riding horses. He told her he knew that the first time he laid eyes on her. Her face was flush and she smiled at him the way he dreamed the girl in the button-up shoes did. He knew she wanted to go again, so he walked to the other side of the horse, played out the line, and sent them into a circle. Around they went. She called out to the girls and they back to her and she laughed. Print made a soft popping sound with his lips and let out more line and Bob Tate eased into a soft, rocking-chair lope and again she squealed, and the girls watching her did too. And for just a moment, he thought of his dream and the merry-go-round. He brought them back to a trot, and then a walk, and finally they stopped.

He helped her remove her legs from the saddle horn and held her under her arms and lifted her down. She steadied herself against him to get her balance and he took her hand and walked her back to the girls. A tiny, crippled girl about as far away from home as she could be, shuffling beside a bowed and bandy-legged old cowboy.

Supper was spent mostly with the men watching and listening to the girls talk to one another. They were more animated this night than any time since Tom and Print first met Fender. Print hadn't felt much like cooking tonight, so he let Heck do the duty. He found a comfortable spot by the fire and smoked and whittled on a new piece of wood and sipped a little whisky for his arthritis.

"Hank, if ya don't mind, I think I'll let you watch things here in the mornin' and Tom an' I'll take the girls inta town an' see if we can find the right people ta take care of 'em."

"Whatever you say, Mr. Ritter. Easy enough for me. Hope it isn't a disappointment for you. The town, I mean."

"So do I, Hank. So do I."

That night he dreamed. But not of little girls or zebra ponies or merry-go-rounds. It was mostly about Virginia and the boys from Carroll County and things he hadn't thought of in many years. He tossed, woke himself up several times with his own snoring, and once he looked about and saw that all the girls had dragged their pallets over and were sleeping around him. He fell asleep thinking of little Number Five going 'round and 'round on old Bob Tate.

Tom had stayed up with the herd and not wakened his uncle, so Print was confused when he woke up and saw that light was breaking in the east. He gingerly got up without waking any of the girls and walked off to pee. Tom came in as Print hobbled back in his stocking feet and slipped on his boots.

"What happened?" asked Print.

"I wasn't tired. It was a pretty night, so I thought I'd let you sleep."

"Can't believe I slept through the night."

"Must have needed it. What are your plans for today?" asked Tom, nodding in the direction of the girls, who were getting up and rolling up their blankets and bedrolls.

"Gotta do it. Gotta take 'em inta that town and see what we can do. Ain't fair to them nor us ta keep 'em on the trail. We don't put an end ta this, we'll lose the herd and God only knows what'll happen to them. No, you an' I'll take 'em in after breakfast."

Tom looked off into the distance and saw the rising smoke from the mining camp. "Any thoughts on how you're going to explain it to them?"

"Nope. I'm just gonna take 'em in. They ain't got a say in it."

"I'll be ready to go when you are. Coffee'll do me for breakfast."

"Nice sewin' job," said Print, pointing to Tom's pocket. "Thanks."

Tom walked back to the herd while Print slipped on his boots, tucked in his shirt, and slid his suspenders over his shoulders.

Sun Foy was always attuned to the subtleties of disposition between Tom and Print. The tone and modulation of their voices told her all she needed to know. Not what they were saying, but if they were cross with one another or if something was troubling one but not the other. She knew that how they felt had everything to do with her and the girls' future.

This morning she heard them talk. Not angry, but low. The old man had the new one cook breakfast as he went off for a walk. And Tahm didn't eat but instead stayed with the horses.

When Honkle Pren returned and hooked up the mules but made no to attempt to secure the camp for travel, she knew that something was very wrong. They way the men averted her eyes when she looked at them. Especially the new man. The old man brought his horse up and Tahm climbed into the wagon and took the reins. Honkle Pren called to her and the others and motioned for them to join Tahm in the wagon.

"This is not right. I think it is not good, but be quiet. Here, take this," she said to Ghee Moon as she slipped her a fork she had taken when they packed the wagon.

Number One took the utensil and hid it in her sleeve.

"Hank, this shouldn't take all day, but if it does, don't leave the herd. No matter how much ya might want to. You stay here."

"Yes, sir. I'll have supper ready."

Print turned his horse away from camp, passing the wagon. Tom slapped the reins and the wagon lurched forward.

"Let's get 'er done nephew."

Tom didn't know Chinese, but he could tell that the girls were pretty upset. Number Three would cut them off when they started talking among themselves. Print rode out in front of the wagon and didn't look back to check on them.

As they drew close to the camp, they could see tents and shacks in a gap between two short mountains. It had steep sides and gave the impression that they were all piled on top of one another. Less than a quarter of a mile from the tent town, they came upon a man with a bucket in one hand and a wide brush in the other. He turned at the sound of their approach. He held his hand with the brush high to block out the sun from his eyes. There was an assortment of signs in various sizes pointing in all directions. One said Soda Springs. Another said Christian Cemetery. Beside it, pointing the opposite way, a sign read Catholic Cemetery. One simply said Diggings and seemed to point to nowhere. Next to the man with the bucket and brush was a sign that was getting redone. It read, CARIB—.

"Morning," said the man with the brush, moving the brush so he could see who he was talking to.

"Morning," replied Print. "New town?"

"No. Just a new name. Use to be called Porcupine. Then we became Broken Nose, but now folks thinks that's too rough and common so we're goin' with Cariboo. That's for Caribbo Jack. Heard of him?"

Tom and Print shook their heads.

"Real name's Jesse Farichild. But somehow he got the handle Cariboo Jack."

"Is he the authority in town?" asked Print.

"Well, to hear him tell it, he was the authority on everything. Sort of a windbag, but he was the real deal. He's the first one to hit gold here."

"Where might we find Mr. Cariboo?"

The painter lifted the arm with the paint bucket and pointed to the sign, "Christian Cemetery." "Just follow the sign."

Print looked at the sign and beyond and then back to the painter. The mules shifted their legs and the harness creaked and jingled.

"Ya missed him by about a month."

Uncle and nephew said nothing.

"Prospector come into the High Dollar carrying on about a wounded grizzly cavorting down by Bear River. Jack starts blowing about what he would do to that griz' and someone took him up on it."

The painter set the bucket on the ground and placed the brush across the top.

"So they set out well fortified with whisky and shot. Jack come up on the bear an' tore into the brush, shootin' to beat hell. Trouble was, he was so drunk he couldn't put a ball in the beast."

The painter took a rag from his pocket and wiped his brow. "Forgot my hat. Well, the bear started to work on Jack and finally Jim Havard shot the griz' dead. 'Course by that time, Jack was looking pretty used up. They hauled the doctor up from Malad to tend to him and then they brought him back here."

The painter wiped his forehead again and patted his shirt pockets.

"Didn't work out?" asked Print.

The painter kept patting himself, looking for something. He looked up. "No, it didn't. Doctor did a swell job of sewing him together, 'cept he didn't leave no openings to drain. Blood poisoning took hold and he passed on."

"White of you to name the town after him."

"Had to. Folks over at Soda Springs wanted to lay claim to him. Wanted to bury him there being he's such a big deal in these parts."

The painter gave up on trying to find what he didn't have. "You fellas got a smoke?"

Tom reached in his pocket and tossed his makings to the painter.

They sat in silence as he took a paper and laid it on the tops of two fingers, sprinkled cut tobacco on it, carefully twisted the paper's ends, inserted it in his mouth.

"Yes, the folks in Soda Springs got exercised when they learned we had him deep in the ground."

He lit the smoke and drew deeply. From the back of the wagon, Tom heard the girls whispering and the big one shut them off.

"That wasn't going to stop those hardheaded Mormons. So we figgered we'd take the high ground by naming the town after him."

"Got a hotel?" asked Print.

"How long you planning on staying?"

"Long enough for a bath an' a shave an' maybe a

beefsteak dinner."

The painter tossed the makings back to Tom. "Thanks. Then that would be the Queen of the Rockies. Everything else rents by the hour. You here to do business with those girls?"

"Maybe."

"Then you ought to talk to Miss Becker. Ask for Big Rump Kate. That's her working name. She's always looking for new gals to work the line. She's got the money, too. Worth more than all the panners in town put together. She'll do right by you."

"Queen of the Rockies Hotel?

"Yep. Thanks for the smoke."

Print moved out and the wagon followed.

"You'll know her when you see her," called out the painter to the departing wagon.

CHAPTER NINETEEN

They proceeded toward the town wedged between the two high hills. The trail turned into deep muddy goo the closer they got to town. There were horses tethered, mired up to their hocks. The camp smelled of greasy smoke and over-flowing privies. The sounds of men shouting and a cock-fight came from behind one of the two rows of tents and buildings that lined the road. Paths of planking went in all directions, spanning churned-up mud and manure.

There was little activity visible. Print assumed that the men were in the mines and the whores were resting up from the night before. Everyone else was probably betting on the Shanghai rooster. The main street, the only street, was literally the point where the two hills came together. Everything on either side was sliding toward the street. A second tier of small tents and tents on top of log-walled sides clung to the hills above the front street dwellings.

Farther down it flattened out some and there were pens and corrals in the back. A red-and-white sign read "Seabolt Livery." Beyond that was the biggest building, labeled Queen of the Rockies. It was two stories and had a planked deck that ran the length of the front of the hotel. All the other shacks had stoops or just some boards tossed on top of the mud.

Print stopped in front of the hotel. He heard a roar from the unseen men at the edge of town and then the crowing of a cock and then cursing. He turned in the saddle and, leaning on the cantle with his right hand, said to Tom,

"Better sit tight 'til I get this sorted out."

"Uncle?"

"Why don't ya let me see what's what 'fore we talk too much."

Tom wrapped the reins around the hand brake and started to roll a smoke. He turned to face the girls, who all had the look of impending betrayal on their faces. Number Three held a hard gaze on him, and he turned back around to finish rolling the smoke. The girls talked in whispers behind his back.

Print dismounted and his boots sank up past his spurs into the muck. He tied Bob Tate to the back of the wagon and struggled in the mud to the steps. He wiped the excess mud on the planks and ascended to the porch and into the hotel. He was concerned about all the mud he was tracking in and went back to the door to scrape off some more. He looked down on the wagon and saw the girls looking up at him.

He walked back to a small counter behind which a man was paring his fingernails with a pocketknife. The clerk put away the knife at Print's approach and stood to greet him.

"Needing a room?" asked the clerk.

"Two. Just for the evenin'. You stable my horse an' mules?"

"We don't, sir. Seabolt's next door does. Two rooms, two dollars each."

Print paid the clerk, who handed him two skeleton keys, each attached to a brass disk with numbers pounded into them.

"Is there a mayor in this town?"

"Not hardly."

"How 'bout a town council?"

"Nope."

"Sheriff?"

"No, sir. Not anymore. Mister, this town's as rough as a cob. It's hard on lawmen. Hard enough to put two in the ground in a year. Nobody's signing up for mayor, town council, or sheriff."

"So, who's in charge?"

"Well, the town sorta operates of a 'live an' let live' policy with some 'every man for himself' thrown in. This ain't one of those places where you check your firearms when ya get to town."

Print stood with his hands on top of the counter, palms down. He lightly rocked on the heels of his boots, looking at the clerk. He looked down at the counter and tapped his fingers and then looked back up at the clerk.

"Kate Becker is the big operator here. She and Avery Blanders. He freights in heavy equipment for the mines, but he stays over ta Soda Springs most of the time. You thinkin' of running for office?"

The clerk incorrectly assumed that sufficient time had passed since Print first walked in such that he could attempt some personal humor with the newest clientele. A disingenuous grin accompanied the last remark he made, but it quickly disappeared when he saw the lack of response on Print's face.

"How 'bout a bath? Can I get a bath here?"

"Yes, sir. Right out back. There's an old Chinaman. He'll set you up with soap and towels and all the hot water you can stand. He'll give you a shave, too, if you don't mind the idea of a Mongolian holding a razor that close to your gizzard. But no barberin'. He ain't worth a shit at cuttin' hair."

Print headed for the front door. Halfway, he stopped and turned to ask the clerk, "The Chinaman, does he speak English?"

The clerk, who had revised his opinion of Print based on his apparent lack of any humor, spit into a can behind the counter. "He knows 'soap,' 'water,' 'hot,' 'cold.' Things like that, I guess. I ain't in the habit of conversing with Chinks."

Print walked out the door. He walked down the hotel steps to the last board before the mud. "I got us two rooms for the night. You can park the rig next door. I'll take the girls inside."

"So, what's the deal? Did you find somebody to take 'em?"

Print motioned to the watching girls to get off the wagon. "Not yet. It doesn't sound promisin'. I at least want a bath and ta sleep in a bed for a while."

"What about the herd?"

"Maybe you can ride out after we get dinner."

Print took one step off the planking to lift Number Five off the wagon. His boot sank into the mud. Again he scraped his muddy boot on the steps. "I'm goin' to get them settled into a room an' then I'm taking a bath out back."

"Well, don't leave them up there. I'll be up in a minute."

Print held the arm of Number Five as she navigated the steps. On the porch, Number Three and Print looked back to see Tom steer the wagon around the side of the hotel. Print held the door for the girls. Once inside he led them toward the staircase at the end of the room.

"Hold on there, mister."

Print turned to face the clerk, who had returned to manicuring his fingernails.

"Mister, those rooms are for sleeping in, not cooching. You want to work those girls, you go talk to Big Rump Kate. This here's a real hotel."

Print gave a long pause before answering the spivvy character behind the counter.

"That's good 'cuz we want a bath, a good steak, and some sleep. You got a problem with that?"

The clerk couldn't hold Print's gaze. He swept his hand across the counter as if to remove some speck of dust. With the other, he waved. "Have at it."

He spit into the can behind the counter and took a seat as if to imply that he had gotten his point across. Print led the girls up the steps to the second floor and down the hallway to the last room. He motioned for the girls to go in and he followed, closing the door. He took a seat in a ladder-back chair by the window and faced the silent girls.

"Ya probably think yer about ta be played badly. Well, it just ain't so. I'm tryin' my level best ta make things right by you."

Footsteps down the hall and the door opening interrupted him. Tom walked in with saddlebags over his shoulder.

"Did you find a sheriff?" asked Tom.

"No. No sheriff. No mayor. No nothin'."

"What does that mean?"

"It means these little cherry blossoms ain't goin' nowhere, least not tonight, Nephew. You stay here with them. I'm goin' ta get a bath and talk to a Chinaman out back. When I get back, I'll sit with them an' you can clean up."

Print opened one of the saddlebags and pulled out a pair of long underwear. He draped them over his shoulder and left.

Out the back of the hotel, a catwalk of planking led to a bathhouse that doubled as a laundry. Inside a Chinaman was stirring a large tub atop a woodstove with a stick stripped of its bark. Lines strung across the room held drying clothes and bedding. Three bathtubs were lined up in the center of the room. They were shaped like caskets.

"I come ta get a bath."

The Chinaman made a gesture that was somewhere between a nod and a kowtow. He motioned to the tubs. Print pulled over a stool and started taking off his boots and then stood to remove his shirt, pants, and underwear.

He sat back down to remove his socks and, upon examination, realized the one was in need of repair and the other beyond repair. The Chinaman was filling the tub with hot water, and steam filled the room. Except for his hands and face and neck, Print was pasty white. He gingerly stepped into the tub, pulled back his foot, and waited as the Chinaman poured a bucket of cooler water. He got in, closed his eyes, and sank down. For several minutes, he said nothing. He savored the feel of the hot water as its warmth made its way through his body and into joints, sockets, and ligaments. He took a washcloth and draped it over his forehead and face.

When he removed it, he saw the Chinaman across the room sitting on a bench, his back to the wall, looking at him. The Chinaman rose and approached him with a bar of brown soap and a long-handled scrub brush. Print took them from him and the man returned to the bench. Print soaped up the bristles of the brush and commenced to scrub his back. Again he was momentarily transfixed by the sensation. The Chinaman got up and took a bucket of water off the stove and carefully poured some into the foot of the tub.

"You speak English?" asked Print.

"Yes. Yes," said the Chinaman as he returned the bucket to the stove.

"Well, maybe you can help me. I'll pay you. Ya see, I got these five Chinese girls ... "

The Chinaman looked confused and then nervous. He returned to his seat and looked away from Print.

"Let's start over. My name's Print Ritter. What's yours?"

The Chinaman turned to face Print.

"Your name. What's your name?"

"My name is Lung Hay."

"Well, Mr. Lung Hay, through a series of circumstances, fate has placed five Chinese girls in my care. Now

I ain't in the girl business, and I sure as hell ain't in the Chinese girl business."

Print paused, and the Chinaman, who was looking away, turned to face him.

"I'm in the horse business. I'm headin' ta Wyoming and I got stuck with these little girls an' one's half crippled. I can't converse with them nor they with me. You sabe?"

Lung Hay nodded yes.

"I want ta help 'em. I want to find some authority that can take care of 'em and be reasonably assured that no harm'll come to 'em. Know what I mean?"

Again Lung Hay nodded yes.

"So far ever' place we run up on has been such a shit hole I wouldn't leave a dead dog there."

Print grabbed his ankle and drew up his foot to soap it. "I'll pay you to help me talk to the girls an' get this sorted out. I know they ain't got the slightest idea what's goin' on and spend mosta the time in mortified fear. Ya think ya could help me with this?"

"Yes," said the Chinaman.

"Can ya wash out those clothes?" Print asked, pointing with the bar of soap to the pile he left on the floor.

"Yes," said the Chinaman.

"Good deal," said Print, sinking back into the tub.

Print walked down the hallway in his long underwear and boots, a damp towel over his shoulder. He entered the room to see Tom at the chair by the window and the girls sitting on the edge of the bed. He changed into a pair of pants as Lung Hay knocked at the door. Print opened the door and welcomed the Chinaman in.

At the sight of Lung Hay, the girls froze. Print was taken aback when he turned to introduce them.

"Tom, this is Lung Hay, an he's gonna help us get this all figgered out. Girls, I want ya ta meet Mr. Lung Hay."

Lung Hay made a slight bow, and the girls whispered

to one another frantically.

"Tell 'em I have hired you ta help me talk ta them."

Lung Hay first asked if they all understood Mandarin. They said they did. He then repeated what Print had asked of him. The girls looked to Print and then back to Lung Hay.

"Tell 'em we are sorry for what's happened ta them and that we mean ta make sure that they have a good place ta stay an' are treated well."

Lung Hay repeated Print's words and the reaction from the girls was immediate. They all started talking urgently to the Chinaman. Lung Hay turned to Print.

"They say that they want to stay with you and your son. Please to be good as not to leave them."

Print looked at Tom. "My son?"

"No son?"

"No. No son. My nephew. Tell 'em they can't live out on the trail with us. They need a proper place to live. A regular place and such."

Lung Hay relayed Print's message, and the girls got quiet. Little Number Five started to cry.

"Tell 'em they will be all right. They have my word on it."

The Chinaman did not translate. Instead he looked directly at Print.

"Go on, tell 'em."

"This is an old story," said Lung Hay. "There is no place safe for them. Nowhere. They will be like meat before hungry dogs. They will be eaten."

"I just gave them my word. You doubtin' that, Chinaman?"

Lung Hay continued to face Print. "No. I no doubt your word, maybe your wisdom."

Print's eyes flared. First at Lung Hay and then at Tom. Tom shrugged.

"I think maybe you speak better English than you let on, Mr. Chinaman," said Tom.

"I mean not to argue. I believe you want them only good. I have spent many years in your country and I have learned your language. I also learn your ways. Not to make you mad, but it would be a kindness to cut their throats than to leave them here."

Print turned red and shouted. "I said no harm is goin' ta come ta them! Now we got horses ta get to Sheridan before fall. And there ain't no way around that. Maybe this ain't the place for them, but I tell you, Mr. Lung Hay Chinaman, this whole country ain't all shit, piss, an' corruption. No, sir."

Lung Hay continued to face Print but said nothing. Several of the girls were crying.

"Ah, hell. Tell 'em not ta get upset. They're gonna stay with us for the time bein'. At least until we get it all figgered out. Go on, tell 'em."

As Lung Hay translated, Tom stood up and looked out the window.

"You sure are a hard case. They're going to be stuck to us like jackass burrs."

Print ignored his nephew.

"Lung Hay, can ya watch them while we go get somethin' ta eat? Maybe you could cook somma y'all's food. Bet they'd like that."

"Yes, I can do that."

Print put on a clean shirt and slipped his suspenders over his shoulders. He buckled his holster on. "Better stay heeled while we're in this burg."

CHAPTER TWENTY

Print and Tom walked into the Highgrade Emporium just before dusk. The crowd was starting to build as miners and camp followers came looking for some gaiety. They made straight for the bar. The first thing Print noticed was that it was wider than most of the saloons he had frequented. It was at least twice as wide as others that conformed to the long, narrow, and dark shotgun style. The lighting was better than most, too.

It had the rough perfume of cigars, spittoons of tobacco juice, stale beer, and sweat. The bartender approached. A tall and unattractive fellow who looked as if he was deep in thought or maybe lacked the wherewithal to formulate even shallow thought.

"Gentlemen."

"Some good brown liquor, if you please," said Print, running the back of his forefinger along the bottom of his moustache.

"Glass or bottle?"

"Two glasses."

The bartender expertly filled two tumblers to the rim. Tom looked around the room and then he and Print carefully lifted the glasses and drank slowly and quietly. They replaced the tumblers on the bar top half empty and pondered the taste and burn on the whisky. They lifted them again and drained them. The bartender watched them and held up the bottle to see if they wanted another shot. Print opened his eyes and nodded. "Oh, yes."

He recharged their glasses and this time they sipped slower.

"Where's a good place ta get a beefsteak dinner 'round here?" asked Print.

"We can fix you up. Got a kitchen out back. Good as any in town."

"What's your name, sir?"

"Vincent."

"Well, Vincent, how 'bout you take that bottle and lead us to a table where we can have a couple of yer best beefsteak dinners."

The bartender gave a vacant smile that confirmed the shallow-brain theory. The men followed Vincent to a table close to the window. He placed the bottle on the table and then the glasses with his fingers on the inside. Tom took his kerchief and wiped out both glasses and poured two shots. More miners came in. Some from the front of the saloon and some from the back, escorted by tired-looking prairie flowers working the dinner shift.

"We seem to have gotten off the trail ta gettin' these horses ta the Moncrieffe brothers," said Print as he ran his finger around the rim of his glass.

Tom poured more whisky into his uncle's glass and then his own. "I ain't as cold feeling toward them as you might think I am. I'm not for dumping them off. We'll get the herd delivered," replied Tom.

Print looked up and nodded in agreement as two plates heaped with meat and potatoes arrived. "This almost makes the visit worthwhile. Too bad young Heck is gonna miss out on this supper."

A nasty little creature from the kitchen brought them a plate of green beans and a big stack of biscuits.

"Speaking of Heck," said Tom. "I think we oughta skin outta here when we finish."

"Much as I was lookin' forward ta a night in a bed, I

think ya may be right."

The men sat and watched the saloon fill with hard-rock men. By Print's count, the men coming in the front were almost equal to the more relaxed ones returning from the rear. Tom noticed one lad who was making his third trip to the "delights" out back with a lady that Tom thought had the general contours of a turkey. It was obvious that the young colt intended to pass judgment on as much of the female talent as he could until his purse was empty.

A large woman in a bright blue satin dress came over to their table as they were nearing the finish line on the dinner.

"Evening, gentlemen. I'm Kate Becker. Big Rump Kate," she said, slapping her haunch to drive the point home. "I'm the owner here. Enjoying your dinner?"

Tom had never seen hair on a woman the color of Big Rump Kate's. He hadn't seen that color on anybody before. It was susceptible to change when she moved. It was a henna–champagne pink combination that could only be replicated just before sunset out on the range.

"We are, thank you. Nothin' like a bath, clean britches, and a little whisky ta make a man feel almost human again."

Big Rump Kate laughed. And when she did, there was a lot of independent motion going on in that blue satin dress. The cuffs and the bodice were trimmed in a white ruffle. The front was cut down to reveal two magnif-icent breasts that were trying to escape their restraints. Tom figured that, conservatively, each one was bigger than his head. He poured himself another shot and continued on that train of thought.

"That ain't all a man needs to feel human. How about topping off the evening with some Highgrade sporting gals?"

Print pushed a big chunk of steak around his plate with a fork, collecting the last of the mashed potatoes, and put it in his mouth. He sat back and chewed, looking at the big operator of Cariboo. Tom was wondering if he was contemplating the steak or the proposition. He swallowed and took a sip of whisky.

"A fella can only handle so much humanity at one time."

"Come on, now. Don't be shy with me. I know you boys want to get under the sheets and talk to the boss. I bet you do."

Print pushed his empty plate away and took another sip.

"Maybe a matinee tomorrow?" Big Rump Kate turned to Tom with her offer. "Come on, lad, take your pick. I got a quadroon from New Awleens, brown as a berry and twice as sweet."

Tom said nothing. The whisky was slowing down his calculations on exactly how big each one of Big Rump Kate's breasts were.

"Not up for the sable gals? Hey, Rose. Rose, come here," she said, waving a big flabby arm in the air. "I call her my English Rose. Newest girl to work the line for me."

A big blonde girl lumbered over to the table. She was every bit as big as Big Rump Kate but without the appearance of amplitude. A different kind of density. Nothing bouncy there, thought Tom. She looked like she could milk a lot of cows, and probably had back home. Until she discovered she could make more money milking the miners and cowhands. To her there was little difference in getting knocked around out back and getting cow-kicked in the barn three hours before sunrise.

"Rose, we got a strong lad here that needs to have the knots worked outta him. I told him you're just the one to do it."

The blonde towered over the men and smiled at Tom with teeth that were in dire need of some attention. Tom leaned back as she leaned in. He looked over at his uncle and then back at the yellow-haired giant.

"I'll work out the knots, straighten your spine, and when I get through, you won't remember your mama's Christian name."

"A tempting offer, Miss Rose, but I was just about to leave, as I have an engagement down the track."

Big Rump Kate's face, caked with heavy makeup, hardened. She stepped closer, placing her hands on the table and leaning closer to the men. Both men stared at her magnificent orbs, which seemed twice as big at close range. Tom could not imagine what kind of rigging she wore that could possibly keep them from bursting forth and filling the empty dinner plates on the table.

"Maybe you prefer gettin' some trim from those Celestials you brung into town. You thinking of setting up shop here? Couple of cowpunchers goin' inta the skin trade?"

Uncle and nephew were listening, but they remained transfixed on the heaving mountains, framed in blue satin. She slammed her hand down on the table. The plates clattered and whisky jumped in the tumblers. Suddenly all the folks in that end of the saloon were watching her, including Print and Tom.

"Let me set you boys straight. The gold I mine from this burg I don't get from digging. There ain't a shot of whisky, a hand of poker, or any fella that wants to dip his pecker in some poontang that I don't get a cut of."

"Easy there, Miss Becker. My nephew and I are just passin' through."

Droplets of sweat were making their way down Big Rump Kate's breasts, disappearing into cleavage that still held Tom's attention, despite her table thumping.

"Then what you got those Chink girls stashed up in your hotel room for? You planning on opening a laundry here?"

Print wrinkled his nose and chewed his moustache.

He said nothing. He stared at the plastered face of the woman. "That ain't none of your business, lady. By that I mean we got no designs on stickin' our finger in your pie. We're movin' on, an' that's all you need ta know, madame."

Big Rump Kate backed off a bit. "A woman's got to protect her ground. Tell you what. I'll buy them gals from you. I'll pay you top dollar."

Again Print waited. "We didn't come here to get laid or sell women. We wanted a bath, a drink, and dinner. That's all."

"Come on, old whiskers. Everything has a price," Big Rump Kate sneered at him.

Out of the side of his vision, Print could see Tom slightly change his body position. The timbre of Print's voice changed. "No, ma'am, it don't. Not ever'thing."

Big Rump Kate straightened herself. "Well, it's a stupid sack of shit that believes he can waltz all over this country with a wagonload of women and thinks he ain't in for trouble."

"You kiss your mama with that mouth?" asked Tom.

The contempt deepened on the big woman's face. "Come on, Rose," she said and walked away.

Both men watched the Teutonic women leave.

"English Rose, my ass," said Tom.

"Looks more like a Dutch elm to me," replied his uncle.

"I'll get the girls and meet ya out front," muttered Print as he worked a toothpick on some morsel of the dinner.

Just then they heard screams from the hotel. They bolted from the bar. Tom sprinted ahead of his uncle and was up the stairs by the time Print had cleared the lobby. Tom took out the door and most of the framing it hung on. What he saw was the back of a man with his pants down at the foot of the bed. Number Four, Ye Fung, was under him. Another man was on the bed on all fours, holding the girl's arms and pinning her down. A blonde woman was beating her fists on the man at the edge of the bed. Lung Hay lay motionless on the floor, his head covered in blood.

The man with his pants at his ankles swung his elbow at the interfering woman and clocked her right in the nose. She staggered backward and tripped over Lung Hay. The other girls were in the corner, screaming. The man returned his attention to the thrashing, screaming girl. He never saw Tom, who drew the heavy .44 Colt from his holster and calmly walked toward the man. He grabbed a handful of oily hair and brought the big hog leg down on the man's skull. Even with all the screaming in the room, Print, who was stepping through the doorless opening, could hear the quiet sound the man made as he slumped to the floor.

The man slid off Tom's right side. The other man, still pinning the girl down, looked up in amazement to see Tom shove the barrel of his gun deep into the man's eye socket. The sensation that traveled down the steel barrel into his palm told Tom he had popped out the man's eye. By the force of the blow and the pain, he raised up on his knees, clawing at his face. Blood poured between his fingers.

Print was at the side of the bed. He grabbed the cyclops by his collar and dragged him off the girl and onto the floor. Tom and Print worked with a calmness and surety of motion that one might see in two men unloading a freight wagon. The one-eyed man struggled to his feet as Print cracked his head with the butt of his pistol. The man buckled at the knees. Print placed his boot in the small of his back and shoved him into the wall, where he slowly sank, leaving a bloody smear down the wallpaper.

Tom stood over the other man splayed out on the floor, facedown. He placed his boot on the unconscious man's wrist and took careful aim. The big Colt roared and filled the room with the smoke of spent powder. The body jerked as one of its thumbs was blown off. The report silenced the room. Tom stepped over to the other side of the body and placed his boot of the other wrist. He fired but missed, and Print stepped forward and helped by steadying the arm with the application of his boot at the elbow. Tom fired again, this time with better results.

For the first time, Print noticed the woman with the smashed nose sitting on the floor, her hand to her bloody face. He turned and looked out the window to the street below. The shots had brought out the curious and the bored.

"Better get down to the livery and get the wagon while you can."

"Not yet."

Tom stripped a sheet from the bed and dragged the thumbless miner over to the window. He tied an end to the man's ankle and the other to the metal frame of the bed. He lifted the man by the collar and his belt and slid him out the window. The falling man made the bed lurch across the room to slam against the sill. He grabbed the other man off the floor and tossed him like a bale of hay through the room's other window. He turned and looked at his uncle. Mitigated fury, Print thought.

"Get the wagon up. I'll meet you out front."

Tom dashed down the hall as Print got the Chinaman to his feet.

"Tell 'em to help their sister. We gotta get down ta the wagon. Can you walk, old man?"

Lung Hay nodded that he could but hung on to Print to steady himself.

Print turned to the woman with the smashed face. "Ma'am, could you help this fella? I got to carry the little girl."

The woman said nothing but went to the Chinaman's side. One and Three were helping Four off the bed. Print scooped little Five up in his arm and led the way down the hall.

At the landing, the hotel clerk and two other men

met Print. The clerk was carrying a shotgun. Print set Number Five down and drew his Colt Peacemaker. He sighted it on the face of the clerk.

"Just lean that against the wall and back off!"

The clerk complied and turned, pushing his way past the other men. They stumbled and fell over one another all the way to the lobby. Print holstered the Colt and picked up the shotgun and Number Five as he made his way down the stairs. The lobby was empty as they crossed to the front door. He peered outside in both directions. Tom was bringing up the wagon. Bob Tate was tied to the back with just a halter and no saddle. Print ushered the group out onto the porch and down the steps. Broken glass crunched under his boots, and to his right, one of the miners lay in a heap.

Tom was out of the wagon to lend a hand. First Number Five, then the other girls, followed by Lung Hay and the woman, who helped shove him into the wagon bed and fell in after him. The crowd was growing and sounding ugly. Print snatched Bob Tate's lead rope from the wagon. He turned to Tom.

"Nephew."

Tom took the shotgun and held the rope as Print tried to jump up on the horse's back. Between the mud, the height of the horse, and his age, he couldn't do it. Tom leaned the gun against the wagon wheel and helped give Print a leg up. He handed the rope to Print, then tossed the shotgun to him. The winded Print settled his legs around the horse's sides and wheeled him to face the crowd. Catcalls and brave talk were shouted from the back of the crowd as it carefully slogged closer to the horse and rider. Print steadied Bob Tate and leveled the shotgun on the advancing mob.

"First one lays a hand on us, I'll open 'em up like a Christmas goose!"

Big Rump Kate waddled down the planking, yelling to the men in the muddy street. Print noticed the other miner hanging out the window. Blood ran down the paint of the hotel. No one seemed interested in helping him.

"I'll pay five hundred dollars for every one of the girls you bring back to the Highgrade!" she hollered.

Print swung the gun in her direction. He aimed from the hip, high and wide. And fired. The pellets broke window glass and sent chips of wood and flecks of paint flying. Big Rump ducked at the shot as debris rained down on her and the men behind her.

"You skinny old bastard!" she roared. "Somebody give me a gun!"

She turned to the man on her right, but he was unarmed. Then to the one on her left. She snatched an old heavy Colt Dragoon revolver from his side. Pointing it at the ground in front of her, she struggled to pull against the slow action of the hammer. Everyone in the street was watching her. Tom started up the mules, who leaned into the weight of the wagon, deep in mud.

Big Rump Kate cocked the gun, but before she could aim, it discharged. It bowled her backward into the cadre of miners huddled behind her. They all put their shoulders into it to keep her upright. Print responded by firing the second barrel even closer into the front of the hotel. More chips and paint flew and the flying buttress brigade behind Big Rump Kate melted away. The lack of support made her stumble backward, and she dropped the old pistol in the mud before she recovered her balance. Print held on to the empty shotgun and the lead rope in the same hand as he drew his pistol.

"I want those girls!" she screamed to no one in particular.

"No sale, lady," replied Print as he reined back his horse with only the lead rope.

"I want those girls!" she repeated.

"Not today. That's the price a bein' a capitalist, lady."

The mules pulled hard, and the wagon moved forward. Bob Tate kept stepping backward, allowing Print to cover the wagon's retreat. Big Rump Kate was now down in the muddy street, her blue dress held high.

"Just remember, you old goat, it's money that greases the wheels of this world."

"Maybe," Print called back. "But not tonight."

"Somebody shoot that son of a bitch!"

To make sure the mob was listening to him and not Big Rump Kate, Print fired a round into the deep mud at their feet. The slug slammed into the muck and splattered the crowd, especially the blue satin dress of Big Rump Kate.

"Will somebody please shoot him?" she screamed, turning to face the crowd. The veins stood out on her neck and temple.

Print fired another slug into the mud, which left an interesting pattern up the back of her dress. She spun around.

"Gimme a gun, I'll kill him!"

She turned back to the miners. "You titless old women!"

Print slipped a look over his shoulder to see that Tom had the wagon on its way. He held the crowd at bay but could see that several were getting bold and creeping along the sides of the buildings and tents. Big Rump Kate squatted in the road and scooped up handfuls of mud and started flinging them at Print in frustration. Bob Tate backed out of her range. She turned to a hapless fellow standing behind her. She hit him in the chest with both of her open palms. A Missouri mule could not have done a better job. With two muddy handprints on his shirt, he flew back into the audience, taking several to the ground with him.

"What are you looking at?" Big Rump Kate screamed to the onlookers.

The crowd momentarily distracted by Big Rump

Kate, Print wheeled Bob Tate to catch up with the wagon.

Once the wagon hit some solid ground, Tom picked up the pace until he heard his uncle hollering at him. He pulled the mules up and turned as Print came alongside.

"Nephew, my days a bareback ridin' are long gone."

They were well clear of Cariboo, and it didn't look like anyone was anxious to take a chance on Big Rump Kate's offer. Print tossed the shotgun to Tom, who stowed it behind him. Print holstered the Peacemaker, bent forward, and then slid off the horse. His legs went rubbery on him. He walked to the back of the wagon to tie Bob Tate.

"I tossed your saddle an' bridle in the back."

He looked into the wagon bed and saw Lung Hay stretched out. The girls and the woman were crammed in there too.

"I'll ride up front 'til we get to camp."

He walked forward, steadying himself on the wagon's side. He pulled himself up and saw that Number Three was sitting next to Tom. She moved over to make room. Shoulder to shoulder they sat, and the wagon moved out. Tom felt the warmth of the girl's thigh through his pant leg and that got him to thinking about the colossal prow on a certain blue satin prairie schooner.

The three up front rode in silence until they could make out the light of Heck's campfire. Print tapped Sun Foy's knee and pointed to the fire. "There ya go, Number Three. We're gonna make it. Ever'thin's goin' to be okay."

She looked in the direction he was pointing and then back to him as he talked. He patted her knee. "Ever'thin's gonna work out."

Tom slowed the wagon as they got close to camp so as not to spook the herd. Heck was waiting for them when the wagon rolled to a stop. Tom handed the reins to Sun Foy and jumped down. Print was slower getting off.

"Heck, we gotta roll. I'll turn the hobbles on the

mares. Help my uncle break down the camp. Toss every-thing in the wagon!" yelled Tom.

"I'll saddle the horses," said Print.

"I should assume things didn't go well."

"No, they didn't," replied Print. "We'll be on the move all night, I suspect."

Soon Tom was leading the herd out into the darkness, with Print and Heck flanking and Number Three driving the wagon. The ground had lots of rock outcropping, so the going was slow. Sun Foy soon figured out that by watching the way the herd parted, she could steer clear of most of the obstacles. She still hit the smaller ones, which made the wagon roll and lurch violently.

The flea-bitten gray mare stayed right on Tom's tail, and he led them through the night. They rode the moon out of the sky, in and out of blankets of low-lying fog. When all that was left in the sky were the morning stars, Tom brought the herd to a stop. They milled about on the banks of a river as Tom paused for a smoke. The struck match shone on his face in the dark as Print rode up.

"Want to wait 'til it's light?" asked Tom.

They studied the river as best they could. They could make out the sound of rippling water, which usually meant shallows.

"Let's put this behind us."

Heck rode up and joined in the inspection. "What do you think?" he asked.

"I think we're swimmin' the Hellespont tonight, Hank," Print replied.

"Come on, boys. Come on," Tom called to the herd in a soft voice.

He eased down the bank and into the water. Print and Heck peeled off and returned to the herd's flanks to keep them going in. Although the gray mare wanted to move faster, she allowed Tom to pick his way. Some of the horses got balky, but Print and Heck turned them in and stayed on the bank until the last of the stragglers were in.

"I'll bring the wagon over. You follow them ta the other side an' give Tom a hand."

Across the water they could hear Tom calling to the horses. Heck waded in behind the last of them. Print joined the wagon at the bank's edge. He dismounted and stripped the saddle and bridle from Bob Tate. He tossed them in the back of the wagon and climbed up on the front seat. He took the reins from Sun Foy.

"I'll take it from here. Ya done a great job drivin' tonight. An' if Mr. Lung Hay survives his smashed head, I'm gonna make sure he tells ya so."

Print gathered the reins in one hand and kept the other on the hand brake as he nudged the mules forward. The wagon swayed violently as it slid down the bank. Sun Foy held on, looking at Print and then over her shoulder to the others in the wagon bed. Once Print heard the Chinaman moan. The wagon straightened as the mules edged into the water. The mules were now telling Print what they were going to do, and he didn't argue. They were sure-footed and smart enough to go slowly. Water reached the wagon bed but didn't breach the top, and by taking it easy, they made it to the other side. There wasn't much of a bank, and Print drove the wagon forward into the back of the herd.

He stood and looked back to see Bob Tate climbing out of the water and shaking himself. Light was now in the east and he could see that they had arrived on a bend in the river and that it formed a meadow that was ringed by large evergreens. The meadow looked to have grass and was high enough not to allow the river to jump its banks. The hemlocks and ponderosas formed a natural corral.

"This'll do just fine. Let's get the mule undone an' call it quits."

Heck rode up beside the wagon. "Why don't I cross back over just in case they tried to follow us?"

"Suit yourself, son. I doubt those miners are goin' ta take up that lady's offer. Tom's got another pistol he keeps in his saddlebag. You take that with ya, an' don't be shy about usin' it ta let us know if ya need help."

Heck trotted off to find Tom, and Print got down and started unhitching the mules. The morning stars were gone by the time the Print-Harte party fell asleep.

CHAPTER TWENTY-ONE

The sun was overhead when Print woke. The girls were asleep, but Tom and Heck were sitting by the fire, drinking coffee. He got up stiff and sore, slipped on his boots, and went in search of a tree to stand behind while he relieved himself. Upon returning he finished dressing, ran his fingers through his hair, and put his hat on. Tom poured a cup and handed it to him.

"Thank ya, son." Print sipped and then stretched his back and shoulders.

"Didn't start breakfast. Wasn't sure if we were staying long enough."

"Did ya see anything back there, Hank?"

"No, sir. I came over about an hour ago. I don't believe anyone's coming."

"Me neither. Guess we better take a look at the damage."

The woman with the smashed nose was out of the wagon and sitting in its shade. Print approached with a bucket and knelt beside her. He placed his hand on her shoulder.

"Mind if I take a look at that, ma'am? I just need ta get this cleaned up. I know it's sore, but it'll feel a lot worse if an infection takes holt."

He cradled her neck in one hand and wiped away the dried blood with a piece of muslin. He squeezed the cloth and let the water run down her face.

"It hurts a whole lot worse than it looks," he said reassuringly.

Tom and Heck helped Lung Hay out of the back of the wagon and walked him over by the fire. Number Three was up and carried an armful of wood to set beside the fire.

"Ma'am, if you'll just hold this on your face 'til I can wipe somma that dried blood off. I'm gonna help them with the Chinaman, but I'll be right over there, and when I'm done I'll be back. Okay?"

She held the wet cloth to her face and nodded yes. Print got up and walked over to the others.

"This old boy's taken a pretty good whack to his brain pan," said Heck as he and Tom were bent over, inspecting Lung Hay's head.

"Now Hank, that's Mr. Lung Hay you're workin' on. You any good at sewin'?"

"Not on the hide of something's that's still alive, Mr. Ritter."

"Guess you're the one then, Tom. If ya can make as good a job of it as that fancy pocket yer wearin', I think Lung Hay won't complain too much, will ya now?"

Lung Hay shook his head as Tom poured hot water from the kettle into a saucepan. Print retrieved a small kit from his saddlebag and tossed it to Heck. "Got that from a saddler in Klamath. Great for workin' on leather and not too bad on scalps, either. Three. Three, come on over here."

Print pointed to Sun Foy and motioned for her to join him. He gave her the saucepan to hold as he washed the Chinaman's head.

"I could whipstitch it," said Tom.

Tom and Heck leaned closer as Sun Foy dutifully held the pan of water.

"I don't know, Nephew. One thing 'bout these Chinese fellas is that they seem to set a lot of stock in their head's appearance. Don't think Lung Hay here wants an ugly scar across the top of his pate. If I was you, I'd go with a tight little chain stitch. Kinda like the way that fancy pocket a yours is done. This is your lucky day, Lung Hay. You are fortunate enough to have two barbarians who have considerable experience at repairin' top notches."

Tom took one of the large, curved needles and threaded it. Print poured whisky into a tin cup and held it out to Tom.

"Sock 'er in there, son."

Tom dropped the needle and thread into the whisky and then retrieved it.

Print offered the cup to Lung Hay. "Ya look ta be a tough old bird, Mr. Lung Hay, but ya might want a jolt 'fore my nephew starts ta work on you."

Lung Hay sniffed the cup and rejected it.

"In that case," said Print as he took a drink and splashed the remainder on the Chinaman's wound, "let 'er rip, doc."

Tom sat himself down on an empty nail keg they used for storing gear. He placed Lung Hay's head between his thighs and clapped the sides of the Chinaman's head with his knees. Print took hold of Lung Hay's hands. He looked over at Sun Foy. She was intently watching as Tom prepared to poke the needle through the man's scalp. She saw Print watching her. He winked and gave her a nod.

Tom punched through the Chinaman's scalp and Lung Hay went stiff from the pain, but he didn't make a sound. Tom did the same to the skin on the other side of the wound. He drew the thread up, made a knot, and waited for Print to cut the remainder with his pocketknife. He repeated the process.

"Ya got one hell of a grip there, Chinaman," said Print.

Tom stitched and Print snipped until the wound was closed. When they were finished, Print indicated to Sun Foy to wash the wound. He struggled to his feet and went over to the wagon and bent down. He reached under and came up with a glob of axle grease on his fingers. He walked back and proceeded to smear it over the wound.

"Now usually I'd make that lard, but this'll do just as well an' keep the bugs off, too."

He took a closer look. "Not bad. Not bad at all."

"A man among men at stitching up scalps," said Heck.

They helped Lung Hay to his feet, and Print held on to him as they walked over to the shade of the wagon. He eased the Chinaman down and went back to the fire to pour a cup of coffee. He took it to the woman with the bad nose. He offered her the cup. She placed the bloody cloth beside her and took the cup and sipped.

"Not ta worry, ma'am, I won't turn them loose on you. Name's Prentice Ritter, an' that's Heck Gilpin, an' my nephew, Tom Harte. The ladies are One, Two, Three, Four, an' Five."

She looked at the girls.

"Well I had ta call 'em somethin'. More for convenience sake. Your nose might be broken, but it's too swollen ta tell right now. Why don't ya find a cool spot ta lie down an' we'll talk later."

Print left her and walked back to get a cup of coffee for himself. He poured for Heck and Tom. He looked at their surroundings.

"It might do us some good to rest for a few days. Couldn't pick a better spot. We go slower, we might get there quicker. We're bound ta have a few sore-footed ones after last night. Let's picket 'em in the river mud for a day. Cool them hooves out."

"We're burning time, Uncle."

"Way I see it, this deal is gettin' more interestin' every day."

"Seems to be getting less profitable every day to me."

Print looked at his nephew for a long time. "Never

use money ta measure wealth, son. Let's get them sore-footed cavvys in the water."

Print and Heck went about running picket lines in the shallows as Tom found lame horses and walked them down to stand in the cool water. The girls busied themselves setting up the camp, and the woman and Lung Hay slept.

Tom brought the last of the horses down and tied them along the line. Heck walked back to the wagon, and Print helped Tom with the horses.

"You know, Tom, back there in John Day, when I said I didn't know what went on between you an' your ma, I meant it. I know my sister could be a difficult woman. Hell, they all can. Her bein' German Huguenot and Appalachian stock. That can make for tough stock. It also makes for the kinda people that could up and leave a place like Galax and ride an' walk across this country to find a new life."

Tom stopped tying horses to look at his uncle.

"It can also make for pretty starchy people ta have ta live with."

Tom went back to securing the horses.

"Now your pa was a regular hand. He was definitely the best thing that ever happened ta my sister. If she was here right now, I believe she'd agree with me. No matter how knotted up she might get, she couldn't put a dent in him. He was as serene as a Sunday afternoon."

"For all the hard praying she did, deep down I think she felt she got out here on her own steam," interrupted Tom.

"Ain't no one made it out here without some divine intervention attached. What I'm tryin' ta tell you is that was a man-sized thing ya done back there with that shit-bird Fender. And it was appropriate for what he done. Ya didn't blink an' that's good. We didn't go lookin' to save no Orientals an' a broken-nosed whore. It just happened.

Sometimes ya just gotta roll with what's thrown at ya."

Print bent down and picked up a small stone and skimmed it across the water. It hopped a half a dozen times. He straightened and looked at his nephew. "I'd like ta see some more of your father in ya sometimes."

Print walked back to the wagon, leaving Tom to tend to the remaining horses.

The woman was lying on a blanket in the shade of some junipers. She sat up at the sound of Print's footsteps.

"How's the nose doin', ma'am?"

The woman raised her hand to hide her face.

"I didn't mean it that way, ma'am. It's bruised and swollen, but that'll be gone soon enough. We're gonna stay here a few days. Let the horses rest. We're takin' them ta Sheridan, Wyoming. We've been on the move from Oregon. You're welcome ta join us until we reach a place of your choosing."

The woman kept her hand over her face and extended the other. "My name's Nola. Nola Johns. Thank you."

"Well, thank you. I don't know what happened back there. You seemed ta be doin' your best ta help these girls. Would ya like a cup of coffee? A little whisky might buck up your spirits."

Nola shook her head.

"We eat simple on the trail. Mostly cowboy chuck, but I'll see if Tom can bring in some fresh game. If you're up ta it, you could join us for supper."

"Thank you."

Print walked over to Lung Hay, who was talking to the girls. "How ya feelin', Lung Hay?" asked Print. He tapped his forehead with his finger. "How's the noggin feelin'? Maybe ya could tell the girls that we're goin' ta stay here for a few days to rest the horses. So we can all relax an' rest up for the trail."

Tom was riding less than a mile from the wagon when he saw five pronghorns grazing. He dismounted and removed the rifle from the scabbard. He ground-tied the gelding and moved forward a half dozen steps. He knelt and took a pinch of grass and let it fall to test the wind. He raised the Remington and steadied it and fired.

That evening by the river the campfire was burning bright. An antelope was on a makeshift spit, and everyone but the woman was watching Print grind the pepper mill over it and sprinkle salt. They all looked up at Nola's approach. Tom, Print, and Heck stood and removed their hats.

"Evening, Miss Johns," said Heck. "Glad you could join us."

"We got biscuits, beans, an' fresh antelope," added Print.

Tom offered her the nail keg for a seat, and Heck handed her a plate prepared by Print. Print noticed that her face was a mess. Wine-colored bruises covered a good part of it.

"Lung Hay, I'm gonna let you talk ta the girls about whatever the rest of us are sayin'. You tell 'em as much or as little as ya see fit, it that's all right with you."

Lung Hay agreed, and Print proceeded to tell Nola the circumstances of their journey. She sat in silence with the plate balanced on her knee, eating and listening about Billy Via and Captain Fender and the sheepmen and Fort Hall. When he was through, he offered her more food and was surprised as she polished off a second plateful. There was the muted voice of Lung Hay in the background, much like the sound of the river. Once in a while the girls would turn their heads from watching the Chinaman to look at the men, as if they didn't remember the events that way.

Print finished the story about the same time the last of the food gave out. Everyone lent a hand to cleaning up.

Heck stoked the fire, and Tom checked on the horses.

"The boys made a place for you an' the girls ta sleep. It's hard ta maintain much privacy on the trail, but we'll do our best ta give ya room."

Tom and Heck had rigged a fly sheet that stretched off the side of the wagon and put blankets and bedrolls under it. The increase in the members of the party was putting a strain on the bedding supply. The men opted to sleep on their horse blankets and cover up with slickers. Heck, who had come to them missing boots, much less a duster or slicker, said that he was just fine and laid his horse blanket close to the fire. Lung Hay preferred to sleep in the bed of the wagon. Tom felt sure the horses weren't going anywhere but promised to get up and check on them. Soon the camp was silent, save the sound of the water and the peepers.

Print was deep in sleep, having dreams about Lung Hay's head and Nola's smashed nose, and at some point, he dreamed about the Chimborazo hospital high on a bluff above the James River. He was sitting in the grass and it was evening and the boys were all joking and swapping stories. A soldier would say something about home, or the pretty girl back home, or the thought of a mother doing all the fieldwork back home, and the men would get silent. They would look over at the lights of Richmond, the biggest city most of them had ever seen. Then someone would start up about a fellow who had shit in his pants the first time he heard a twenty-gun battery unload. They would all laugh and then go on to another story. At one point the Chinaman was sitting with them, and he saw Nola pass by dressed as a nurse.

He woke and got up to relieve himself. He saw that Tom was gone and looked into the night to see if he was with the horses. He walked back and added wood to the embers. He could hear Nola snoring loudly. Considering the damage done to her nose, it was not surprising. He lay down and went to sleep and dreamed no more, or if he did, he didn't remember in the morning.

The morning was busy cooking and getting the horses out of the river mud and back to the rest of the herd. Except for a couple of young horses, the herd was in good flesh, according to Tom's assessment. The girls were anxious to walk with Lung Hay as he told them what he knew of this country they had been brought to. He told them what he thought of the uncle and his nephew and Sun Foy told him her thoughts.

Heck tended to Nola's face, cleaning the last of the dried blood. Tom left to hunt more game, and Print took a hatchet that they had found among the gear in the wagon and set about lopping branches from the spruce and junipers and dragging them back to the wagon.

When the girls returned, Lung Hay was carrying plants that had been pulled up from their roots, which he obliquely referred to as medicine. Print felt a momentary twinge of resentment, but it passed. Always be open to knowledge, he thought. He had the girls set about pulling the sprigs of evergreen from the larger boughs and had them start a pile under the fly sheet. Then he started to spread the pile and indicated that it would serve as a bed.

"An' it'll have a nice smell, too."

Later Nola took the girls upriver to bathe. Print warned them not to go too far and to yell loud if there was a problem. Armed with bucket, brush, and soap, they departed.

Tom returned with a saddlebag full of partridge and doves. Tied to the saddle horn was a brace of grouse. He was letting his horse set his own pace as they followed the river line. He passed a stand of stunted chokecherry trees. Below, he saw the woman and the girls bathing. Nola was cradling little Number Five in her arms as Number Two poured water from the bucket over the little girl's head. Their backs were to him except for Number Three. He tugged lightly on the reins, and the horse was content to stop. He moved his head from side to side as the breeze moved the branches.

Sun Foy looked up and saw him beyond the river-bank, looking down. He froze, hoping she could not see him. But she had. She was in water up to her waist but made no move to cover herself. She looked past Nola and the girls and up at him. Finally she broke the moment, as she didn't want the others to know he was there, spying on them. She helped Nola with Ghing Wa, and when Tom felt they were sufficiently preoccupied, he moved the horse along and out of sight. Sun Foy looked up again and saw that he was gone.

Print made a big deal out of supper that night and everyone ate well. Lung Hay translated the dinner conver-sation. The girls and Nola retired to the bed of evergreen sprigs and the men settled in around the fire and sipped some bug juice. Print whittled, Tom smoked, Lung Hay rebraided his long pigtail, and Heck kept the cups supplied, although the Chinaman was not a drinker of the spirits.

"Nothing like a couple of hot meals and some extra sleep to put a shine on things," said Tom.

Heck lifted his cup. "Relax, ruminate, and reflect."

Uncle and nephew joined in hoisting their cups.

"Ta be wild, woolly, an' hard ta curry," added Print.

Again they lifted their cups and drank. Print lay aside his knife and a piece of wood to take out his pipe. He packed the bowl with burly cut.

"What brought you out here, Hank?"

Heck still got thrown occasionally by the way Print interchanged his name. He swirled the whisky in his tin cup, then looked at Print. "Ever been to Philadelphia?"

Tom and Print shook their heads.

"It was all a little too neat back there. Too many people. Like all the air had been used up. I got a good education and all it did was make me want to travel. I knew there was more to life than Sunday strolls along the Schuylkill River. So I cashed out. Broke my parents' hearts, but I didn't look back.

"What about you, Mr. Ritter? What's in this for you?"

Print puffed his pipe, then took a sip and looked into the fire. "Well, ya see, Hank, I've spent mosta my life on the hurricane deck of a cow pony. An' more than a few evenings, I listened ta them cows settlin' down for the night an' asked my maker that very question."

"So what did he say?"

"Well, he didn't send me no telegram. Ya know, I've had ice water down my back, dust up my nose, an' boils on my butt. I've been rolled on, busted my ribs, a foot, an' my nose," he said, pointing to the parts of his body with the pipe stem.

"Had my heart stomped more 'n once. Truth be told, I spent a good deal of my life never bein' worth more 'n a hundr'd dollars. Boil all that down an' I don't believe there's been too many days I ain't felt that life was grand, that I've been a lucky fella to watch it."

Print clamped his pipe between his teeth and relit it.

"What about women?" Heck asked.

"Women? There's been a few. One I even set up house with. Black-haired an' green-eyed. We was bedded but not churched, ya might say. She did make me get baptized. Even held me under water. Guess they shoulda used som' soap 'cuz it just didn't take. In the end I think she wished they'd held me under for about ten minutes."

"You're just a pushover for the ladies, Uncle."

Print snorted and took another puff. "Nephew, there ain't a man alive that can stand up ta the power of that little cooter. The holt it has on a man is unbreakable. It'll bring a strong man ta his knees. Read your history. Look at the kings an' kingdoms that have fallen ta that little split tail."

Print looked from one to the other to make sure they understood him. "A road agent 'ill demand your money or your life. A woman requires both."

The men chuckled, and Lung Hay nodded with a sagacious smile.

"The mysteries of women are like the Egyptian hieroglyphics, an' I sure ain't found the Rosetta stone yet. Truth is, I never really understood their language."

"I think I'll stick to horses," said Tom, rolling another smoke.

"Don't let my lack of success put ya off. There's a lot ta be said for the companionship of a woman. Ain't that right, Heck?"

"I'm not sure I can shed much light on the subject. Other than the most shallow of dalliances with the ladies, I tend to keep wanting to move on. My standards require a statement of honesty about my lack of long-term interest. That usually busts it with the ladies. I find myself taking comfort in the arms of soiled doves."

"There's som' safe an' soberin' advice."

"A short-term cure for a long-term ailment, I'm afraid," replied Heck as he added another splash to every-one's cups.

Nola lay on the bed of evergreens, listening to the men. Number Four tossed in her sleep, chased by some nightmare only she saw. The firelight reflected on the tall trees. Tom tossed a chunk of wood on the fire and a shower of sparks ascended toward a canopy of brilliant stars.

"What do you think about marriage, Lung Hay?" asked Tom.

"When I was a boy, my father told me that a man without a wife was like a stallion without a fence."

"Well, shit. That sounds pretty good to me," said Tom.

"Nephew, how many stallions ya seen out there on the range? Sure it's dandy there in the beginnin'. All those fillies winkin' at ya. You out there laying claim ta as many as ya can jump. But pretty soon you're spendin' most of your time fightin' off ever' stiff dick in the neighborhood 'til ya get your teeth kicked in or a hock busted bad enough and then you're gummin' hard grass. An' some other swingin' dick 'ill be takin' care of your ladies. No, the Chinese make a good point. Marriage is an institution."

"So's the state penitentiary," chuckled Heck.

"Ah, come on, Hank, it ain't suppose ta be a death sentence. It's about give an' take. Ain't that right, Lung Hay?"

"Chinese say a deaf husband and a blind wife make a good marriage."

"There ya go! Exactly my point," replied Print, pointing with his pocketknife at Lung Hay. "The Chinese are a smart people. I've always said that."

Heck rolled his eyes and Tom shook his head.

"Look, I already admitted that I don't understand women too much. An' I ain't been lucky with 'em. But that don't mean that I can't see the logic in marriage. ... A little bug juice, if you please," asked Print as he held his cup out to Heck.

"Ah, hell. He's getting wound up now," said Tom, tossing another piece of wood on the fire.

"Livin' out here has changed a lot of things. Suspended the conventions of eastern life. That's probably why you like it so much, Hank. Women plowing land and pannin' for gold. Men sewin' up their own britches, cookin' for themselves. That's well an' fine. It's good for the people an' good for the country. But too much? No, sir. Without women an' marriage, we'd all be shot or drunk ourselves ta death or died of the clap. No, sir."

"Don't think ya can die of the clap, Uncle."

"A small point. You'd wished ya had ever' time ya had

ta make water, so I've heard."

Print slipped the figure he was carving back into his vest and closed his pocketknife. "All I'm sayin' is that you two colts are still young enough ta make a run at it. I'm the ol' caballo here. Out there, with the bunged-up hock an' no teeth eatin' prickly pear choy waitin' for the blizzard."

Tom winked at Heck. "Guess we better take you and old Bob Tate out and shoot you both right now. Sounds like the only kind thing to do."

Print shot his nephew a look that had a smile attached to it, but not much of one. "The blizzard ain't here yet, Nephew."

Heck got up and stretched. He took his cup and dropped it in the washbasin. "Boys, I'm off to the Land of Nod. See you in the morning."

The others watched him head for the woods before turning in. Tom turned to his uncle and said, "Maybe I ought to go to Sacramento or down to Denver and find a rich woman to marry."

Print quit whittling and moved his pipe from one side of his mouth to the other. "My advice would be ta never marry for money, son. Neither of ya will be gettin' or givin' love. You'll both just be rentin' it out. If ya need money that bad, go to a bank. That's what they was invented for."

"Damn. There's no pleasing you tonight."

Print brushed the shavings from his lap. He removed the pipe from his mouth and tapped out the ash. "If you was ever lucky enough ta find a woman that could stand your stubbornness for more 'n three days and in fact ya did get married, it might not work out. But if you never marry, sure as shit draws flies you will be sorry."

Tom said nothing. Print rose and walked over and patted him on the shoulder.

"Why don't ya get yourself some sleep, son. I don't

think ya have ta worry 'bout no wedding bells in the next couple a weeks."

Print walked off to the trees to pee. Tom called out to him, "Be careful not to bump into anything out there in the dark, old man."

Print replied, "The best thing I found in my life I bumped inta in the dark."

Print laughed and Tom smiled.

Tom looked across the fire at Lung Hay. "You ever married?"

The Chinaman nodded yes.

"A long time?"

"Many years. Still have wife in China."

"What brought you to America?"

"Gum San."

"Gum San? What's that?"

"Gum San. Gold Mountain. All Chinese hear California was Gold Mountain. Gum San. I leave my young wife with my parents and come to be a rich man. Now my wife is old, my parents are dead, and I am not a rich man."

"Think you'll ever see her again?"

"Maybe. We are old people now."

Tom nodded and they sat in silence. Tom sighed deeply.

"Lung Hay, you play checkers?"

"Oh, yes."

"Good deal. First chance I get, I'm gonna get a board and chips. A helluva lot more civilized than poker."

"Oh, I like poker," said a smiling Lung Hay.

CHAPTER TWENTY-TWO

A purple skink crawled into the sun and onto a flat rock to warm his reptilian blood in preparation for a breakfast of some juicy bug. Not far away, smoke from Print's campfire curled above the tallest pines. Print was late getting up, and when he did, he felt a headache. He also noticed that none of the girls was next to him. They had stayed the night with Nola. Again Heck had breakfast going and the others were eating. Print made a trip behind a wide tree and then went down to the river to splash water in his face to clear his head. He returned to the group and tipped his hat to Nola.

"Mornin', Miss Johns."

"Morning, Mr. Ritter."

"Honkle Pren," said Number Five.

"That's right, 'Honkle Pren.' How's the head feelin', Lung Hay?"

"Much better, thank you. How is your head?" asked Lung Hay in the most innocent tone.

Print shot him a look but wasn't sure about the question so he let it pass. He took a plate from Heck and clasped a biscuit in his mouth. He found a spot and sat down. He took the biscuit and used it to push food onto his fork.

"I wish som' smart fella would invent a way ta take a couple of hens on the trail. I would surely enjoy some fresh eggs."

"Ya mean the Romans didn't already figger that one out?" asked Tom, with as much of a straight face as he could muster that early in the day.

"You'll hafta excuse my nephew, Miss Johns. He takes great delight in thumbin' his nose at my attempts to impart a drop 'r two of historical knowledge."

"Maybe you should take Miss Johns for a walk and you can tell her all about ornithology and the wonders of city waterworks systems. It makes for facinatin' conversation."

Print started to reply, but food almost fell out of his mouth. He stopped it with the back of his hand. Swallowed and cleared his throat. "Ya can see the task I have before me."

They all cleaned the camp. Tom announced his intention to hunt for more game, and Heck volunteered to check the horses, which were grazing in the meadow. Tom gestured to Sun Foy to ask if she wanted to join him. Lung Hay cleared up the matter, and the girl agreed. Nola went with Lung Hay and the rest of the girls for a walk. Print sat with his hangover and poured another cup.

It wasn't long before his solitude was interrupted by movement across the river. He got up and casually walked to the wagon, where his gun and holster were. He made no attempt to retrieve them but stood and watched a procession of riders and packhorses walk along the opposite bank from this camp. The rider leading the procession was dressed in buckskins. Print took a quick glance in the wagon bed to find the location of his gun.

The buckskin rider called out, "Hey over there."

Print reached for the big Colt, withdrew it, and slipped it into his waistband.

"Mornin', neighbor," the voice called out.

"Mornin'," Print called back.

"Mind if we cross?"

Print did not reply.

"I'm guiding these folks on a hunting and fishing trip."

The buckskin rider had the horse in the shallows,

prepared to cross. Print saw several men, definitely not turned out in local attire, and a woman. He replaced the pistol in the wagon and walked toward the river's edge.

"Come on. Quietly. I got a herd an' mustangs grazin'."

"So I see. Quite a string you got there."

"Come on. Just give the herd a wide berth."

The rider waded on in, followed by the others. Print stood on the water's edge as they forded the shallow crossing. The buckskin man walked his horse out of the water in front of Print.

"Huntin' an' fishin'," commented Print.

"Yes, sir. It's all the rage these days." He reached down and extended his hand to Print. "They're from back East. Dudes, but they're all right. Good people." He bent lower and whispered, "Even if they are Yankees."

Print smiled and turned to walk up the bank.

"Mind if we rest a while? I been pushin' 'em hard since dawn."

"Sure. Just mind the herd."

Soon all were across, and still mounted. The buckskin man did the introductions.

"Name's Yip Dawes."

"Print Ritter."

"Well, Mr. Ritter, this here is Mr. Robert Bentingcourt. That's Mr. William Rice Findley, Mr. G. G. Pollard, and the lovely Mrs. Bentingcourt."

Print tipped his hat to the lady. "How 'bout som' coffee? We got a fresh pot workin'."

"That sounds good. Thank you."

They all dismounted, and an Indian in buckskins took the reins of the horses and led them away. Print watched the man leave.

"That's Kaybo. He's a Mandan—white man cross. He's all right too. He's the packer, tracker, skinner, an' cook," said Yip.

Print kept watching and then turned to his new guests. "Anyone that don't want coffee?" he asked. "Might have ta rinse out a few cups first."

Print started pouring as Kaybo returned with a packhorse and quickly untied several folding chairs and opened them.

"Ain't that handy," remarked Print.

Yip retrieved more cups from the washbasin and soon everyone was sipping hot coffee.

"So huntin' an' fishin' is the thing to do these days?"

"People back home can't get enough of it," said Pollard.

"Where's home?

"I am originally from Elmira, New York. Mr. Findley and the Bentingcourts are from Boston, where I now live," replied Pollard.

"You a fisherman or a hunter, Miz Bentingcourt?"

"Both, actually. This is our honeymoon. And please call me Eva."

"Well, if you folks want ta camp here for the night, we'd enjoy the company for supper."

"Marvelous," said Bentingcourt. "But you must let us provide the repast. Are you on for fish tonight, Mr. Ritter?"

Print shoved his hands deep in his pockets and rocked back on his heels. He looked to Yip. "Why sure. We ain't had fish in at least a week."

"Then if you will excuse us, Mr. Ritter, we have dinner to catch."

Print gestured toward the river. "Help yourself. You fellas need any bait? I could grub up som' worms for ya."

"No, indeed," said Findley. This is fly-fishing we'll be doing. Wet and dry flies are all we will be using."

Yip and Kaybo started unloading the mules, while the anglers opened leather tubes and took out bamboo sections that they assembled into rods. Bentingcourt struggled into a pair of rubber pants.

"What ya got there, Mr. Bentingcourt?"

"Chest waders made of vulcanized rubber so I can go where the fish are."

The dudes headed for the river as Yip and Kaybo started setting up camp.

Lung Hay, Nola, and the girls returned to find large, elaborate tents up and two collapsible tables set up with numerous chairs. Print did the introductions. And then did it again as Heck walked in.

"Where you been?" asked Print.

"Actually, I took a nap over there in those hemlocks. Too much whisky and too little sleep last night."

Print lifted Number Five and carried her on his hip and started for the riverbank. He pointed to the people by the river's edge. "They do any fly-fishin' back in China?"

Ghing Wa couldn't care less what he was talking about. She just liked to be carried around by the old man. He found a spot on the west side of the bend in the river and lowered the girl. He sat down too. The three men and the woman were strung out along the riverbank with Bentingcourt going into the water wearing his vulcanized rubber pants.

Print told the little girl what the people were doing, and she listened as if she understood him. The long poles bent as they moved back and forth in the air. Gossamer fishing line floated high overhead, and the sun caught the damp line and it looked liked long loops of silver thread moving ever so lightly in the air. The poles moved back and forth like metronomes and Print saw that there was, if not a rhythm, then at least a cadence to what the anglers were doing. He explained this to the girl, and when he filled his pipe and took out the matches, she held out her hand and he let her strike the match and light his pipe. He bent close so she could reach the pipe's bowl. He drew deeply and blew a perfect smoke ring. The girl squealed and tried to put her finger through the smoky circle. She tugged on his shirtsleeve and he blew another. And he said to himself that there was a lot more to life than being worth more than a hundred dollars.

The poles swayed and Print and Ghing Wa were content to sit and watch them. From the top branches of a huge ponderosa an eagle fell, pulling up just before it hit the water, and then skimmed along in front of the fishermen. It hit the water with its talons and stopped on the surface. There was splashing and the bird struggled to get airborne, a big trout in its grasp.

"There goes dinner, boys!" hollered Print.

"God, wasn't that magnificent!" cried Eva Bentingcourt.

"Yes, it was," Print whispered to himself.

"Means the fish are rising," called out Findley.

Means that eagle gets supper tonight, Print said to himself.

Soon they were in the thick of it, reeling in fish. Every time the line hit the water, a fish took it. Yip walked up and sat down next to Print. Ghing Wa had no more pipes to light, so she wandered closer to the water.

"Too hot ta be workin' in buckskins," said Yip.

"I was meanin' ta ask you about them. You look like ya gone native."

"The easterners lap it up. I think of it as a costume."

"A while back we had three rank-lookin' bucks get up in our faces an' wolf us out of a damn fine horse. It ain't exactly Boston out here."

"Hell's fire, man, if I could raise Sittin' Bull hisself up from the dead ta swoop down an' plunk a couple a arrows in their arses, I swear I believe they'd pay me double. They can't get enough of this."

Yip pulled out a pipe and tamped tobacco into it. He

offered his pouch to Print, who declined.

"Ya like what you're doin', this fishin', huntin' deal?"

"This? Man, I wouldn't trade this ta be the top rump rider in the finest whorehouse in San Francisco. I done 'bout everything out here ta earn a nickel. Trapping, lumber, pannin'. Even cleaned out piss pots for a hotel down in Julesburg. No, this is the best deal this dog's ever had."

The fishing party was walking toward them, loaded down with big, shiny trout.

The men were preparing the evening meal. Tom had brought back pronghorns and plenty of birds. Print enlisted the help of the girls to pluck and clean the fowl, while Tom and Heck field-dressed the antelope. Yip and Kaybo were at the river's edge, squatting on a long, flat rock, cleaning fish, as the men of the Bentingcourt party watched.

Tom and Heck had rubbed the carcass in pepper and Print took the cuts and skewered them on the spit. First the shank, then the rump, the loin, and the flank. Next the shoulder, rib, and brisket. He took the liver, sliced it into long strips, and had it simmering in a saucepan of bacon fat and wild scallions that Lung Hay and the girls brought back with them. In another pot, huckleberries, with a liberal application of whiskey, were bubbling slowly.

He sent the girls out to pick prairie sage and quizzed Lung Hay on his knowledge of wild mushrooms as opposed to toadstools. The Chinaman assured him no one would be poisoned. Upon the girls' return, he rinsed the birds in water, then stuffed their cavities with prairie sage and wrapped them in muslin.

Kaybo and Yip returned with the cleaned and filleted fish. Kaybo set up shop on the other side of the cook fire. Soon both Print and the other cook were preparing a varied dinner. Kaybo had the advantage of more pots, pans, spices, and condiments at his disposal. Before long the trout were sizzling in pans garnished with various herbs and seasonings. Not to be outdone, Print skewered the quail and doves on sticks to hang above the fire to cook.

Nola walked up, a shawl about her, her face heavily bruised, but the swelling was going down. Print stood, wiping his hands on his pants. He introduced her. "Miss Johns is employed to take care of the girls. She had a nasty spill, but she's on the mend now."

As a dozen birds were roasting over the fire and four large skillets of trout sizzled, a large pot of beans with molasses and strips of bacon on top bubbled. The Dutch oven, buried in the hot coals, was baking biscuits. Pollard hoisted a bottle in the air.

"Some Madeira, ladies and gentlemen?" Pollard started pouring into the extended tin cups.

Lung Hay, Kaybo, and Nola declined.

"Sir, to your hospitality, a virtue for all fellow travelers," said Pollard.

They all toasted, and more Madeira was poured.

"To Robert's honeymoon—before he starts working for a new boss."

They laughed and drinks were downed. Yip stood and held out his cup for a refill. He held it in the air. "To Mrs. Bentingcourt, who skinned a wolf and got a mink."

Robert Bentingcourt stood.

"Now, with gusto and God's good graces, let us devour our hard-won dinner."

Plates and utensils were passed as Print and Kaybo ladled food. Cuts of meat, filets of trout, beans, and golden biscuits were served. The camp fell silent save the clinking sound of plates and forks. Lips and chins shone with drippings from the bird meat. Yip brought bottles of wine to be opened and passed around.

"I'm feeling more like the guest than the host here," said Print.

"Nonsense. Not everyone offers to share their fire

with strangers," quipped Bentingcourt.

Heck stabbed a thin slice of lemon from his fish and held it up on the end of his fork.

"How do you get fresh lemons up here on the Divide?"

"Shipped in to Rawlins from Saint Louis. Packed in sawdust. Keeps them fresh," answered Findley.

More food and drink were consumed. Biscuits sopped up the last of the beans and molasses and bits of trout. Print leaned back. "It don't get much better than that."

"Oh, yes, it does. Kaybo, if you please."

Kaybo had removed a covered dish from the coals and lifted the lid to reveal the contents of a brown-and-golden confection.

"Apple pandowdy, à la Kaybo."

"Say your prayers, boys. I think we just passed through the pearly gates," said Heck.

Fresh plates with the dessert were passed around and all ate in silence. After dinner, more wood was added to the fire as all sat around drinking coffee or sipping some of Bentingcourt's aged port.

"This is a truly magnificent country out here," said Bentingcourt.

"Well, you'd better enjoy it while ya can, 'fore the bankers, lawyers, and politicians ruin it," said Print.

The easterners looked at one another. Finally Pollard spoke up. "I take it you do not care for men of those professions."

"No, sir, I do not. You can take a banker, a politician, and a lawyer, shove them in a barrel, kick it down a hill, and there'd be a son of a bitch on top every time. Pardon me, ladies. Too much of Mr. Bentingcourt's fine wine makes me forgetful that we are in the company of such lovely ladies."

"That's quite all right, Mr. Ritter," said Eva

Bentingcourt. "You just happened to have dined with two bankers, two lawyers, and a politician. You see, my husband is a banker and a lawyer. Mr. Findley is a banker, and Mr. Pollard is a lawyer and a state assemblyman for the Commonwealth of Massachusetts."

"You'll have to excuse me, ma'am," said Print. "At my age I cannot touch my toes, but I got no problem puttin' my foot in my mouth."

Everyone laughed.

"Why do you feel men of our professions are so bad for your part of the country?" asked Findley.

"You're askin' me ta skate on thin ice after such a wonderful supper."

"We didn't get to be who we are by being thin-skinned, Mr. Ritter. I'm curious. Why are we such a blight?"

Print paused, took out his tobacco pouch, and started to fill his pipe. "I was referring ta the professions in general as opposed ta our present company. From what I seen of men in your profession, they don't care for gamblin'. See, the West was made on gamblin'. The whole country is thick with gamblers. I seen waddies bet a month's wages on who had the most bedbugs in his blankets. I heard a two pistoleros down in Raton that bet all they had as to who could sustain the most nonlethal wounds at twenty paces. I seen a man shoot a coffee can off his wife's head ta collect a fifty-dollar bet. And he done it, too. Course, he was a Mormon and had a solid inventory of wives ta spare."

He struck a match, puffed the pipe, and took a sip of port. "That's just the picayune stuff. Nobody come out here that wasn't gamblin'. Rich or poor. White or colored. They bet against the weather. They bet against locusts, cattle fever, and prairie fires. Cave-ins, floating 'cross rivers, child-birthing. Every morning out here ya draw a breath, it is a gamble, and it ain't going to stop. The West will always be a gamble."

Print paused to flick a small piece of tobacco from his tongue. He wasn't sure if he was being entertaining or insulting to his dinner guests but decided to continue wading in.

"What about Lung Hay?" interjected Tom.

Print nodded in agreement while attempting another sip at the same time. "Mr. Lung Hay here came all the way to California to gamble that he'd be a rich man in the goldfields. Now he's gamblin' if he'll ever see his bride back in China. Tom and I are gamblin' we can get these horses 'cross country ta Sheridan. Only person I seen out here that ain't gamblin' is the red man. He's been forced inta a game that he just keeps drawing bad cards from, and his pot is dwindlin' fast.

"It's all one big gamble, cept house odds don't always apply. Sometimes caution can be almost criminal."

"I will drink to that one," said Tom, holding up his tin cup. "Cautious bankers foreclosin' on a man. Timid politicians back East afraid to help the non-voters out in the territories."

"And lawyers sometimes impeding justice and the need for immediate action," added Heck.

"Are we to assume you prefer vigilante justice?" asked Bentingcourt.

Print could tell that Yip was uncomfortable with the way the conversation was going. "One can be as bad as the other," said Print. "There is an element out here that can't abide with the odds and they have no problem adoptin' a more larcenious attitude ta make things fall in their favor."

"So you've seen frontier justice in action?" asked Pollard.

Print looked from Tom to Heck to Yip and nodded.

"Tell us one ... one that won't incriminate you."

Print relit his pipe and took full advantage of the dramatic pause. "I was privileged ta see the conclusion of a business transaction years ago. Fella name a Ted Arns. Rancher east a Worland was havin' trouble with the unexplained disappearance of som' a his cattle. Now there was a flashy fella that come into that part of the country 'bout the same time Ted and som' a the other ranchers started seein' their inventories dwindle. Now the flashy fella was always turned out in clean pants an' a silk scarf an' a stylish tilt ta his Stetson. Name was Dwayne Fowler. When it came ta brandin', he was said ta be an artist with a runnin' iron."

Print paused for another sip and Tom raised his eyebrows as a signal to hurry it up. "Well, Ted Arns finally tracked the sporty Mr. Fowler down in a saloon in Meeteetse. Back then Meeteetse was a small joint. No sheriff. No magistrate. So Ted called him out right in front of the whisky sippers an' card sharks. He did give him the option ta relocate to a different hemisphere, but a fella that wore his hat the way Dwayne Fowler did wasn't goin' ta be showed up in front of a crowd."

Print peered into his empty cup and made a face. Bentingcourt solved the problem with two fingers of port.

"Fowler said if this wasn't a business issue, it was about respect. Ted Arns disagreed."

Print looked at his audience, milking every dramatic drop that he could. "Fowler was fast in trying to get his point across, but Teddy Arns was more accurate in statin' his case—and the placement of two slugs here an' here," said Print, pointing first to his neck and then to his chest.

"And what happened?" urged Pollard.

"Rancher Arns ended that transaction by putting the flashy Dwayne Fowler inta the 'bills paid' side of the business ledger."

Broad grins were on the faces of all the people who understood English. Print was beginning to see what Yip meant about their love of western color.

"What about the girls?" asked Eva Bentingcourt.

Print shifted his weight to get more comfortable. "Sometimes I bloviate too much. Let Tom tell that one."

So Tom proceeded to tell the story about the girls and Fender and Cariboo. He left out the part about Big Rump Kate and skirted around Nola's involvement. Kaybo, Sun Foy, and Heck cleared dishes as Tom told the story.

" ... and that Captain Billy Fender, he was a gambler too. He was a miserable son of a bitch. Excuse me, ladies. You'll have to take my word for it. He was the kinda fellow that'd steal his own blankets, but he was a gambler, right up to the moment he cashed out."

The group was silent as they pondered Tom's words.

"Is there a musician in your party, Mrs. Bentingcourt?" asked Heck. "I saw the violin case."

"Mr. Findley is a fine musician," replied Eva.

"Would you honor us, Mr. Findley?" asked Heck.

"I would, Mr. Gilpin, except that I managed to run a fishhook in my thumb the other day and I am afraid that you would regret having to hear me. Do you play, sir?"

"I do, some."

"Then, sir, be my guest, and put a topping on this lovely evening."

Heck retrieved the violin case, took out the instrument, and tuned it. He started to play. All the faces of the party shone in the campfire light as they watched Heck. It was exquisite. Lyrical. As he played, he bowed and winked at the girls. All were transfixed. And when Heck finished, they all applauded.

"Bravo, bravo, Mr. Gilpin. What was that piece?" asked Bentingcourt.

"*Caprice*. By Fritz Kreisler," replied Eva Bentingcourt.

"Indeed it is, ma'am," said Heck, nodding to the lady.

"Who would have thought that we would hear one so contemporary as Kreisler under the stars of Wyoming? Surely that is rarer than fresh lemons," said Eva.

"I heard him play when he toured back in eighty-eight," said Heck as he tuned one of the strings.

"Please, Mr. Gilpin, another piece."

He bowed slightly to Eva. "Ma'am." He turned to the others. "*MacLeish's Waltz.*"

Heck played a haunting melody, a work more emblematic of the times and the region. After a few bars, Bentingcourt stood and reached for his wife's hand. He started to lead her in a waltz. The men backed up and moved to give them space. Eva was radiant. Nola watched her and instinctively covered her bruised face with a hand. Print noticed, struggled to his feet, and extended his hand to Nola.

"Miss Johns, may I?"

She tried to turn away, but Print took her and gently brought her to her feet. The two couples danced around the fire to the slow waltz. Even on the rough ground, they were graceful. Nola averted Print's attempt at eye contact.

"You're lighter than my biscuits, Miss Johns. Positively weightless."

She smiled slightly but shook her head in denial.

"Don't take my word for it."

He stopped and waited for the Bentingcourts to pass, and then he tapped Robert Bentingcourt on the shoulder. They changed partners, and Bentingcourt danced with Nola around the fire. Heck played on, and then they changed partners again.

"See, I ain't the only one thinks you're a fine dancer, Miss Johns."

Heck drew long notes from the violin, which resonated in the night air. When he finished, Eva curtsied, and Nola followed suit. The men bowed and everyone clapped.

"A perfect topping on the evening, Mr. Gilpin."

Heck bowed.

Slowly the girls got to their feet. Nola escorted them

back to the wagon and their pallets. The Bentingcourt party retired. Print banked the fire, and Heck piled the last of the cups into the big washbasin.

"I think I'll go sit with the horses a while," said Tom.

Print placed his blanket close to the fire, removed his boots, and lay back to fall asleep. Kaybo joined him at the fire, spreading his bedroll on the other side. The cream-colored tents blinked out, one by one.

CHAPTER TWENTY-THREE

The next morning after breakfast, the Bentingcourt party prepared for another day of fishing. Nola had gathered up a bundle of laundry, and Number Three and Number Two followed her with bundles too.

"Anything you want washed, Mr. Ritter?"

"I think I'm fine, thank ya. Mind if I join you? Probably a good idea ta stay downstream of the fishermen."

He picked up little Number Five in his arms and led the way down to the riverbank. He found a spot downstream from the camp with a big, flat rock that jutted out into the water. Soon Nola and the girls were scrubbing laundry and rinsing it at the water's edge. Print found a comfortable spot to sit and watch.

"Ya haven't said what happened back at that hotel room."

Nola continued scrubbing and didn't bother to look up. "I went to check on the girls. ... I was sent to check on the girls."

She turned and looked at Print. "I worked for Kate Becker. I believe you met her."

She went back to washing. She wiped away a strand of hair that had fallen in front of her face. "She wanted to know what you were up to with these girls. When I got to your room, those men were already there. I tried to stop them, really I did."

"Pretty obvious from what they done to you that you tried."

"We were fortunate that you and your nephew came upon us when you did."

"I appreciate what you did to protect the girls, Miss Johns."

"What you told them last night at supper about how you came to have the girls—is that true?"

Print gave her a questioning look. "Yes, ma'am, one hundred percent true."

"Why did you do it, Mr. Ritter? Take in the girls, I mean."

"What was I supposed to do? Give them a canteen and a tin of crackers and say adios?"

"I wasn't suggesting that, Mr. Ritter. I only wanted to know why you took them with you."

"Miss Johns, I'm a thoroughly failed Christian person, but I wasn't about ta leave them out there in the middle of nowhere. No, sir. And I didn't have no carnal designs on 'em neither, if that's what you was thinkin'."

"I didn't think either of those thoughts, Mr. Ritter."

Print took out his pocketknife and a little figurine of a girl and started to whittle. Nola continued to scrub and rinse the clothes, and the girls took them and spread them on the rock to dry. Print and Nola sat in silence for several minutes.

"It's Mrs. Johns."

There was more silence as Print took the knife blade and ran it against the rock he was sitting on to sharpen it. "How'd ya wind up in the employ of Miss Big Rump?"

"One dance with a girl and you want to know all about her, Mr. Ritter."

Print smiled sheepishly. The girls took more linen to spread on the rocks.

"We came out here from Illinois. Mr. Johns's people had a small farm near Moline. We lived with his folks, working the farm. Kel's—my husband's—ma died and about a year after his papa died. Turns out they left the farm to Kel's sister and her husband. We were left with almost nothing. Kel said he couldn't live in Illinois after that. Said he wanted to make a new start in the West. So we took what little we had and struck out for the 'New Canaan,' so to speak. Spent our first winter in Omaha. Next year we moved to Laramie. Kel got a job freighting supplies to a mining camp up in the Centennial Range. Thirty-seven miles each way. Twice a week. We were making do until he drove the wagon off a switchback.

"They brought him back to Laramie. He survived, but they took both his legs off. We barely had a nest, much less a nest egg. I worked at whatever I could and got a job clerking in a dry goods store. But he'd sit upstairs in the boardinghouse all day. They came to the store the first day of May to tell me he had shot himself."

She paused and looked at Print. He had been looking at her, but he dropped his gaze as if to concentrate on the little figurine he was whittling. With no more washing to spread, the girls were playing down by the water's edge.

"I had no money and there was no going back to Kel's people."

"Families sure can be hard 'n one another."

"You think so, Mr. Ritter?"

"Absolutely. It was family hardness that set Tom an' I on this course for Wyoming."

"Maybe if I'd been as brave as my husband, I would have put an end to it right there. But I was young and scared. Fear and hunger will make a person do things they never pictured for themselves. You sure you really want to hear this?"

"You tell me as much or as little as ya like. I ain't a judge or a preacher."

She looked out across the water, away from Print. "I started there in Laramie. Then it was Walcott, Medicine Bow, Rawlins, all over, wherever the mines were hitting pay dirt or the cattle were selling." She spoke in a level voice devoid of emotion.

She turned to look Print right in the eyes. "It's a rough trade, Mr. Ritter. Easy enough for you men, but rough if you're on the receiving end."

She looked back out across the water. "I was in Rock Springs. A man split my scalp with a bottle and dumped me out the back door. It was around the middle of November. They found me the next morning. My hair was frozen to the ground."

Again she turned to look at Print. "They had to cut my hair off."

Even Print could not hold her gaze, and he looked away.

"You know what a whore with no hair is worth in this world, Mr. Ritter? Not much."

Print looked up into the sky at the sound of a hawk keening high above them.

"Thing is, sometimes even a bald-headed whore wants to keep living. Your hair grows out. Life goes on. But time's against you."

Print interjected. "Nothin' more unforgivin' than time."

Nola continued. "You feel it setting in like a hard freeze. You start out in the parlor houses if you're young and have any looks at all. But youth and beauty start to go fast. I never understood how something that God meant to be so wonderful could wear a woman out so fast. Soon you're at the rooming house at the end of town. Next stop are the cribs down the line. Finally, if you haven't been killed or done yourself in, it's the hog ranch. Ever pay a visit to a hog ranch, Mr. Ritter?"

Print, who was looking down at the little figurine, raised his head to meet her eyes. He shook his head.

"That's the last rung. I'm about halfway down that ladder.

"Still think you want to go dancing with me, Mr.

Ritter?"

Print looked down at the palm of his left hand while he rubbed it with his right thumb. "I guess you're down on men."

"I don't hate all men. Most of you aren't bad. They just wanted to pop their cork. A lot of lonely men in the West. I believe most wanted a brief, bright moment of companionship. I had a miner pay me just to watch me hang laundry on a clothesline. Never touched me. And he was a young man, too. In the end, I think it's as much about being lonesome as anything. Sure, you want to pop your cork. That's natural. We do too."

Print shifted his weight and turned to look upstream.

"Does that make you uncomfortable, Mr. Ritter? The idea that women want it just as much as you fellows? Why shouldn't we? There ought to be some payoff for the pain of childbirth. What isn't much of a bargain is being kicked and hit and cut up. It's not natural, and it doesn't fit the definition of companionship. There's no creature on the face of the earth lonelier than a whore, Mr. Ritter."

Ritter looked up at her. "You think you could call me Print?"

Nola ignored the question and brushed back an errant wisp of hair from her face. She rose and gathered up the laundry. The girls returned from the shallows to help her. Print gathered up Number Five in his arms and followed Nola back to the wagon.

Just as she reached the top of the riverbank, Print spoke to her back. "You're the best dancer I ever twirled with."

Nola stopped and stood for a long moment. She turned to face him. "You don't scare easy, do you, Mr. Ritter? ... Print."

She turned and continued walking back to the camp.

Print said nothing, and simply shifted the little girl to his other hip, following Nola and the girls back to camp.

Soon he was joined by Bentingcourt, returning from the riverbank.

"Mr. Ritter, we are going to move upstream a few miles before nightfall. I wanted to thank you for your hospitality. Please take this and enjoy it as the memory of our brief visit."

He handed three bottles of Scotch to Print.

Findley stepped forward and held out his violin case for Heck. "Mr. Gilpin, thank you for last night's recital."

Heck, with a look of surprise, said, "I couldn't. That's much too generous."

"Sir, you must. The image of you playing out under the stars of this western sky will warm the long winter nights in Boston for me. Please."

Heck took the violin case and bowed slightly.

They all stood around the camp and watched as Yip led the party back across the river.

"They're going to make me have to say nice things about Yankees," Print said. With his hands jammed in his pockets, Print turned to face Tom and Heck. "Much as I'm enjoying this spot, figure we ought to strike out in the morning. Can't count on summer holding on forever."

That evening, after supper, while Nola went about collecting the pots, the girls sat on a blanket, watching Heck run rosin down the length of the bow, with the violin lying beside him.

"I think I'll take advantage of all this fresh water and give these pots a good scrubbing," said Nola.

"Let me give you a hand," said Print, standing up to help.

Print took a heavy iron skillet and a stewpot and followed Nola. You could hear Heck in the background, tuning the violin.

At the river Nola knelt and took a handful of river sand and started to scour the pots. Print took a position on a rock and rolled himself a smoke. Faint strains of Heck's violin could be heard in the background.

"I didn't notice you smoking cigarettes before."

"Once in a while, a night like this calls for a good smoke."

The full moon reflected on the rippling water.

She paused at scrubbing the pots. She rose and walked over to a rock and sat down and removed her shoes. She raised her skirt, rolled down her stockings, and soaked her feet in the cool water. Print got up, walked over, and sat down beside her.

"Oh, that feels good. You ought to try it, Mr. Ritter … excuse me, Print."

Print flipped the last of his smoke into the river and proceeded to remove his boots and socks.

"Do you really think women are so puzzling? I heard you talking the other night."

"Oh, that. You mean about the Rosetta stone? No. Maybe I just had bad luck."

"What was it you really wanted from women?"

"I see this is going to be a two-smoke night." Print reached into his shirt pocket to take out his makings. He took the paper, filled it with tobacco, and then rolled the cigarette. He lit up and took a deep draw while Nola watched.

"Same as most fellows, I suppose. What did you call it—a bright, brief moment? How 'bout a partner, a companion? Somebody to keep your feet warm at night."

Nola splashed her feet in the water in response.

"I would like to have known just once in my life that I was truly and deeply loved by a woman, a woman with a heart as true as a rancher's wife."

"You're quite the romantic."

"Romance is for pikers. I ain't talkin' 'bout infatuation. I'm talkin' 'bout something way beyond romance.

Bone deep. You just feel it between the two of you."

Print brought his feet out of the water and looked at them in the moonlight. He gestured with his feet. "If you stub the right toe, the left one feels it."

Nola raised her feet out of the water and held them next to Print's.

"Ain't no he or she or you or me. You're both just one."

"You sound like an expert on the subject."

"Me? Nah. Hell, I don't know what I'm talkin' 'bout half the time. But I do believe it does happen to the lucky few."

"But not to most folks?"

"No. That's why there's so many hard-edged and fearful people out there. It's like livin' your life without salt."

"You don't seem to be lacking any salt in your diet, you know, all hard-edged and scared."

"Oh, I can get spooked, same as everyone else."

"Really? When?"

Print paused to think for a moment. "I get rousted out of my sleep sometimes for nature's call. I find there's something frightnin' about that hour of the night. There ain't no foolin' yourself about what you've done and what you haven't done with your life."

"What do you do?"

"Well, I try like hell to get back to sleep."

They sat for a moment in silence.

"So, have you given up on women?"

"No, ma'am. But I figure I got about as much chance of findin' that gal as becomin' the King of Siam."

Nola laughed. "I have a hard time seeing you as the King of Siam, Mr. Ritter."

"Sure you just can't you call me Print? Everybody else calls me Mr. Ritter."

She looked at him for a moment, smiled, and then said, "I like to think that when I say it, it has a different ring to it."

A broad grin came across Print's face as he looked out onto the water. Then he looked back at her.

"You have a unique sense of humor, Miz Johns. Shall we go?"

Print took his feet out of the water, and as he did, Nola grabbed his ankle. She dried his foot with the hem of her dress, then the other. They put on their boots and shoes. Print stood to help Nola up. They faced one another and Print reached for her face. She drew back.

"I'd pay forty dollars just ta watch you hang laundry any time, Miz Johns."

Slowly he reached again. She didn't resist. He let her hair down and, with a Braille-like touch, ran his fingers over the long white scar on her scalp. He held her head in his hands and drew her to him and kissed the scar.

"Yer a good woman, Miz Johns, you really are."

With her arms at her sides, she rested her head on his chest. They gathered the pots and pans and turned to the sleeping camp.

Where the meadow met the riverbank, she stopped and put the pots down. Print turned and she took the pans from him and put them on the ground too. She untied his kerchief and slipped the suspenders off his shoulders and opened his shirt. She unbuttoned the top of her dress and clothes fell like flags on a field of surrender.

His white body was the color of soap as he lay on the meadow grass. He shivered, and when he felt her body next to his, he shivered again. She pulled him close to her, and she rolled on top of him. She looked down at him and her hair hung down on his cheeks. He couldn't see her face but saw the Great Milky Way in the night sky behind her. It looked like a bride's veil on her. He shook violently, he felt so cold. She kissed his face and held her lips next to his ear and soothed him.

They moved in a pantomime that was older than the

river that ran beside them. They moved alone and they moved together. Then they passed through each other into nothingness. No river. No horses. No stars. He felt himself falling endlessly backward into oblivion.

CHAPTER TWENTY-FOUR

Print was up an hour before the first light appeared in the east. A front had rolled in during the night and left a skin of frost on the camp. He walked over to where the saddle horses were picketed and brushed the crystals off Bob Tate's mane. He sniffed the air; it smelled of horse. He stroked the chestnut's mane and neck. He couldn't ever remember a horse that smelled bad. Unlike the countless humans he had come across. The boys in butternut wool from a summer of marching and the metallic sweat of fear. Miners so drunk they soiled themselves. Whiskey-sick cowboys. The hermits up in the big woods and their huts so rancid that he always slept outside. The Russians who had drifted south from the Yukon and as far as Kamchatka, following the timber trade, smelling of tinned fish and rotten teeth. The gamey tang of the doughy whores. The cheap cologne, their own musk, and the sweat of other men. He doubled-up the cinch strap and flopped the stirrup down. Yes, horses smelled just fine to him.

When the sun came up it burned off the frost, but the day remained cool and sunny. A big magpie alighted on the bough of a hemlock. The bough swayed under its weight. In its beak was a purple skink.

Print joined Tom at the fire, where a pot of coffee was working.

"Bit of fall in the air," said Print.

"All the more reason to push on. I don't want to get trapped in these passes," said Tom.

"We can wheel them once or twice," said Print, "and then we'll send them on."

They broke camp, and Sun Foy, at the reins of the wagon with Lung Hay on one side and little Number Five on the other, steered the wagon to the edge of the meadow as the men went about bunching up the herd. Nola and the other girls sat in the back of the wagon, watching. Number Four was sitting on the edge, her legs dangling off.

Print signaled to Tom and Heck to start the horses. They started turning the herd in a large counterclockwise circle. As it picked up momentum, the men continued to keep the herd tightened up. Print broke away and went over to the wagon and said, "We're going to pull out. You all stay behind us."

And then, as an afterthought, he turned and looked back at where they camped and said, "I'd like to try that fly-fishing some day."

He rode back to the wheeling herd of galloping horses. He signaled for Tom and Heck to circle one more time and then let them go.

Number Four kept watching the horses, then turned to see the people in the front. Just like that, Ye Fung jumped off the back of the wagon. She stood for a moment, looked back again at the girls, then dashed straight into the thundering herd. The first horse dodged her to the side and missed her. But then, a second later, another horse hit her, sending her flying into the air, and she fell into the dirt and dust of the pounding hooves.

Tom saw what happened and gigged his horse around the edge of the turning herd to where the girl disappeared. He swept in, low in the saddle, and grabbed at the girl. He grasped her clothing and pulled her up and across his saddle and pulled out of the churning horses.

Tom cleared the herd, the limp body across the pommel

of his saddle. He swung out of the stirrups and lowered Ye Fung to the ground.

A stunned Print rode up to Tom and joined him on the ground. Heck kept looking across the backs of the horses from the other side of the turning herd, which was slowly starting to come to a halt now that the other riders weren't there to keep them going. Nola jumped from the wagon and ran to the men and the lifeless form before them. Sun Foy thrust the reins at Lung Hay and followed her, while the rest of the girls looked on in shock.

The climbing sun had warmed the day as the men went about digging a grave. The girls, along with Lung Hay, had pulled tufts of tall grass to use to line the bottom of the grave. Tom and Print picked up the blanket at either end that held Ye Fung and gently lowered her into the hole. Tom pulled back the blanket that covered her face. He bit his bottom lip and covered it again. He rose, and he and Print started to fill in the dirt. When they were through, Print said to him, "Anything you want to say?"

"I already said it."

Print nodded. He looked at the girls. They came forward and knelt, placing a bunch of Indian paintbrush at the foot of the grave. Print removed his hat, and the other men did too.

"We're all travelers in this world," he said, "from the sweetgrass to the packinghouse. Birth 'til death, we travel between the eternities."

He put his hat back on, turned, and started to walk off, and said, "Nephew."

The sun was directly overhead when at last the herd moved out, followed by the wagon and riders. A light wind ruffled the bunch of Indian paintbrush left at the foot of the fresh grave on the bend of the Snake River.

CHAPTER TWENTY-FIVE

They had been on the move for three days when the herd crested a flattened-out hill. In the distance, they saw a building that sat in the open country by itself. The mounted men tightened up the herd as they drew closer. The building was a low-slung affair made up of a half-dozen stalls facing the intersection of two dusty drovers' trails.

It was really an intersection from nowhere and to nowhere. Several horses, saddled, waited in a corral in the back. A man in a bloody apron was butchering a steer suspended from a tripod of poles. Several women came out of the stalls. Hard, tragic beings. They were the worst of whoredom. The toothless, the diseased. Cankered shells of what were once women. There was a sign that said "Runyon's."

Print pushed his horse into the lead, passing Tom. "Keep 'em movin', Tom. I don't want 'em stoppin' here."

Print pulled up ahead and was greeted by the man in the bloody apron.

"You folks going to put up for the night?"

"We got two hours of daylight 'fore we call it a day," said Print.

"How about some fresh beef? You can put your herd in the big corral out back. My gals could sure use some money."

"We're shy on time today. Gotta grease a few more miles 'fore we make camp."

Print pushed his horse forward to keep up with the lead mares. Soon the wagon rolled past and Tom stopped to make sure it continued on. Nola and Lung Hay looked out as the wagon glided like a ferry passing a dock of passengers waiting to board. The sad women waved at them and the girls that were looking out the back. The man in the bloody apron stepped forward.

"See you travel with your own girls."

Tom turned in the saddle and looked at the girls peering out of the back. "They're my nieces," he said coldly.

With a blood-caked hand, the butcher grabbed the reins of Tom's horse. "Mister, you must have a strange-looking brother-in-law."

Tom leaned low in the saddle and in a whisper said, "Get your hands off my horse 'fore I blow a hole in your liver, fella."

The butcher let go of the reins and backed up. Horse and rider moved on.

"Go on. We don't need you cheap-ass people 'round here anyway," said the aproned man.

Tom stopped his horse, his back to the man, and cocked his head as if to hear more. The butcher turned and walked away, and Tom moved on.

A tragic old hag was standing in one of the doorways. She called out, "Hey, cowboy, how about a ride? Come on. Won't take long. You won't even have to take your boots off. Come on. Us professional ladies got to eat too, you know."

From within one of the darkened stalls of the hog ranch, heavy breathing and groaning could be heard, and a creaking bed. A figure rose in the darkened stall, leaving an old, world-weary woman on the mattress. The figure watched the last of Print's procession go by. And the shadow on the wall showed a man, one arm against the wall and a head with unusually large ears.

The faces of other women from hell could be seen peering out of the darkness of the stalls as Nola and the girls looked at them. The dust rolled up behind the departing wagon. The Ritter-Harte party moved eastward, away from this ignominious spot where two cattle trails crossed in the middle of nowhere out on the prairie.

Print pushed them along 'til almost sunset as he wanted to put as much distance between the herd and the hog ranch they'd passed. As they went about setting up camp, the girls went out looking for wood for the fire. Suddenly, there was a cry and then whimpering.

Tom and Nola ran to where the girls had gathered around little Number Five. Lung Hay followed close behind. Ghing Wa had stepped into a gopher hole and twisted her ankle. Lung Hay pushed through everyone and said, "Please, let me look. I want to look at her."

He knelt and carefully touched her leg, from the knee to the calf to the ankle. He turned to Sun Foy and said to her in Mandarin, *"Please, I need you to hold her. Please hold her strong."*

Tom knelt on the other side of the girl as Lung Hay removed the slipper, then slowly removed the binding around her foot. What was revealed was a tiny, deformed foot, toes broken and bent under and mashed up into the sole of the foot. All of the adults except Lung Hay were taken aback.

Lung Hay turned to Sun Foy and said, *"We are lucky. It is just a sprain."*

Print rode up, dismounted, and walked over, bent low, and looked. "Sweet Jesus. What the hell is that?"

Lung Hay, without looking up, said, "It is an ancient custom," to which Tom replied, "And they call us barbarians."

Lung Hay rubbed the ankle carefully. "It is not broken. Please hold her tight," he said to Sun Foy.

Lung Hay carefully bound up the foot again. The little girl was in great pain. She grabbed Tom's hand, and he stroked her brow. Lung Hay talked quietly to the little girl.

"What did you say to her?" asked Print.

"I told her she would be all right. I told her Ghing Wa was a brave girl."

"Ghing Wa?"

"Yes. Ghing Wa, that is her name. Ghing Wa."

"How come you never told me that?" asked Print.

"Why, you never asked."

Lung Hay turned and pointed to each one of the girls. "Sun Foy. Ghee Moon. Mai Ling. Ghing Wa."

Tom mouthed the words. "Sun Foy."

Print pointed to the little girl on the ground. "Ghing Wa?"

"Yes, Ghing Wa," repeated Lung Hay.

"And the little one that was killed by the horses?"

"Ye Fung." Lung Hay nodded.

Print repeated the name. "Ye Fung."

"She did not die from horses. She died from shame," said Lung Hay, looking directly at Print.

Print sat up late that night, and he thought about why he hadn't asked Lung Hay the girls' names before. And he thought about the little Chinese girl whom he barely knew, and her rash death.

He recalled the years out on the trail and how talk would drift to the war and the younger boys wanted to hear all about it. He had sat and listened to some fellows that wolfed and bragged about battles they'd been in and what a high time they had. There were the others who never talked about it and would get up and walk away from the fire rather than listen or talk. He talked some, but not much. He figured that if a man had not been there, then it was a waste of air to go on about it.

And he didn't want to talk to any Yankees about it. He didn't hate them, but he sure found most to be tedious at times. Thing is, they were always right. Not that they thought they were right—most of the time they *were* right. At least on things like commerce and efficiency of all things.

He found they missed the mark on people most of the time. They were naturals at telling other folks what to do. He decided that they had been that way ever since the first one tiptoed over Plymouth Rock. He didn't expect them to be changing much in the next couple of hundred years.

The boys would ask him if he was afraid before the fights. Yes, he said, he was afraid.

The one time he was scared down to his toenails was an afternoon engagement against a battery on a hill overlooking the Rapidan. They were ordered up the hill to take out the four-gun battery. He was in the second or third line and they were almost on top of the placement when a shell from one of their own howitzers hit the magazine on the Yankee caisson and exploded as the first line breached the guns.

In slow motion he saw a leg, from boot to hip, turning in the air, end over end, hit a fellow in the line in front of him and knock the lad's head half off. The fellow must have been leaning into the incline of the hill because it didn't knock him over. The impact had straightened him up, the head hung back between his shoulder blades, and the soldier then sank to his knees and toppled over. He had seen worse gore—surely at the hospital. But the incident was so random. So violent.

Except for the time a quartermaster's wagon ran over his foot and smashed it and they sent him to the hospital in Richmond, he was never touched. It was the strange and utterly random way the boy died that afternoon on the Rapidan that still filled Print with fear.

CHAPTER TWENTY-SIX

Early the next morning, before the sun was up, Tom and Sun Foy sat in the short grass away from camp, on a small rise facing the east. It was cold. Tom didn't mind it, but Sun Foy shivered slightly. He looked out at the prairie as they sat in silence.

Just before the sun broke over the horizon, he held a finger to his lips. A covey of doves broke out and rose from a nearby clump of cottonwoods. Then another covey. Tom got up and extended a hand to help Sun Foy up. They picked up two buckets and walked toward the bushes.

Later, when they walked back into camp with the buckets full of water, Tom asked Lung Hay to tell her that "the birds fly to water in the evening and from water in the morning." Lung Hay translated, and Sun Foy nodded.

The day was hot as the herd and wagon moved across what seemed like the endless expanse. They were now out on the buffalo range, long, rolling hills that went on for as far as the eye could see. In the afternoon the sky to the west darkened as magnificent columns of a thunderhead built and rolled down toward them. Soon the skies opened up on them and the rain fell in sheets. There was thunder and lightning; the darkness was lit by blinding flashes that hung the scene in suspended animation. And then more darkness. The procession came to a halt. The horses bunched up, their tails turned into the storm. The riders were in slickers, and rain poured off the brims of their hats. Sun Foy parked herself on the little horse next to Tom, hair plastered to her face. Tom took off his hat and put it on her head. Nola and the girls and Lung Hay huddled in the wagon as rain poured down the canvas sides. And then it lightened, and then it stopped and the storm was gone. The sun returned and the prairie was washed and puddled.

"Damn, if the Old Man didn't toss his hammer down the canyon walls that time!" yelled Tom to Heck as they started the horses up again.

"Smell that sage? You don't find that back in Philadelphia," replied Heck.

Sun Foy's soaked shirt revealed her breasts. Tom was staring at her. She looked at him, knowing that he was. She had a benign look on her face that was neither shy nor offended. He looked at her face and then averted his eyes.

The wagon moved on, following the herd as it trailed the departing storm.

Print was on point, and in the late afternoon, he saw something off to the herd's right. He waved Heck up to his side. "Hank, keep 'em movin' on. I'll be right back."

Print loped over to a piece of planking sticking out of the ground. It might have been a floorboard of a wagon. The ground in front of it had been tunneled and dug up. Probably coyotes, thought Print. The sole of a boot green with mold lay several feet away. Someone had carved into the wood plank "A Texas Cowboy."

Print called for a break an hour later as he wanted to give the herd a lot of time to graze. After making camp, Tom, on the little red roan, was playing with Sun Foy and Mai Ling. He was trying to separate them by cutting them with his horse. The cow pony feinted left and then right. He backed up and stopped. Then he jumped forward again, the giggling girls dodging one way and then the other. Tom smiled and then uncoiled his riata. He swept left and laid a loop over Sun Foy. He gently hauled in his rope, bringing her to the pony's side. She smiled at him as he loosened the loop and removed it from her.

Heck was sitting on a nail keg with Ghee Moon next to him. The violin sat in his lap, and he showed her how to draw the bow across the strings, and he placed her fingers on the correct frets with the other hand. She slowly drew the bow across and a soft, sad sound was heard.

After dinner Nola and Print collected the pots and walked to the little creek they'd camped by.

"Never knew Uncle Print to take such an interest in dish washing."

Heck chuckled. "Wasn't he the one that said something about bringing a strong man to his knees? Think he left out the part about going to the river."

At the side of the creek, Print and Nola both knelt, scrubbing and rinsing the pots.

"You're quite the domestic cowhand, Mr. Ritter—I mean Print."

"No, you're right. I do like the way you say way 'Mr. Ritter.'"

"What are you going to do with the girls?"

Print wiped his hands on his pants and started to roll a smoke. "We got seven, maybe eight days 'til Sheridan. I still have time to get it figured out. What about you, Miz Johns? You made any plans?"

Nola said nothing. She continued washing the pots.

"You don't have to go shy on me."

She stopped and looked at him. "Like you said, it's seven, eight days until we get to Sheridan. I have time, too. Now, if you'll excuse me, the only clothes I now own are the ones I was wearing when I left Cariboo. I need to do some washing."

Print was at a complete loss. He stood and then took the pots and headed back to the wagon. At one point, he turned around to look back and saw Nola undressing, her strong back and wide hips in the starlight. He lingered a moment and then moved on. As he walked back into the camp, Lung Hay and Tom looked up.

"Not much skillet cleaning tonight, Uncle."

Print shot him a frosty look, dropped the pots by the fire, and went to get his bedroll. In the background, Heck was playing a rendition of *Aura Lee*.

◎ ◎ ◎

The fire was crackling in the predawn light, the coffeepot perking in the coals.

"Where's Uncle Print?"

"He walked out of here way before daylight. He's prickly this morning," said Heck.

"He must've got some dust up his nose," replied Tom.

Both men looked at Nola. Nola looked at them and simply said, "No salt."

Neither of the men understood what she meant.

"Well, before we pull out, I'm going to go scare up some game for tonight while we wait for him."

Tom and Sun Foy lay side by side behind a large clump of Russian thistle in the short grass out on the buffalo range. A hundred yards in front of them was a small group of pronghorns. Tom eased the carbine forward and placed it beside Sun Foy. He reached around her to steady the butt against her shoulder. He placed her index finger in the trigger guard, and then he helped her aim. He had his arm around her. Their cheeks touched momentarily, and he pulled back. Sun Foy looked down the barrel. Tom leaned close to help her sight. He breathed in her scent and smelled her hair and he forgot about the pronghorn.

Suddenly the carbine roared. The recoil hit Sun Foy hard. She was wide-eyed and stunned. For a long moment Tom held her to him, his eyes closed, his cheek against her hair.

Tom was dressing out the pronghorn back at camp, the girls watching him skin the hide from the carcass, when Print rode back in. He dismounted, loosened the cinch on Bob Tate, and saw a group of mounted men approaching the camp from the east. Tom saw the men too. He stabbed his knife into the ground several times to clean it and then sheathed it. He rubbed grass and dirt on his bloody hands. The girls scurried to the wagon.

"Company coming, Uncle."

Tom drifted over to the picket line to blend in with the horses. Nola and Lung Hay joined the girls by the wagon, and Heck moved back from the fire as Print walked toward the men.

Five mounted men and a packhorse came to a halt in front of Print.

"'Morning, folks. I'm Bill Miller, marshal out of Sheridan. These are my deputies: Dick, Doug, Don, and Dana McNeary."

"That's handy," said Print.

"Who's the jigger boss here?"

Print said nothing. "You men care for coffee?"

"Thank you. So, you the honcho here?"

"My name's Print Ritter. This is my party."

"Good-looking bunch of horses you got there, Mr. Ritter."

"Yep."

"You got papers on them, I suppose."

"You bet. ... You got a badge, I suppose?"

The men dismounted.

"No need to get puffed up," Miller replied as he pulled back the left side of his coat to reveal the brass badge. "I should be eating ham and eggs at The Blue Goose back in Sheridan instead of sleeping on the ground, eating jerky, and looking for horse thieves."

Nola had come forward with cups for the men and

then poured from the pot. The men tipped their hats to Nola. The one called Don took his off and then replaced it.

"Thank you, ma'am," said Miller, and then he turned to Print. "I'm after a rough lot run by a fellow name of Big Ears Bywaters." He smiled and shook his head. "You can't be on the wrong side of the law and not have some ridiculous name attached to your reputation these days."

"Well, if I run into him, I'll give him your regards, marshal."

"It ain't a name he responds to well. Don't let that name fool you. He's trickier than a redheaded woman. They steal horses 'round here and tail them up to Alberta. Sell them to the Metis renegades. Then kype horses up there and bring them south to sell. Been pretty active down Carbon County way. I'm surprised Big Ears ain't paid you a visit. They say he can hear a horse at twenty miles."

The marshal pulled on his earlobe.

"Point taken," said Print.

"Steer clear, if you can. They're all well garnished with weapons."

Print pointed to his horses. "These horses are from John Day country. I'm deliverin' 'em to William and Malcolm Moncrieffe in Sheridan."

"The Moncrieffe brothers? You can't touch them with a million. They'll pay good money too—if you get them there."

"You want to see my papers?" asked Print.

Miller handed back his coffee cup and mounted up. "That won't be necessary."

"Good luck locatin' Mr. Big Ears."

"My plan is to catch up with them soon enough. Then I'll put the kibosh on them." He patted the coiled rope on his saddle. "We'll straighten them out and make good citizens out of them. With any luck I'll be wearing his ears on my watch chain."

The rest of the men handed their cups back and mounted up too. The marshal turned to go, then wheeled the horse toward them again.

"Folks don't take to yamping livestock in Carbon County."

He tipped the brim of his hat to the women. "Ladies." The riders departed.

Tom walked out from the picket line and was joined by Heck.

"Ambitious fellow," said Tom.

Print stuck his hands in his pants pockets. "All the more reason ta get these horses there soon as we can. We'll all sit a double watch from here on out."

◎ ◎ ◎

It was a moonless night. The camp was sound asleep. The horses browsed on the short grass. Tails switched. Tom and Heck were out nighthawking. They slowly circled the herd, in opposite directions. They didn't tighten it up too much, but they didn't want any of the horses straying. As they passed one another, they stopped and Heck said, "I been meaning to ask you about what you did back there in the hotel. Pretty hard on that fellow, weren't you?"

"You think so? There's men that had a lot worse done to them."

They walked on in a long circle away from one another until they met up on the other side of the herd and stopped again.

"My uncle told me about a time he was down in Elko years ago. He and some hands caught a fellow that had raped a woman. He didn't get far."

"Did they hang him?" asked Heck.

"No, they prunced him."

"Did what?"

"They prunced him," said Tom. "They cut his nut sack off."

"Oh. Did he die?"

"No. He just got fat and grew old."

The men pushed their horses on as they circled around the herd again.

◎ ◎ ◎

By noon the next day, the herd had made good time. They had found water twice, and Print intended to move the herd along until it was dark. Still in a bad mood from his conversation with Nola the other evening, he turned in the saddle to look back and saw that Tom had fallen way behind. He turned Bob Tate and loped around the side of the herd and back to meet Tom.

"What's the problem?" he yelled to Tom as he pulled up.

"Nothing. I just feel like we're being dogged."

Print looked over Tom's shoulder and beyond. "Ah, that marshal's got ya jumpy."

"Maybe," replied Tom. "I'm not sure. Why don't you push on for an early camp? Pick a good site for us. I'm going to hang back and stretch out the distance for you. Then I'll close up quickly."

Print agreed and loped back to the herd.

◎ ◎ ◎

It was evening, and Print had picked a spot to camp that was in a small coolie. There was a rock outcropping on either side a hundred yards up. Print had built a big campfire and was sitting in front of it whittling, the wagon behind him and no one else in sight. He heard footsteps coming up from behind him. He knew it was his nephew, Tom.

"Stay in the dark and pick a good spot. Up in the

rocks to the left would be the best."

"Where's Heck?" asked Tom.

"He's up in the rocks on the right. He's got the rest of 'em up there well hid."

"Where are you going to sit?"

"I'm gonna sit right here."

"Like a big piece of cheese waiting for the rats to show up?"

"Well, let's not make it Swiss cheese. We can't shoot it out with these fellas. We're going to have to face 'em, listen to what they have to say."

"Then what?" asked Tom.

"We'll find a spot and we'll play it by ear."

Print pulled out a tattered copy of *The Writings of Anatole France* and read by the fire.

An hour later he could hear the sound of horses walking in from the darkness. One rider emerged; several others were visible in the half-light. He rode his horse into the firelight. He was tall and thin with a pinched face and very large ears.

"Evenin'. Saw your fire. Got some coffee to spare?"

Print closed his book and placed it beside him. "We're fresh out of coffee."

"Too late for supper?"

"Supper's over."

"Where are the rest of your people?"

"That's none of your concern, mister."

The pinch-faced man started to dismount.

"Whoa, there," said Print. He waved his finger back and forth to indicate no.

"Ain't a friendly camp you're running here, mister." The rider settled back in the saddle.

"You been cutting my sign all day and now you ride in here at night with a hard lot. What did you expect?"

"Well, I thought you might want to do some horse business."

"I ain't in the horse business."

"What business you in then?"

"You got shit in your ears, mister? I told ya, my business is none of your concern."

"I come in here peaceful. All I wanted to do was some horse business and be respectable."

"Respectable?" Print looked the rider up and down and then the riders behind him. He shook his head and chuckled. "Fella, my daddy told me a long time ago you can't shine shit."

"I ought to burn you down right where you sit, mister. You ain't going to talk to me that way and live."

Print said nothing.

"I ain't afraid of you."

"You should be," said Print. "See, I'm in the blanket business."

"Blanket business?"

"Yeah. I sell blankets, mostly ta the tribes in need of smallpox and typhoid."

The men behind the pinch-faced man looked at one another and muttered.

"I ain't afraid of no blanket," said the pinch-faced man.

"Like I said, you should be. Ya ever seen a white man's face after he's had the pox? With those dinner plates you got for ears, I figured you might have heard the name of Smallpox Bob."

Print stood and walked over to pick up a saddle blanket. Coming from up high, out in the darkness, they could hear the distinct sound of a round being jacked into a carbine. Big Ears looked up and then back at Print. And then they heard the same sound come from the right. Big Ears and his men looked left, and then back to the right again, and then at Print.

"I didn't ride in on the turnip wagon, Mr. Big Ears."

Print walked toward the riders with the blanket extended. The horses behind Bywaters started snorting and backing up, and two of the men turned their horses and started to trot away. Print stopped and looked over at Big Ears.

"Tonight's your night, old man," said Bywaters, "but I'm going to make a point of meeting you again."

Print shook the blanket again, and the rest of the riders spun their horses and bolted into the night. Big Ears simply backed his horse up slowly, turned it slowly, and walked into the darkness. Print watched him leave and listened to the footfall of the horse until it was gone. He took a bucket of water and doused the fire. Soon he could hear Tom coming down out of the rocks. And then Heck and the rest of them joined him in the darkness.

"Where'd you come up with that stuff about the smallpox?" asked Tom.

Print smiled slightly, "Books, son. Readin' books.

"I don't think we'll sleep tonight. We need to put some distance on these fellas."

Print tightened the cinch on Bob Tate and mounted. He took up a position at the rear of the herd as they moved out, realizing that there was now more at stake.

Books indeed, he thought. Books and memories, memories that hurt and haunted him, at times so bad he couldn't eat and couldn't talk. He had worked hard in the beginning not to think of the woman and the little girl. He thought he was losing his mind. He drank alone and he drank with others. He wanted to take it out on the working girls, but he couldn't. He couldn't slap them. He couldn't have them. In the end, all he could do was bury his face deep in the big Swede's breasts and cry. Afterward he was ashamed, and she told him not to be. That he would be surprised how many men had shed tears on her bosom.

He drank again, then sobered up and made inquiries. Someone said they had gone to Laramie. When he got there, he was told they had left for Denver. Denver was big, and all he found was someone who knew someone and that they had heard she was going south. How far? Maybe Springer or Las Cruces. He wired his old boss Mr. Wallop, who had told Print that he would help. And he did. Print took the money the old man sent and drifted south along the eastern front. Over Raton Pass to Cimarron and then to Springer. No one had heard of them, and he knew they hadn't been there. But he kept going. Wagon Mound and Las Vegas. In Tularosa he almost died from the mescal. Between there and Las Cruces he pulled up and camped and looked at the line of blue mountains that stretched into old Mexico.

He said to himself that he was a fool and that he probably always had been a fool. He had gotten into the wrong deal and he knew it from the start. And that was why he was a fool. He looked at those blue mountains for two days, and then he turned that skinny cow pony around and started back. He didn't drink. In Santa Rosa he bought a book, Barnes's *New National Reader*. When his mind drifted back to the woman and the girl, he stopped and got down, sat on the ground, and started reading. After that he'd saddle up and move on until thoughts of them overcame him, and then he'd stop and read some more. He read Hawthorne, Hardy, Richard Dana, Cooper, and Dickens. He quoted Tennyson. He memorized Gray's *Elegy Written in a Country Church Yard*, reciting it over and over to the cow pony. He didn't drink for two years, until he knew he didn't have to drink. He bought another book, Irving's *Tales of the Alhambra*. He swapped that one out for the writings of Bret Harte. Robbie Burns and Carlyle were pretty tough sledding, but he couldn't get enough of Kipling. He made it back and worked off the money he'd borrowed from Mr. Wallop.

He came to believe that the little girl had got him reading. That it was somehow a bond between them. Every time he started feeling sorry for himself or wondering what she would look like or where she might be, he reached for a book.

CHAPTER TWENTY-SEVEN

The herd moved over the rolling hills of the old buffalo range. With the failing light of a rustler's moon, it looked like chain mail sliding over the country. The wagon tottered along behind.

They pushed on all night and through the day and stopped only briefly for a cold meal and coffee. That night they camped on the banks of the Tongue River and had a proper supper.

"We're getting close to Sheridan, aren't we, Mr. Ritter?" said Heck as he put his plate and fork in the washbasin.

"We should be at the Moncrieffes' by tomorrow afternoon."

Everyone looked surprised. Nola got up to gather the pans and tin plates, and Print went to lend her a hand. They walked off toward the river again.

"There's somethin' to be said for eatin' off clean dishes every night," said Print.

"I don't mind doing the dishes," she replied.

"I don't mind helpin'. I enjoy your company."

"You mean you enjoy my company 'til we get to Sheridan."

"No, I do not mean that. Look, I'm old enough to have owed your daddy money. I tried to tread lightly around you. You probably had your fill of men. You had no need, I felt, of my sniffing around."

She threw the handful of sand into the water and looked at him.

"Sniffing around? Look at me, Mr. Ritter. I've had countless sweaty men in my life. I can't change that fact. But none of them, not one of them, did I let in here," she said, touching her chest.

"I didn't mean to insult you."

"There's a big difference between selling it and offering it, Mr. Ritter. Why don't you go have a smoke and leave me alone?"

The next day Print was out on the point, way ahead of the lead mare, the flea-bitten gray, and her lieutenants. He was in a foul mood, and he spent much of the time thinking about Nola and last night. Off in the distance he saw a small group that was on a course that would intersect theirs. It looked like a skiff out on the ocean. As they drew closer, he could see that it was a small group of tired-looking Indians. As they drew abreast of them, he saw an old man lying on a travois pulled by a raw-boned Indian pony. A woman and a little boy were mounted on another pony, and a slightly older boy walked.

Print raised up in the stirrups, turned, and called for Tom to stop the herd. Shortly he was joined by Heck and Tom, and the wagon drew up behind them. Heck eased his horse forward and, using sign language and various dialects, asked, "Where are you coming from?"

The woman looked at him for a while and then said in perfect English, "We are Brule Sioux from the Rosebud Agency."

Print was taken aback by her English. "Well, why ain't you there?"

The woman looked at him. "The buffalo wallows are empty. All our horses have been taken."

"You speak pretty good English," said Tom.

"My name is Cecilia Spotted Calf. My father was a peace chief. I was sent to the East to your school. He died, so I came back to help my grandfather."

"Then you oughta know it ain't safe out here."

"My grandfather wants to die in the North, where there are no whites. Soon the Cheyenne and the Arickaree, and even our enemies, the Blackfoot and the Crow, will be gone. Then our voices will be in the rocks and the grass, and we will wait for the time when our Great Father inclines his ear upon us and we will tell him our story."

"Well, Miss Spotted Calf, we got some jerky and supplies," said Print. "We'd like to help you out if we could. Heck, see what you can get for these people."

Cecilia Spotted Calf looked at the girls. And they looked back at her.

Sun Foy whispered to Mai Ling, *"She could be our sister."*

Heck gave them a bundle of food.

"That ought to get you where you're going," said Tom.

"Better steer clear of the wolfers and the whiskey traders," Heck said.

The woman stopped and turned her pony to look back.

"If anyone asks about ya', we'll tell them you're headed south and west," said Print.

Cecilia Spotted Calf turned her pony to the trail and they moved on.

Meeting the bedraggled Indians had cast a pall over Print's party. Print, Tom, and Heck got the herd going and they trailed behind it for a ways.

"It's an old story," said Print. "Egyptians done it to the Israelites. Romans done it to the Egyptians. Mongols done it to the Romans. We did it to the Negroes. Now everyone's doin' it to the red man."

"We call them savages for takin' scalps, but look at Cold Harbor," said Heck.

"I've been north and seen the blood on the rocks. Their enemies lost more than their scalps, and they stole and trafficked in a hell of a lot more human freight than my grandpappy ever did," replied Print.

"You don't think they've been given a pretty raw deal?" said Heck.

"Worse than raw," added Tom.

"Well, of course they have. It ain't that simple. Can you honestly imagine a world today with all of us piled up in Europe and them havin' a grand time here, chasin' buffalo? No, sir.

"Humanity sometimes walks forward on heavy boots. Now that's a cold, hard fact," said Print.

"Well, I don't want to be around when their Great Father lends an ear to their story," said Tom.

Print stopped his horse, looked at him, and said, "Oh, you will be. We'll all be there. And that's a cold, hard fact, too."

◎ ◎ ◎

Later in the day Print pulled up the herd. He motioned for Tom and Heck to join him, and then he waved his arm for Sun Foy to bring the wagon up. When they were all together and the men still mounted, Print addressed them.

"Well, folks, we got a decision we gotta make. We're almost there. Those fellas back there, I suspect, are still followin' us. What I propose is that, Heck, you take the wagon, Mr. Lung Hay, and the girls, and you proceed on down the track here. Tom and I'll take the herd. Now, you see that over there? It's too small to be a mountain and too big to be a hill."

Print was pointing to a large outcrop in the distance. "That's the whale's back."

When Tom looked at it for a while, he could see that indeed it looked like the back of a big whale breaching the surface of the prairie.

"Now, here's the deal. You all go on down the track.

Tom and I will take the horses. You can't tell from here, but there's actually a river cut down into the ground. We'll bring the horses down in that, and if the water ain't too high, we can snake our way along that 'til we get to the tail of the whale's back. We'll go up over the spine, drop down, and meet you on the other side. I don't think that those fellas are as interested in that wagon and the girls as much as they are in these horses. But it's a risk. If we all go down the track, there's a chance we'll lose the herd, and there will be spilt blood too. The only other thing to do is to ditch the wagon and put everybody up on horseback. But I don't like the idea of everybody mounted going over the whale's back. Do you think you can handle it?"

"Yes, sir, I do."

"Miz Johns?"

She nodded.

"Lung Hay?"

"Yes," he said.

"All right. You probably won't need it, but here, take this." Print slid his rifle out of its scabbard and handed it over to Miz Johns. "If ya have any problems at all, you're on your own for the next fifteen miles. We'll meet ya or you'll meet us on the other side. Think it's the safest thing for all concerned."

Tom and Print waited as they watched the wagon move on down the trail, and then they got the herd going. They slipped in along a forest of ponderosas, and they followed it for a half a mile. Then they dropped down into the river. There wasn't much water in it, and there were high banks, so the horses couldn't go anywhere except upstream. Print led the way, and Tom brought up the rear. They snaked their way up that river. It turned and it bent and it turned again. Then, when they looked out of the walls of the river and saw the whale's back, they drove them up a bank into a small clearing. Print led the way up the hill. It wasn't a mountain, but it sure wasn't a hill, either. It was steep and it was narrow in the spine, and he just trudged on with Bob Tate. The flea-bitten mare and the other mares followed, and everybody pretty much fell into line as they went right up over the spine. Toward the back of the herd, some got nervous and started pushing to keep up with the leaders and that started about twenty of them scrambling and slipping. Print and Tom could not get to them and had to let them sort it out for themselves. Before it was over, two slid on their sides downslope. Tom was on the rear of the herd, and as he passed, he could hear the two whinnying down below to the herd as it continued on.

Tom and Print picked their way all the way 'til sunset. Then, as the sky turned purple and darkened, they dropped down the far side. It was dark when they saw the canvas top of the wagon in the distance.

When they arrived at the wagon, Print gathered them together. "Everything all right?"

"Yes, Mr. Ritter," said Nola as she handed the rifle back to Print.

"Hate ta have to ask this, but I think we really should push on through the night. Think it's the safest thing we could do. It's the last night. I want ta get these horses in the Moncrieffes' pens, and I want ta get all of you ta Sheridan. So we'll move on one more night and then we'll be done with it."

So, slowly, they pushed the herd on. The herd was tired and they hadn't grazed much for the last day. But they had been watered, so they moved on into the night. The little wagon swayed along behind them.

The night was ink-colored. The dawn was rose. And by midday, the sky was yellow. The herd crested a low rise, and down before them in the distance lay the Moncrieffes' spread. Print conferred with Tom and Heck.

"I think I'm goin' on in to give the Moncrieffes a heads-up. You boys bring 'em on in slowly." Print turned and loped off on the big chestnut.

Print passed under the lodgepole entrance of the Quarter Circle A Ranch. The gate was adorned in elk antlers. He rode up to the front yard of a white ranch house and was met on the lawn by a moustached man who was wearing a blend of English country, cavalry twill, and western attire.

"Mr. Moncrieffe?"

"I am. Malcolm Moncrieffe," said the man with a strong Scottish accent.

"My name's Ritter, Prentice Ritter. I wired you in April about bringin' horses from John Day."

"Ah ha," said Moncrieffe. "The man from Oregon. Welcome. We've been following your journey with anticipation, Mr. Ritter."

"I'm not sure I understand, Mr. Moncrieffe."

"I received correspondence and packages from a Mr. Bentingcourt in Boston, and just the other day, Marshal Miller wired me from Cody asking about you. That's more news than I get from my family in Scotland.

Sorry you just missed my brother. He's off the ranch on business."

"Where would you like me to put these cavvies, Mr. Moncrieffe?"

"We'll put them in the south pasture, over there," the Scotsman said, gesturing to the poorman's gate that was coiled and laying on the ground. "Keep them separated from the others for a week. I'll get my boys to lend you a hand."

Print and the Moncrieffes' hands rode toward the approaching herd. The Moncrieffe spread was a vast grid of corrals, large paddocks, and pastures, and there were literally thousands of horses there. The Ritter-Harte herd started picking up its pace as they got closer. There was excitement in the air, and soon the herd was galloping, then thundering. Print and the Moncrieffes' cowboys split to either side as the herd rolled at them. Heck and Tom were trying to keep them closed in, but to no avail. The wall of galloping horses thundered toward the south pasture. Print and the hands formed a moving line to try and turn them in. Finally, the lead mares buckled, turned to the right, and swept inside a huge pasture. Inside, the horses were leaping and bucking and rearing. Tom, Heck, and the mounted riders pushed in the stragglers. Two Moncrieffe cowboys secured the poorman's gate as the dust-covered wagon rolled up moments later.

Print and Tom rode over to Malcolm Moncrieffe. "Mr. Moncrieffe, my nephew, Tom Harte."

Moncrieffe looked past Print at the wagon's occupants. Turning in the saddle, Print followed his gaze and noted, "The rest of my party."

"You put on quite a show, Mr. Harte."

"Tried to keep 'em in good flesh, sir. This is first-rate stock you're getting. No yew necks, no pin ears, no pig eyes. Three weeks, they'll be fat as ticks."

"Let's get you settled in, and then we'll do some business."

The ranch office was a small building off to the side of the main ranch house. Inside, Malcolm and Print talked.

"This draft is drawn on the Stockmen and Merchants Bank in Denver, but our bank in Sheridan will honor it."

"Couple of times back there, I wasn't sure this transaction was goin' ta happen," said Print.

"That's a good deal of money, Mr. Ritter. Will you buy more horses?"

"Not really sure. I'm thinkin' of gettin' some land."

"Hard to go wrong with land. You might want to talk to Oliver Wollop, my cousin. He's got his finger on the pulse of the state's politics. Good thing to know when you're buying land."

"I think I knew his daddy, or it mighta been his uncle." Changing topics, he said, "If we're through here, I think I'm gonna take my crew inta town for some shoppin' and a bath. We'll see you again in the morning."

The wagon rolled down the main street of Sheridan with the mounted men behind it. They pulled up in front of one of the storefronts. Everyone dismounted. Print walked over to Nola.

"Miz Johns, I want you ta outfit yourself and the girls for all your requirements. Don't go thin on the expenses. I'll be back ta settle up. Think we'll go have a drink and then a bath and a shave."

◎ ◎ ◎

Later, when Print, Tom, and Heck caught up with Nola, the girls were all dressed in little denim trousers, shirts, and straw hats.

"That's what they wanted, Mr. Ritter. I got them dresses too, shoes, everything. I got myself two dresses, if you don't mind."

"Of course, not. That's what I wanted."

The next morning, in the pens at the Moncrieffes', Tom was helping the ranch hands work some horses. Sun Foy watched as he roped the colts. Malcolm Moncrieffe, Print, Heck, and the girls were watching through the poles of the corral.

"Your nephew seems to have a way with horses," said Malcolm Moncrieffe.

"He always has."

"Not an overly talkative lad, though."

"For sure. What's your plan for all this stock you bought?"

"We're in partnership with our cousin Oliver. We're supplying mounts for the British army. We've already shipped over twenty thousand horses to South Africa for their war."

"That's one hell of a lot of horseflesh."

"Not nearly enough, from the reports we get. They're calling for upward of a half a million animals. Horses and mules, that is. Between the Brits and your Spanish-American dustup, the price of horseflesh is going through the roof. But enough talk. We're having a picnic this afternoon. I hope you'll all join us, as we don't have guests here at the ranch that often."

As the tables were being prepared, the ranch hands got up a game of baseball. The men played with big three-fingered mitts. They invited some of the girls to join them.

Print sought out Tom. "Tom, you got a moment?"

"Sure."

They walked off to the side, and Print took a thick envelope from inside his vest pocket and handed it over.

"Your share of the proceeds an' then some. That should square it between you and your ma."

Tom looked inside, surprised at the amount of cash it contained. "What about you?"

Print, with his hand palm down, passed it between them. "More than square," he said.

They shook hands and Print walked off. Tom watched him for a long time as he walked away, and then he returned to watch the game.

One cowboy playing shortstop was paying extra attention to Sun Foy. He was standing behind her with his arm around her, showing her how to catch the ball. Tom turned back once again to look for Print and then turned back to Sun Foy and the cowboy. Tom walked to his horse, mounted up, and trotted over to home plate.

"Gimme that bat."

A bewildered cowboy looked up at Tom and handed it over. Tom centered his pony over the home plate.

"Come on. Toss it in here."

A smiling ranch hand complied and gave a slow, easy pitch across the plate. Tom stood up in the stirrups and swatted the ball out across the lawn in the direction of the cottonwoods. His pony jumped out, rounding first base, then second. He aimed the pony at the cowboy who'd been helping Sun Foy and almost bowled him over, the ranch hand having to dive for the dirt. There was a smile on Sun Foy's face as Tom headed for home. He crossed the plate, waved his hat high in the air. "Yee haw!"

And he kept on going. Tom spun the horse around and raced back to home plate and brought the horse up short. He swung down out of the saddle at the same time the dinner bell rang. He walked his horse over to the hitching rail, loosened the cinch as Sun Foy joined him, and they walked toward the picnic tables set up in the backyard.

It was quite a spread, and the girls and Nola and Lung Hay and the ranch hands all enjoyed the afternoon. But Print was nowhere to be seen. When finally Tom asked Malcolm Moncrieffe where his uncle was, Moncrieffe told him that he had gone back into town to do some business.

CHAPTER TWENTY-EIGHT

Print had the big chestnut in a good trot going down the road to Sheridan. The weather was good, and his mind was elsewhere. At one point he eased back to a walk and checked his pocket watch. He opened it up, shut it, put it back in his pocket, and turned in the saddle. He thought he heard horses. Barely visible in the distance behind him, he saw dust from a rider. … Print looked forward, scanned the skyline, and moved on. Five minutes later, Print looked back and saw that the rider was closing on him. He fanned Bob Tate with his hat, and they raced along the dirt road for a mile, leaving billowing dust behind them. He kept looking over his shoulder and didn't see the three riders who rode up out of the blind ditch to block the road until he was almost on top of them. He pulled Bob Tate up hard. With the late afternoon sun on his face, he saw that one of the riders had the unmistakable silhouette of a pair of big ears.

"Well, I told you we'd be together again."

Print rested his forearm on the saddle horn, his horse blowing hard.

"You a praying man?"

"Not much."

Big Ears looked up at the sky as if to tell the time. "You will be, time I leave my mark on you."

They escorted Print and his horse off the road and down to a thicket of cottonwoods. There they stripped him down to his long johns and seated him astride the trunk of a blown-over tree. Big Ears fingered through the horse money and then stuffed Print's money belt into a saddlebag and removed a small fencing hammer from the other side. It was the kind used to repair barbed-wire fencing. He took out some sixteen-penny nails as well and placed them between his teeth.

"Thanks for the donation, old man. First thing I'm going to do is nail your credentials to this log. Then I'm going to push you over backward. We're gonna to see how much sand you really got. Then you're going to find out how good I really am with a running iron."

Two of the rustlers stepped up to grab each of Print's arms. Big Ears straddled the log to face him, and he sat and took a nail from his mouth.

"You're going to wish the Mandan squaws got hold of you, time I get through with you, mister blanket man."

Big Ears got ready to set a nail between Print's legs. Print mumbled under his breath.

"What'd you say to me, old man?" said Big Ears as he leaned close to Print's face.

With all the strength he had, Print head-butted Big Ears, bringing his forehead square on the bridge of the man's nose with a fierce thud. Big Ears rocked backward, screaming, blood pouring down his face. He stood up and with all his strength hit Print under the right eye with his fist. The force knocked Print over.

Big Ears sputtered through blood flowing from his mouth. "All right, blanket man, you just booked yourself a ticket to hell. You're going to leave this world a miserable, old, toothless man."

Print was splattered with blood as Big Ears spit out his words. The men set Print back upright on the log. Big Ears wiped the blood from his mouth with the back of his sleeve, the hammer in the other hand. Print looked up at him, his right eye already swollen shut.

Suddenly the chest of Ed "Big Ears" Bywaters opened up. It exploded, though there was no sound, and he and his entrails were pitched onto Print. There was the delayed sound of a distant rifle report. Then confusion, as the men scrambled. Print struggled to get out from underneath the dead and mangled Big Ears Bywaters. A rustler took a slug in his thigh and screamed, cursing. The other man mounted. There was gunfire. Print wiggled out from underneath the dead body. The outlaw in the saddle aimed at Print. Print rolled over and over in the dust as the rider fired at him from his hysterical, turning horse. Then the rider was blown out of the saddle and hit the ground hard. Print rolled up as close as he could to the log in hopes that he wouldn't get stepped on by the scrambling horses.

Print tried to get his bearings. He looked around and saw a man against a tree. He was shot in the leg and the gut and bleeding badly. Their eyes met and locked. A rifle roared behind Print and the man's head snapped backward as the back of his scalp flew away. Then there was silence. Print lay back and looked up to see Tom looking down at him. Tom bent down and grabbed his uncle and lifted him to his feet. Print held onto Tom at the shoulders as he tried to gain his balance. A big gash ran down the side of his jaw below his ear and down his neck. They looked at each other as if they might embrace. Breathing heavily, Print simply nodded.

A piano played in one of the saloons on the darkened front street of Sheridan as the two riders led three horses with bodies strapped across the saddles. The rider stopped in front of the marshal's office. A light glowed inside. Tom dismounted, and a tired Print, his eye swollen shut, sat astride his horse, unable to move.

Marshal Miller and Deputy McNeary were inside

playing cribbage when Tom entered, and they looked up at him. Tom said nothing. He took a wadded-up handkerchief and placed it on the table between the two men. The marshal and his deputy just looked at him. Then, gingerly, Bill Miller opened the kerchief. Inside were two large, bloody ears.

"My uncle said they were for your watch chain, marshal."

Miller and the deputy looked up at Tom, then back at the handkerchief. Tom simply turned and walked out into the night.

◎ ◎ ◎

There was a dry wind blowing out of the West when Print walked out onto the veranda the following afternoon. He watched the Chinese girls as they attempted to play croquet. Nola was sitting on a bench, watching them too. He stepped off the veranda and walked across the lawn to Nola.

"Evening," said Print.

"Good evening, Mr. Ritter. How's your eye feeling?"

"Oh, I can't see much right now, but it'll be all right." Print reached for his makings.

"Every time I talk to you these days, you seem to have a sudden urge for tobacco, Mr. Ritter."

"I had a long talk with Lung Hay," he said. "I proposed that you take the girls to San Francisco. He says there's a place there that will look after them in a more permanent way."

"And you volunteered my services."

Print said nothing.

"That's very generous of you. Thank you. If Ghing Wa is fit to travel, I'll make plans to leave immediately."

"No need to rush off."

"No need to delay either. I can be ready by tomorrow, if necessary."

An awful silence fell between the two of them. Both were prideful and both were hurting.

"Nola," he said. He realized it was the first time he had ever addressed her by her first name. "My one attempt at havin' a family and settlin' down turned out badly. The truth is, I'm neither brave enough nor strong enough to go that way again."

She said nothing. She got up and walked back to the house, leaving Print to watch the girls as they played on the lawn.

Three days later the fickle weather of early autumn in Wyoming had changed again. It was cold and overcast and threatened snow. Everyone was assembled in front of the Sheridan-Laramie stage line. Ghing Wa was lifted into the coach, then Ghee Moon and Mai Ling. They were all very quiet.

An embarrassed Tom motioned for Lung Hay to join him as he stood beside Sun Foy. "Could you translate for me?"

"Yes."

"I thought I had this all worked out."

Lung Hay started to translate, but Tom cut him off. "No, wait. This ain't easy."

Tom looked at Sun Foy. "I ain't got much. Well, that's not right. Actually I got a pretty good wad of dough now."

Lung Hay translated.

"I don't even know how to get in touch with you. I want to know what happens to you. I … I … I want to know you had a good life."

He took a step backward, and Lung Hay helped Sun Foy into the coach.

Then Nola walked out of the stage office to the waiting coach and Print. He took his hat off and faced her. She turned to him.

"Most men are afraid of failure in this world. It seems

like some are afraid of success. Good-bye, Mr. Ritter."

She kissed him on the cheek, then quickly stepped into the coach and looked away.

A bareheaded, black-eyed Print put his hat on and watched as they shut the door, and with it his life.

CHAPTER TWENTY-NINE

The Royal Coachman landed lightly on the pool between the bank and the quiet run that diverged from the fast current of the river. In the cool water a fat trout swept its tail back and forth, considering the fly that had landed on the surface.

It was the middle of September 1915 on the Snake River, and a wagon passed under the entrance of lodgepoles adorned with moose and elk antlers. A sign hung below the cross pole, "Siam Bend." Lung Hay walked out from the vegetable garden at the side of a log house. It was long with a stone chimney at either end. Two dormer windows protruded from the shake roof. A veranda ran the length of its front. It faced the river, where Print was fishing.

Lung Hay, a hoe in hand, walked to the wagon to meet the driver, who handed him a packet of mail and several parcels. Down by the river, Print was casting. The wagon turned around in front of the log cabin and passed Ye Fung's grave. Print stayed in the river until almost dark, as it was a good time to fish since the fish were biting.

Later, inside the log cabin, he sat in a deep, stuffed chair and read the mail. There was a blue envelope with a San Francisco postage mark on it. He put on his spectacles, opened the letter, and read.

Dear Mr. Ritter,

I hope this letter finds you well. I am

embarrassed that it has been so long since last I wrote to you.

Summer must almost be over at Siam Bend. You have no idea how it touched me to learn the name you have given that point on the river.

I seem so preoccupied these days with time. You told me right there on the river that nothing was more unforgiving than time. You would not recognize me now, as time can be ruthless, especially to women.

You, on the other hand, I am sure, are as stout and straight as a ridgepole. You also have Lung Hay to keep a mindful eye on you. Ghee Moon, Mai Ling, and Ghing Wa have grown into wonderful young ladies. I see them often and they always ask after you.

I do so hope that I can visit you. Lung Hay is better at writing letters and the girls tell me everything about your fishing camp. Promise me that you will not laugh at an old woman when I tell you that she wants to sit with you by the river and splash her feet in the water.

There are so many things that one wishes they might change about their lives. I know for me, one would have been to be less prideful when we were last together.

It is my fear of time and how it stands between us that prompts me to write to you this evening. I want to say without shame or guilt that it is you and only you who will abide in me in my final hour.

Thank you, Mr. Ritter, for giving me

back my life, even if I could not share it
with you.

With warmest thoughts,
Nola Johns

Late in the night, Prentice Ritter had fallen asleep
and the letter rested on his chest. The lamp beside him on
the table was burning low. An ancient Lung Hay shuffled
into the room and silently placed the letter on the table
and turned the lamp out. Print opened his eyes. They flut-
tered. He woke momentarily and looked at Lung Hay and
then dozed off. Lung Hay went and took a seat in a chair
across from him and waited for the morning light to fill
the room.

EPILOGUE

If you have no family or friends to aid you, and no prospect opened to you there, turn your face to the great West, and there build up a home and fortune.

—Horace Greeley

Nola Johns died in the influenza epidemic of 1918. She was buried at Siam Bend on the Snake River, next to Ye Fung.

Lung Hay never returned to his wife. He died in 1921 and was buried at Siam Bend.

Prentice Ritter joined them in 1924.

Heck Gilpin escorted the herd from Sheridan to Capetown. He later settled in the Republic of South Africa.

Mai Ling stayed at the Cameron House in San Francisco and worked with Donaldina Cameron in her continuing efforts to rescue young Chinese girls from the privations of the slave trade.

Ghing Wa graduated from Stanford University School of Medicine and returned with Ghee Moon to China and started a hospital. They were lost in the turmoil of Mao Tse-tung's revolution.

Tom Harte married Sun Foy. Their grandchildren still ranch in Wyoming.

ACKNOWLEDGMENTS

I would like to thank the late Waldo Haythorn and Beldora Haythorn of Arthur, Nebraska, Maxine Brocius Bushong, Major James Rumpler, and Doug Gardiner for so many stories that helped in the writing of this book. Thank you to Horton Foote and Ulu Grosbard for vetting the story in its early stages. I would like to thank the Cameron House in San Francisco for help in researching the history of Donaldina Cameron and the trafficking of Chinese girls. Special thanks to Mark Stewart of Lippan, Texas, and the entire Bews family of Longview, Alberta, Canada, for making sure I didn't sound like a dude; to Scott Cooper and Wes Morrissey for telling me when I missed the mark; and to Dave Barron, who helped me find Bob Baron and Fulcrum Publishing; to Sam Scinta, its associate publisher, who spent long hours on the book's development; and to the hardworking team at Fulcrum, who made this book a reality.

I want to thank Luciana Duvall for her encouragement in writing this story, and most of all my friend Robert Selden Duvall, who told me to "write that story down" and was there to help me, from start to finish. Thank you, Bobby.

READER'S GUIDE

Five Questions for Author Alan Geoffrion

Your story, while well-rooted in the Western-novel genre, has some unusual traits, particularly the incorporation of many strong women, notably the five Chinese girls. How did you come upon this story?

I am always asked, "Is this a real story?" My reply is that it is a collection of real stories. The horse drive came from a conversation with a rancher in Nebraska. The Chinese girls came from my interest in Donaldina Cameron, who worked for forty years to rescue young Chinese girls from the underground slave trade. In fact, the working title for the story, *Daughters of Joy*, focused on these girls. And the ranches and places along the journey are all real, though some of the towns are only ghost towns today.

How much did your long friendship with Robert Duvall shape the character of Print Ritter?

I have always felt that Bobby is the actor of the proletariat. Regular folks identify strongly with the characters he portrays, especially in Westerns. It was easy to write the dialogue for a Duvall character. It was hard not to make that character a thinly veiled knockoff of his other roles. I think we both believe that you can define the big story from a small action or thought. I always want to use a sentence of dialogue or a gesture or action to say, "Ah ha, so that's what that person is about."

Your use of colloquial language is remarkable, giving the book an authentic feel. How did your years as a horseman shape the language you use in the book?

The world of horses is populated with "characters," and those characters lead to others and they lead to great stories. Not all the people and dialogue came from the horse world. I am always prospecting and mining—a word, a story, a physical gesture. I try to sock it all away for the future.

While the story is quite serious and filled with many dramatic events, there is also a keen sense of humor that fills many moments. Who are some of the writers who have influenced you and your own writing style?

I was always drawn to adults in my youth. I thought they had great stories. Stories that Hollywood would never accept as possible. It was the voices of those adults that impressed me. Writers? Certainly Twain and O. Henry. Sherwood Anderson, Horton Foote, Kipling, Hemingway, Dickens, Beryl Markham, J. P. Donleavy, Alan Paton. Many of these authors are not very politically correct these days and won't be found on college syllabuses next semester. In the Western genre, I am a big fan of Thomas McGuane and Cormac McCarthy.

You have lived with the characters for more than a year, throughout the writing of the novel and the screenplay. Which character have you grown to like the most?

Asking this question is a lot like asking which of your children you like the best. Surely Prentice Ritter is the tent pole of this book. However, it is the character of that place of undefined borders that starts at my doorstep in the Virginia Piedmont and can stretch to Hawaii, to Alberta and British Columbia, and deep into old Mexico: The West. It is the character that I most respond to. For better or worse, it has helped define us as a people. Personally, I think it's been for the better.

Questions for Discussion

While the novel is, in many ways, a traditional Western, it is also a story of love, as Print Ritter discovers feelings he thought were long buried. Discuss the different levels of love discovered by Print and how this love shows his growth.

When Print and Tom discover the theft by Captain Billy Fender, each immediately takes a different path, one of violence and one of nurturing. Discuss this juxtaposition and what it tells us about the two characters.

The five Chinese girls remain a bit of a mystery throughout much of the novel, obviously dealing with fear, an unknown language, and an uncertain destination. How does this represent the American immigrant experience?

Throughout the novel, Print wrestles with painful memories of the Civil War. By the end of the novel, do you feel he has exorcised these memories, and, if so, which relationship helped him the most in doing so?

The author provides very limited physical descriptions of the characters in the novel, instead describing characters through their words and their deeds. Based on this, how would you describe each of the novel's characters?

In her words, Nola is halfway down the ladder to a life of misery. Why do you think she trusts Print enough to be intimate with him, both in words and in action, and does this relationship ultimately pull her back to a good life?

There is sense from early in the novel that Ye Fung, Number Four, is destined for a bad fate. Discuss the role that fate and chance play in the lives of the major characters. Are they able to overcome the odds that fate has placed before them?

Do you feel that Print was happy at the end of the novel?